Counseling Crime Victims

LAURENCE MILLER, PhD, is a clinical and forensic psychologist based in Boca Raton, Florida. Dr. Miller is the police psychologist for the West Palm Beach Police Department and mental health advisor for Troop L of the Florida Highway Patrol. He is a forensic psychological examiner for the Palm Beach County Court and a consultant with Palm Beach County Victim Services. Dr. Miller serves as an expert witness in civil and criminal cases and is a consulting psychologist with several regional and national law enforcement agencies, government organizations, and private corporations.

Dr. Miller is a certified trainer by the International Critical Incident Stress Foundation (ICISF) and a member of the Special Psychology Services Section of the International Association of Chiefs of Police (IACP), the International Law Enforcement Educators and Trainers Association (ILEETA), the Society for Police and Criminal Psychology (SPCP), the Consortium of Police Psychologists (COPPS), the American Academy of Experts in Traumatic Stress (AAETS), and the National Center for Victims of Crime (NCVC).

Dr. Miller is an instructor at the Police Academy and Criminal Justice Institute of Palm Beach Community College and an adjunct professor of psychology at Florida Atlantic University. He conducts continuing education programs and training seminars across the country, appears regularly on radio and TV, and is the author of over 200 print and online publications pertaining to the brain, behavior, health, law enforcement, criminal justice, forensic psychology, business psychology, and psychotherapy. He is the author of six previous books, including the most recent: *Practical Police Psychology: Stress Management and Crisis Intervention for Law Enforcement* and *From Difficult to Disturbed: Understanding and Managing Dysfunctional Employees.*

Dr. Miller can be reached online at docmilphd@aol.com.

Counseling Crime Victims

*Practical Strategies for Mental
Health Professionals*

Laurence Miller, PhD

SPRINGER PUBLISHING COMPANY
NEW YORK

This publication is designed to provide accurate and authoritative information in regard to the subject matter covered. It is sold with the understanding that neither the author nor the publisher is engaged in rendering a legal, clinical, or other professional service. If individual legal, clinical, or other expert assistance is required, the services of a qualified professional should be sought. The material in this book is for educational purposes only and is not intended to provide specific clinical or legal advice. All instructions for emergency response, crisis intervention, and individual clinical strategies should be supplemented by proper training, practice, and supervision.

Copyright © 2008 Springer Publishing Company, LLC

Springer Publishing Company, LLC
11 West 42nd Street
New York, NY 10036
www.springerpub.com

Acquisitions Editor: Jennifer Perillo
Production Editor: Julia Rosen
Cover design: Joanne E. Honigman
Composition: Apex Publishing

08   09   10   11/   5   4   3   2   1

Library of Congress Cataloging-in-Publication Data

Miller, Laurence, 1951–
    Counseling crime victims : practical strategies for mental health professionals / Laurence Miller.
        p.; cm.
    Includes bibliographical references and index.
    ISBN 978-0-8261-1519-5 (alk. paper)
    1. Victims of crime—Mental health.   2. Victims of crime—Mental health services.   3. Crisis intervention (Mental health services)   I. Title.
    [DNLM: 1. Crime Victims—psychology.   2. Counseling—methods.   3. Psychotherapy—methods.   4. Stress Disorders, Post-Traumatic—therapy.   WM 165 M648c 2008]
RC451.4.V53M53   2008
616.89'14—dc22   2007045882

Printed in the United States of America by Edwards Brothers.

Dedication

To those who give voice to the voiceless,

Names to the nameless,

And hope to the hopeless.

You know who you are,

And we remember what you do.

Contents

Foreword

Victims of crime, particularly violent crime, face some unique challenges. They are thrust into a universe most never could have anticipated. Their formerly trusting perspective on human goodness surely will be threatened. Their assumptions of justice and the legal system can be contested in ways that defy how they can order their personal world.

If victims are fortunate enough to recover from physical injuries, many discover that the emotional impact cuts deeper than they would have suspected. That can further complicate their recovery as they second-guess whether they are "normal" after all.

Those who are committed to supporting victims in the aftermath of their emotional trauma discover that learning a whole new language and culture is a necessity for providing meaningful assistance.

Dr. Miller's work is a practical primer on the recognized language and culture of crime victimization, particularly at the emotional and psychological level. While intended specifically for mental health professionals, this book is a valuable reference for all who serve victims in any direct capacity. He provides a sensible and functional breadth and depth of knowledge that exposes the extraordinary dimensions associated with victim response and intervention.

Those who have field experience will immediately recognize the functional nature of Dr. Miller's labor while certainly discovering new insights for serving victims of all kinds.

Will Marling, MDiv, DMin, CCR
Interim Executive Director
The National Organization for Victim Assistance
January 2008

Preface

He didn't just attack my body; he stole my soul.
—Sexual assault victim, 1997

More than an accidental injury, more than a serious illness, more than a natural disaster, the trauma of crime victimization goes beyond physical and psychological injury: It robs us of the very faith we have in the human world. Although eclipsed in recent headlines by terrorism, the common everyday violations of civilized behavior that our own citizens continue to perpetrate on one another are no less wrenching.

As more and more mental health professionals are becoming involved in the criminal justice system—as social service providers, victim advocates, court liaisons, expert witnesses, and clinical therapists—there has not been a commensurate improvement in the quality of teaching material to address this expanding and diverse field. Until now, students and practicing professionals have had to content themselves with either overly broad texts on criminology or trauma theory, or with narrow tracts on one or another subarea of victim services.

Counseling Crime Victims: Practical Strategies for Mental Health Professionals provides a unique approach to helping victims of crime. By distilling and combining the best insights and lessons from the fields of criminology, victimology, trauma psychology, law enforcement, and psychotherapy, this book presents an integrated model of intervention for students, trainees, and working mental health practitioners in the criminal justice arena. In this volume, I've tried to creatively integrate solid empirical research scholarship with practical, hit-the-ground-running recommendations that mental health professionals can begin using immediately in their daily work with victims. This includes direct advice to impart to victims and their families on how to stay alive during a crime in progress and on how to cope with police, clinicians, lawyers, judges, and social service agencies.

As in any solidly grounded but user-friendly volume, this book is part scholarly review, part practical clinical wisdom, and part personal journey. My own work with crime victims has converged from two directions. The first is the field of neuropsychology and traumatic brain injury and other traumatic disability syndromes, such as chronic pain and posttraumatic stress disorder. Many of these patients have been involved in motor vehicle or workplace accidents, but a fair number are injured in the course of a criminal assault. My work with physical and psychological trauma patients led to an interest in traumatic stress syndromes in law enforcement and emergency services personnel, and I soon found myself clinical director of the Palm Beach County Critical Incident Stress Management Team serving the county's police officers, firefighters, and paramedics. This in turn led to my close and fruitful involvement with the West Palm Beach Police Department and other local and regional law enforcement agencies.

Around the same time, my practice in forensic psychology had been focused largely on civil cases involving workers' compensation and personal injury but, as I became more involved with law enforcement and the criminal justice system, I began to see more and more criminal cases, both from the perspective of evaluating suspects for competency to stand trial and insanity defenses and evaluating victims for symptoms of stress and psychological disability. In addition to evaluations, many of these crime victim cases were referred to me for treatment. Thus, I've had the professional opportunity to experience the forensic psychological aspects of crime and crime victimization from the clinical psychology, law enforcement, and criminal justice perspectives.

For this book's title, the term *counseling* is not chosen lightly and, as used throughout this book, has a number of important overlapping meanings and implications for treatment. To begin with, counseling encompasses all the phases and components of helping crime victims: psychological, legal, social service, philosophical, and spiritual; counseling is not just limited to weekly clinical sessions. An especially important dimension of counseling is its proactive nature: As I've emphasized elsewhere, *the best form of crisis intervention is crisis prevention*, and the best way to help a crime victim is to keep him or her from becoming one in the first place. Thus, this book places great emphasis on what might be called *preventive mental health*, by analogy to preventive medicine. Many of the strategies you'll learn in the following pages can be used by your patients (and yourself) to keep them (and you) from being a victim, or in the case of a crime already committed, the strategies in this book can help mitigate the harm done.

But bad things do happen to some good, bad, or in-between people and counseling also incorporates a number of postcrime interventions for victims. Here again, the purview of counseling is broad and encompasses crisis intervention literally within minutes of the traumatic victimization, to short-term psychological stabilization, to later therapeutic processing, to long-term clinical follow-up and guidance through the civil or criminal justice system. To *counsel* your patient, then, is to directly aid him or her in the deepest, broadest way you can and help the patient secure the additional services that can assist further.

While we're discussing semantics: The term *victim* is used purely descriptively in this book, to refer to someone who has had a criminal act perpetrated on him or her. It is not intended to be understood as any kind of a value judgment, as in the sometimes pejorative term *victim mentality.* Another semantic point refers to crime victims under clinical care who I here refer to as *patients*, simply because this is the terminology I was trained in and feel most comfortable with. Some clinicians are more comfortable with the term *clients*, in which case feel free to make that mental substitution while reading these pages. As an interesting linguistic aside, the term *patient* derives from the Latin, "one who appeals for help," whereas the derivation of *client* is "one who depends." Psychotherapists know that words and their meanings carry great weight in our interactions with patients. Thus, we must ensure that we communicate clearly and supportively to those we are trying to help.

The case examples chosen for this book are snippets of either actual cases (disguised for confidentiality) or composites of cases, and you will notice that many of them involve criminal victimizations that are not excessively gruesome or horrific. That's because, in routine outpatient clinical mental health practice, you're more likely to see larger numbers of noncatastrophic traumatic injuries and, consistent with the principle that *everybody's pain is real to them,* it is essential to have the clinical and empathic skills to work productively with these crime victims, just as it is essential for the clinician who works in a hospital or other inpatient setting to have the skills to work with more severely injured patients. The principles in this book will apply to crime victims at all levels of injury and traumatization.

Although each chapter can be read on its own merits, this book is organized sequentially. Part 1 provides a solid clinical and empirical background on types of crime, victimization patterns, and common and unusual psychological reactions to crime victim trauma. I spend a good deal of time delineating various symptoms and syndromes because this richness of clinical presentation is what you'll see in real-life practice and the first step to effective treatment is always proper diagnosis and case formulation.

The chapters in part 2 cover each stage of intervention involving a crime scenario, from preventing crimes from occurring or escalating, to immediate law enforcement and emergency mental health response to the crime scene itself, to short-term symptom management, to ongoing psychotherapy. This includes strategies for working with direct victims of crime as well as family members of deceased crime victims, including children.

Part 3 applies the lessons learned in the previous chapters to addressing the unique needs of what might be called the "special victims" that you may encounter in your work: victims of sexual assault, domestic battery, workplace and school violence, and—in this new and strange age—victims of terrorism. A special chapter is devoted to the care and maintenance of mental health professionals—that's you and me, folks—who do this kind of intense, gritty, demanding clinical work. Strategies are offered for beating burnout, staying sharp, and coping with the costs of caring. And if you work with crime victims, it's inevitable that you'll at some point become involved in the civil and/or criminal justice system; accordingly, the final chapter provides both you and your patients with a practical guide to forensic evaluations, courtroom testimony, and working with attorneys, victims rights groups, and social service agencies.

I'm counting on the fact that *Counseling Crime Victims: Practical Strategies for Mental Health Professionals* will not be the kind of book that readers flip through once and consign to bookshelf purgatory. I intend this volume to be the kind of dog-eared, Post-It–covered, underlined, yellow-highlighted, and margin-scribbled practical guide and reference book that working mental health clinicians consult again and again in their daily practices. This book will also be of use to attorneys, judges, law enforcement officers, social service providers, and other professionals who work with crime victims in a variety of settings. The book can also serve as a text for courses in clinical psychology, forensic psychology, criminology, and criminal justice.

Finally, only you will know if this book has accomplished its therapeutic mission, and the only way *I'll* know is if you tell me. Therefore I invite readers to contact me with any comments, questions, critiques, or recommendations for future editions of this volume. Look, you don't need me to teach you how to do psychotherapy; you're already good clinicians, and the fact that you're even holding this thick tome in your hands proves your dedication to enhancing and honing your professional skills. What this book *will* do is help you expand and apply those skills to the special needs of victims who have been assaulted in body, mind, and spirit so that you can guide these souls back into the human community they have been cast out of. So start reading, get to work, and let me know what you've accomplished.

Laurence Miller, PhD
October, 2007

Acknowledgments

A book like this has many points of origin and convergence, and its influences have been many and varied. The professionals I work with in the fields of psychology, law enforcement, and criminal justice continue to provide me with insights and experiences that I try to utilize in becoming a better practitioner and educator. The students in my courses and training seminars know that they serve me best when they challenge me to back up my ideas and present my practical recommendations in clear, convincing, and usable form. This book therefore represents an exercise in both learning and teaching.

Once again, I want to thank book agent James Schiavone for securing a most appropriate outlet for this work at Springer Publishing Company. Special thanks goes to *International Journal of Emergency Mental Health* editor Dr. Richard Levenson for his continued support of my published work in traumatology, victimology, criminology, and law enforcement psychology over the years. Rich also introduced me to Springer Publishing acquisitions editor Jennifer Perillo, who believed in this project and displayed Jobian patience while waiting for the manuscript to be completed (aw, c'mon, it wasn't *that* late) and then, along with project manager Julia Rosen, she helped refine the manuscript's essential message, with a collectively deft yet restrained redactive hand, into the practical guidebook you now hold.

I had always considered it a kind of cornball conceit for clinical authors to thank their patients (if you were so grateful, doc, did you cancel your bill?), and I've always viewed such acknowledgments skeptically—until it was my turn. My clinical patients and organizational consulting clients continue to reinforce the importance of seeing people—as both individuals and as groups—beyond the diagnostic labels and problem descriptions that often propel them into my office. So yes, they're grateful to me for helping them, and I'm grateful to them for teaching me how to help others. It's so corny, it's actually true.

Other important lessons have been learned from the mental health clinicians, social service workers, victim advocates, support group members, and law enforcement officers I've worked with over the years. While I'd like to say that all of these professionals do their jobs out of selfless devotion to the welfare of others, let's face it, for some it's just a day's work. But *how* they do that day's work is what's important, and I continue to be impressed by the way these individuals use their instincts, training, and common sense to do the kind of work that often necessitates making the impossible routine.

Last, but never least, my family once again earns my gratitude for enduring the prolonged absence of yet another self-imposed exile while completing this book. For better or worse, living with an author who often does his writing after coming home from his day job, they've learned to get used to brief glimpses of me when I pop my head out for air. But I hope they understand that I never stop appreciating their support for the work that I do.

PART I

Crime Victimization

Patterns, Reactions, and Clinical Syndromes

CHAPTER 1

Crime and Crime Victims

The Clinical and Social Context

Certain traumas do more than injure us; they violate our sense of security and stability, yank the existential ground right out from under our feet. More than most traumas—illness, technological accidents, natural disasters—violence deliberately and maliciously perpetrated by other people robs us of our sense that the world can ever be a safe place again. The suddenness, randomness, and fundamental unfairness of such attacks can overwhelm victims with help-lessness and despair. As difficult as it may be to bear the traumas of injury and loss that occur in accidents and mishaps, far more wrenching are the wounds that occur at the deliberate hands of our fellow human beings, that result from the callous and malicious depredations of others. Assaults, rapes, robberies, and even petty but frightening harassments and threats can all nick, dent, and occasionally pierce the psychic shell of security we all envelop ourselves in to get through the day. Violent crimes shatter us in mind, body, and soul.

In some populations, as many as 40% to 70% of individuals have been ex-posed to crime-related traumas sufficient to meet diagnostic criteria for post-traumatic stress disorder (PTSD) and other syndromes (chapters 2, 3, 4), and many individuals have endured multiple exposures to such extreme stressors (Breslau & Davis, 1992; Breslau, Davis, Andreski, & Peterson, 1991; Breslau et al., 1998; Davis & Breslau, 1994; Norris, 1992; Resnick, Acierno, & Kilpatrick, 1997; Resnick, Kilpatrick, Dansky, Saunders, & Best, 1993; Scarpa et al., 2002). Except for rape, men appear to be assaulted under the same kinds of situations as women, but it may be more difficult for a man to report any kind of as-sault for fear of shame, ridicule, or disbelief (Saunders, Kilpatrick, Resnick, & Tidwell, 1989).

TYPES OF CRIMINAL VIOLENCE AND CRIME
VICTIM TRAUMA

While almost any kind of violence can happen to anyone, certain types of criminal victimization appear to be relatively common in the clinical practice of trauma counselors.

Criminal Assault

Each year, more than 25 million Americans are victimized by some form of crime (Herman, 2002). The U.S. Department of Justice estimates that rapes, robberies, and assaults account for 2.2 million injuries and more than 700,000 hospital stays annually. Annual costs due to medical bills, mental health bills, and lost productivity are estimated to exceed 6.1 billion dollars. Indeed, even in this age of terrorism (chapter 14), for many Americans today, local violent crime is *the* overriding social and political issue. The bad guys seem to have gotten more brazen, while the rest of us cower helplessly, feeling victimized not just by the criminals but by the justice system that is supposed to protect us (Bidinotto, 1996; Kirwin, 1997).

> "Give it up, bitch." That was the first and last thing Janet heard before she hit the ground. Just seconds before, she'd been walking to her car in the parking lot of a shopping mall at dusk. Laden with packages, she didn't see the tall figure in the green hooded sweatshirt until too late. The assailant pushed her to the ground and warned her not to look up or he'd shoot her dead. Rifling through her belongings, he apparently wasn't satisfied with the yield and, out of frustration or sheer meanness, he put his foot on the prostrate woman's cheek and proceeded to grind her face into the pavement for several seconds, telling her over and over again that she would be killed. Then, something must have startled him because, as quickly as he appeared, he abruptly fled. Mall security and the local police soon arrived, but the assailant was never apprehended.

> "My whole life is ruined," Janet later told her counselor. Several months after the attack, she could still not go to shopping malls, and seeing dark green clothing of any type produced terrifying flashbacks of the assault. Although she sustained only minor lacerations and abrasions on her cheek, she suffered bouts of excruciating facial pain. She was worked up neurologically for trigeminal neuralgia, but all the standard medical tests were negative. Sleep was almost impossible due to nightmares of being chased and attacked by "wild

animals." Sometimes at night she could hear the phrase "Give it up, bitch" playing repeatedly in her head, which she described as being "like a stuck tape loop." She got frequent headaches and night sweats and had lost more than 30 pounds. Her doctor prescribed tranquilizers and told her to "get some help."

Criminal assault can be all the more psychologically destabilizing when it occurs on home ground, at home or work where we are supposed to feel safe.

His friends and family told him not to take his first Phys Ed teaching job in such a rough high school, but Mark had always prided himself on being a mediator and peacemaker. Besides, as a former high school and college football player and wrestling team member, he was hardly a wuss and could cut quite an imposing presence when he needed to show authority. So he didn't think it would be that big a deal to break up a fight during a recess basketball game—until one of the combatants pulled a shank and stabbed him for his efforts. He recalls the emergency room doctors telling him his wound was potentially life-threatening and "I remember thinking, 'how's that different from *really* life-threatening?' But at no time did I really think I was going to die. I figured I'd just take a few weeks off, get over this, and go back to work."

And, being young, healthy, and enthusiastic, he recovered from his physical injuries. But even during his convalescence, he began noticing problems. Ball games on TV, which he used to love, now disturbed him, giving him "an itchy kind of nervousness" when he watched them. On his first day back at the high school, he was stunned to realize that he couldn't bring himself to walk onto the basketball court. "It was like that force field on the starship Enterprise—I just couldn't get past it. I'd get all dizzy and have to turn back." Embarrassed and dismayed, he took a semester's leave of absence and, as of last contact, hadn't yet returned to teaching.

One of the realities of doing crime victim work is the realization that perpetrators and victims do not come in neat, separate, diametrically opposed packages. Some victims are targeted through no fault of their own, yet may lead questionable or marginal lifestyles that all too often put them in the wrong place at the wrong time.

"Hey, I'm no angel," Manny allowed. "I like to party as much as the next guy. So maybe me and my crew were getting a little wild at the bar, but, hey, you're supposed to go there to have fun, right? All of a sudden, this bouncer is telling us to cool it or we'd have to leave. Hey, between the drinks and the girls, I already dropped a small fortune on that place, so I ain't going nowhere, see? Okay, maybe I had an attitude and used a few choice words, but I sure didn't start a fight. Next thing I know, I'm being bum-rushed out the door, so I kind of pushed back, you know? Then, there must be four, five guys on me, kicking and punching. At one point, I could hear my head crack and I thought I was gonna pass out. Then, I'm lying there on the sidewalk and my friends come out of the bar looking for me. I wanted to go back in, but they talked me out of it. So we went to some other place, but I don't have a very good memory for the rest of that night.

"I figured that was that, but then for the next couple of days, I was feeling kind of tired and foggy and I was forgetting things, so I went to see a doctor who said it sounded like I had a concussion and told me to 'take it easy'—yeah, like that's gonna happen. Those fuzzy feelings passed after about a week or so, but then I noticed that going out with the guys at night wasn't as much fun anymore. I'd sit in a bar or club and just kind of get bored or antsy, like I wanted to be somewhere else, so we'd go to a new place, but then I'd want to get out of there, too. I was starting to feel like a real drag and even my friends said I wasn't much fun anymore.

"And, this is the weird part that I haven't told too many people, but a few times I'd be sitting in a bar and I could swear I could see or feel a bunch of guys closing in on me like they were gonna attack me—but there was nobody there! That's when I thought I was really starting to go nuts. And then, a couple of times a week, I'd be like half asleep, not a dream or anything, just like dozing off on the bus or while I was watching TV in bed or something, and I'd feel a crack on my head, like I got hit with a bat, and I'd bolt right up and feel my head, but there was nothing there. I went back to the doc who saw me for my concussion and he said to see somebody like you, so here I am."

A number of diagnosable psychiatric syndromes may be seen following criminal assault. Depression, anxiety, PTSD, and substance abuse are common psychological disorders (chapters 2, 3, 4) found in victims of robbery, rape, and burglary (Falsetti & Resnick, 1995; Frank & Stewart, 1984; Hough, 1985), and a high proportion of panic attacks trace their onset to some traumatically stressful experience (Uhde et al., 1985). In a follow-up study, approximately 50% of crime-induced PTSD cases were found to persist in a chronic course after 3 months (Rothbaum, Foa, Riggs, Murdock, & Walsh, 1992). Clinical experience suggests that such traumatic effects may persist in some form for far longer—years, decades, or a lifetime.

A criminal act can affect those not directly assaulted or killed. When a family member has been murdered, surviving family members may be plagued by intrusive images of what they imagine the scene of their loved one's death to have been, even if—perhaps especially if—they were not present at the time of the death (Falsetti & Resnick, 1995; Schlosser, 1997). Criminal assault survivors may be scapegoated and blamed for their attack by friends and family members seeking to distance themselves from the contagious taint of vulnerability that crime victims are all too often imbued with (chapters 2, 10).

Abduction and Torture

Perhaps the most extreme form of violence that one human being can perpetrate on another is abduction and torture. These acts typically take place in a military or political context, such as an act of terrorism, or as part of a civil crime such as a botched robbery, attempted extortion, sadistic sex crime, domestic dispute, or revenge. Treatment of captives can range from gracious to atrocious and may sometimes vary between these two extremes within the same event. The duration of captivity may range from minutes to years, but in most civilian crime settings, kidnappings or hostage crises where the victims survive are typically resolved within hours or days (Frederick, 1994; Mollica, 2004; Rosenberg, 1997; Miller, 2002c, 2005c, 2007h).

> Stefan, a middle-aged businessman, was abducted from the underground parking garage of his office building by criminals who mistook him for an errant gang member who'd skipped with a large sum of their money. He was thrown into the back of a van and taken to a remote motel room where he was beaten and tortured for several days before finally being dumped unconscious onto a deserted street where he was found and taken to a local hospital. He claimed to have virtually no memory of the ordeal itself, aside from a few frightening dream-like images. In addition, his overall short-term memory and concentration were seriously impaired.

> One of the differential diagnostic dilemmas in this case was figuring out how much of Stefan's well-documented cognitive impairment was due to head trauma sustained in the beatings and how much to extreme psychological numbing associated with PTSD (chapter 2). Happily, this man was able to obtain a degree of justice in seeing his attackers prosecuted, which aided greatly in his integrating the trauma and getting on with his life (chapter 16). However, he will always

carry a certain edgy wariness about him, and he now tries never to go anywhere alone. Underground parking is out of the question.

It is hardly surprising that kidnapping, with or without actual physical violence, can produce severe posttraumatic stress reactions. Yet many captives manage to survive their ordeals relatively intact, some even emerging somewhat seasoned and ennobled by their experience. Several factors seem to be associated with better outcomes after hostage situations (Frederick, 1994; McMains & Mullins, 1996; Miller, 1998h, 2002c, in press-c; see also chapter 14):

- Age over 40
- A belief in one's own inner strength of self
- Reflective thoughts of loved ones
- Faith in a higher power
- Continuing the hope that the captivity will end favorably
- Using one's powers of reasoning and planning to figure out possible plans for escape or release
- Physical or mental exercise
- Appropriate expression of anger, where safe and feasible
- Ability to focus attention and become task-oriented

Psychological preparedness may promote a sense of control over the trauma (Hoge, Austin, & Pollack, 2007). In a study examining psychopathology in victims of torture, those who were political activists appeared to show more resilience. These individuals were thought to be relatively insulated psychologically by their commitment to a cause, training in stoicism, and prior knowledge about torture techniques (Basoglu et al., 1997). Other researchers have also found that prior training in emergency work appears to enhance resilience (Alvarez & Hunt, 2005; Hagh-Shenas, Goodarzi, Dehbozorgi, & Farashbandi, 2005; Miller, 1989b, 2005d, 2006m, 2007m; Regehr & Bober, 2004).

Crime in the Community

The *Diagnostic and Statistical Manual of Mental Disorders* (*DSM-IV-TR;* American Psychiatric Association [APA], 2000) recognizes that posttraumatic stress reactions can occur in persons who observe terrible events happening to others, even if they are not directly, physically affected. This includes witnessing crimes of violence or threats of violence against others. Indeed, certain segments of the population may be exposed to traumatically stressful events on a fairly regular basis, for example, residents of crime-ridden and socioeconomically depressed inner-city neighborhoods.

Breslau and Davis (1992) and Breslau et al. (1991) studied over one thousand young adults from a large health maintenance organization in inner-city Detroit and found that many of these residents showed classic signs and symptoms of PTSD. Precipitating events included the standard traumatic events of sudden injuries, serious accidents, physical assaults, and rape. But also important was the traumatic effect of having one's life threatened without actually being physically hurt, getting news of the death or injury of a close friend or relative, narrowly escaping injury in an assault or accident, or having one's home destroyed in a fire. Overall, almost half of this sample of young, inner-city adults reported experiencing potentially traumatic events and about a quarter of them developed full-blown PTSD.

Many of the young adults with PTSD continued to experience symptoms for a year or longer. These chronic PTSD sufferers were more likely than those whose symptoms resolved sooner to show hyperreactivity to stimuli that symbolized the traumatic event, as well as interpersonal numbing (chapter 2). They were also more likely to report greater anxiety, depression, poor concentration, and medical complaints. Women were found to be more susceptible to PTSD than men, and subjects were more likely to experience traumatically stressful events if they were poorly educated, more outgoing, and impulsive; if they had a history of early conduct problems; or if they came from families with psychiatric and substance abuse histories. This makes sense: As noted above, people who are more impulsive and disturbed to begin with tend to take greater risks and more often find themselves in trouble-prone situations where they may be victimized and traumatized. Thus, in many cases, criminal activity may be as much related to the impulsivity and maladaptive lifestyle that leads to traumatic events in the first place as it is to the stress syndromes that result from those events; a similar relationship has been noted for impulsive antisociality, aggressive behavior, and traumatic brain injury (Miller, 1987, 1988, 1993e, 1994c, 1998d, 2001d, in press-d).

More recently, Breslau et al. (1998) surveyed over two thousand adults in the Detroit area, aged 18 to 45, to assess the lifetime history of traumatic events and PTSD. They found that almost 90% of the sample had been exposed to one or more traumatic events over their lifetime. The most prevalent type of trauma was the sudden, unexpected death of a close relative or friend. Men, non-White minorities, and economically poorer persons were more likely to be exposed to criminal assault, and assaultive violence carried the highest risk for PTSD, compared to any other kind of trauma. Another class of trauma with high PTSD rates was sudden unexplained death of a loved one. A little less than 10% of men exposed to traumatic events developed PTSD, and this rate was doubled for women. In most cases, PTSD persisted for more than 6 months, and the duration was generally longer for women.

More recent studies have demonstrated that young people as a group are at a disproportionately high risk of exposure to violence (see also chapter 13), with up to 80% of young adults reporting having been a victim of violence, and over 90% reporting being a witness to violence (Scarpa, 2001; Scarpa et al., 2002). Furthermore, this appears to produce a vicious cycle—the so-called cycle of violence—with those victimized showing more aggression themselves. Those most likely to turn their victimization into aggression appear to be characterized by high rates of victimization, avoidant and emotion-focused coping styles, and low perceived support from friends and others (Garbarino, 1997; Scarpa & Haden, 2006).

Real Crime Versus Fear of Crime

Now, some more bad news: Fear of crime may be hazardous to your health. Increasingly, social scientists are finding that the sheer overload of crime and disaster stories in the media, especially on local television newscasts, is giving the public a warped view of reality and contributing to a type of media-induced trauma known as *mean world syndrome* (Budiansky et al., 1996). Because most of the general public have little direct experience with crime, our beliefs about crime and the criminal justice system are largely based on what we see on TV and read in the newspapers, where sensational and violent crimes are often overrepresented. This may have the paradoxical effect of oversensitizing people to nonexistent or insignificant threats, while at the same time numbing the public's understanding of the true impact of crime victimization when it does occur (Miller, 1995a, Miller & Dion, 2000; Miller, Agresti, & D'Eusanio, 1999).

Political scientist Robert Putnam of Harvard University has observed that the rise of television in the 1950s led to a "civic disengagement" of Americans around 1960. Television watching may breed pessimism and apathy. The mean world syndrome makes us paranoid about our neighbors and cynical about society and human nature in general (Budiansky et al., 1996). Just as importantly, if falsely exaggerating the extent of the crime problem contributes to a deterioration of mental health in individuals or groups, are news services liable for damages by engaging in what would amount to journalistic malpractice? Stay tuned.

RISK FACTORS FOR CRIME VICTIMIZATION

In general, women are more likely to be victims of sexual assault, often by people they know, such as husbands, ex-husbands, boyfriends, or relatives (chapter 10), while men are more likely to be physically assaulted by strangers. The risk of sexual assault diminishes with age, while risk of physical assault increases with age earlier in life but then declines as men get older. Having been victimized in the past appears to be a risk factor for future victimization, probably because most people cannot easily escape the sociodemographic factors that put them at risk. Women are likely to develop PTSD at about the same rate following both physical and sexual assault, while the rate of PTSD for men is lower for physical assault but very high for sexual assault, which for men is a rarer and more humiliating event than physical assault (Kilpatrick & Acierno, 2003).

THE PSYCHOLOGY OF CRIME VICTIMIZATION

Russell and Beigel (1990) conceive of crime victimization as comprising several layers in relation to a person's core self:

- *Property crime* like burglary generally hurts victims only at the outermost self-layer (i.e., their belongings), although the theft of certain meaning-laden family heirlooms can have a much greater emotional impact.
- *Armed robbery,* which involves personal contact with the criminal and threat to the physical self of the victim, invades a deeper psychological layer.
- *Assault and battery* penetrates still deeper, injuring the victim both physically and psychologically.
- *Rape* goes to the very core of the self; perverts the sense of safety and intimacy that sexual contact is supposed to have; and affects the victim's basic beliefs, values, emotions, and sense of safety in the world.

Society's response to crime also plays a role in how supported or abandoned victims feel (Russell & Beigel, 1990). For example, when a child comes home from school and tells his parents that the teacher was mean and made him sit in the corner, a common parental response is to inquire, "What did you do to make the teacher punish you?" From experiences such as this, many people grow up thinking that if something bad happens to them, they somehow deserved it. Also, taking the blame for something, even if you logically know it's not your own fault, is often a more existentially reassuring stance than having to believe that something this terrible can just happen for no reason—because, if there's nothing you did to contribute to it, then there's nothing you can do that will prevent it from happening again, or something even worse happening, any time, anywhere (Miller, 1994b, 1996a, 1998e, 1998h, 1999d, 1999i, 2001d).

Society often regards victimization as contagious. In modern American culture, with its emphasis on fierce competition for limitless success and having it all, victims are often equated with losers. Most of us want to believe that crime victimization is something that happens to somebody else. The victim must have done something to bring it on him- or herself, otherwise, the reasoning goes, I'm just as vulnerable to the same bad fate, and who wants to believe that? We may thus be reluctant to associate with the victims for fear that their bad luck will rub off. All of these beliefs and reactions further contribute to the feelings of blame and shame that many crime victims experience (Miller, 1996a, 1998e, 1998h, 2001d, 2007l).

CRIME VICTIMIZATION: THE THERAPEUTIC MISSION

As therapists and counselors, we are not necessarily immune from these natural self-preservatory prejudices. What we *can* do is use our knowledge, training, informed intuition, and common sense to cultivate a comprehensive understanding of the wide variety of crime victim syndromes we will encounter in real-world practice in order to develop a flexible range of options for counseling, treatment, and direct services. As noted in the preface, counseling encompasses a wide range of services, from practical help to psychodynamic therapy. The principles of effective treatment are universal. This book will guide you in applying them to victims of crime.

CHAPTER 2

Psychological Reactions to Crime Victimization

Posttraumatic Symptoms and Syndromes

Any victim of crime that comes to us for help is not a blank slate. A traumatic occurrence does not color a victim in a standard, by-the-numbers way. Rather, each patient is already a complex canvas of temperament, cognitive style, personality, family background, past experiences, and social status by the time he or she is splattered by the sharp brushstrokes of the crime. It is important for counselors and therapists to understand these differences so that our interventions address the unique needs of the person who is before us. This chapter and the following ones describe the main classifications of symptoms and syndromes seen after crime victimization.

POSTTRAUMATIC STRESS DISORDER: THE SYNDROME

In clinical terminology, a *syndrome* is defined as a set of signs (what can be objectively observed by the clinician) and symptoms (what is subjectively experienced by the patient) that occur in a fairly regular pattern from patient to patient, under a given set of circumstances, and with a specific set of causes. Although a number of clinical syndromes may be observed following crime victimization, the most commonly diagnosed syndrome is *posttraumatic stress disorder,* or PTSD, which is defined as a set of emotional and behavioral disturbances that follow exposure to a traumatic stressor or traumatically stressful experience that is typically outside the range of normal, everyday experience for that person. As a result, there develops a characteristic set of signs and symptoms (APA, 2000; Helzer, Robins, & McEnvoi, 1987; Meek, 1990; Merskey, 1992; Miller, 1994b, 1998h; Modlin, 1983, 1990; Taylor, 2006; Weiner, 1992), any of which may be seen in crime victims, although the particular pattern and severity will vary from person to person.

Anxiety. The crime victim describes a continual state of free-floating anxiety or nervousness. There is a constant gnawing apprehension that something terrible is about to happen—largely based on the fact that something terrible has already happened. The victim maintains an intensive hypervigilance, scanning the environment for the least hint of impending threat or danger. Panic attacks may be occasional or frequent.

Physiological arousal. The victim's autonomic nervous system is always on red alert. She experiences increased bodily tension in the form of muscle tightness or knots, tremors or shakiness, restlessness, fatigue, heart palpitations, breathing difficulties, dizziness, headaches, stomach and bowel disturbances, urinary frequency, or menstrual disturbances. About one-half of PTSD patients show a classic *hyperstartle reaction:* surprised by an unexpected door slam, telephone ring, loud sneeze, or even just hearing her name called, the patient may literally jump out of her seat and then spend the next few minutes trembling with fear and anxiety.

Irritability. There may be a pervasive chip-on-the-shoulder edginess, impatience, loss of humor, and quick anger over seemingly trivial matters. Friends get annoyed, coworkers shun the patient, and family members may be abused and alienated. A particularly common complaint is the victim's increased sensitivity to children's noisiness or the family's bothersome questions.

Avoidance and denial. The crime victim tries to blot out the event from his mind. He avoids thinking about the crime and shuns news articles, radio programs, or TV shows that remind him of the incident. "I just don't want to talk about it," is the standard response, and the patient may claim to have forgotten important aspects of the event. Some of this is a deliberate, conscious effort to avoid trauma reminders; part also involves an involuntary psychic numbing that blunts most incoming threatening stimuli. The emotional coloring of this denial may range from blasé indifference to nail-biting anxiety. In the early phases, this avoidance may frustrate criminal investigators who are trying to access the victim's memory for clues that can help them solve the crime (see chapter 5).

Intrusion. Despite the patient's best efforts to keep the traumatic event out of her mind, the horrifying incident pushes its way into consciousness, often rudely and abruptly in the form of intrusive images of the event by day and frightening dreams at night. In the most extreme cases, the patient may experience *flashbacks* or reliving experiences in which she seems to be mentally transported back to the traumatic scene in all its sensory and emotional vividness, sometimes losing touch with current reality. More commonly, the intrusive recollection is described as a persistent psychological demon that "won't let me forget" the terrifying events surrounding the criminal assault.

Repetitive nightmares. Even sleep offers little respite. Sometimes the victim's nightmares replay the actual events of the crime; more commonly, the dreams echo the general theme of the traumatic experience but miss the mark in terms of specific content. For example, a sexual assault victim may dream of being attacked by vicious dogs or drowning in a muddy pool. The emotional intensity of the original traumatic experience is retained but the dream partially disguises the event itself. This symbolic reconfiguration of dream material is, of course, one of the main pillars of Freudian psychodynamic theory (Horowitz, 1986; Miller, 1991b).

Dissociation. During the traumatic event, and for some time afterward, the patient may experience episodes of *depersonalization* (feeling that the self is unreal) or *derealization* (feeling that the outside world is unreal). Patients describe feeling like "this is happening in a dream" or that "it's happening to someone else." There may be extreme distortions of time sense and memory. Dissociation is thought to be a psychological defense mechanism that allows the person to mentally survive the original traumatic experience or the strikingly painful intrusive recollections afterward.

Impaired concentration and memory. The crime victim complains of having gotten "spacey," "fuzzy," or "ditsy." She has trouble remembering names, tends to misplace objects, loses the train of conversations, or can't keep her mind focused on work, reading material, family activities, and so on. She may worry that she has brain damage or that "I'm losing my mind."

Sexual inhibition. Over 90% of PTSD subjects report decreased sexual activity and interest; this may further strain an already-stressed marital relationship. In some cases, complete impotence or frigidity may occur, especially in cases where the traumatic event involved sexual assault. This may be associated with a general decline in enjoyment of life activities, and may shade over into clinical depression (chapter 3).

Withdrawal and isolation. The crime victim shuns friends, neighbors, and family members and just wants to be left alone. He has no patience for the petty, trivial concerns of everyday life—bills, gossip, news events—and gets annoyed at being bothered with these piddling details. The hurt feelings this engenders in those he rebuffs may spur retaliatory avoidance, leading to a vicious cycle of rejection and recrimination.

Impulsivity and instability. More rarely, the crime victim may take sudden trips, move from place to place, walk off his job, disappear from his family for prolonged periods, uncharacteristically engage in drunken binges, gambling sprees, or romantic trysts, make excessive purchases, or take dangerous physical or legal risks. It is as if the trauma has goaded the traumatized crime victim into a what-the-hell-life-is-short attitude that overcomes his usual good judgment and common sense. Obviously, not every instance of irresponsible behavior can be blamed on trauma, but a connection may be suspected when this kind of activity is definitely out of character for that person and follows an identifiable traumatic event. Far from taking such walks on the wild side, however, the majority of trauma survivors continue to suffer in mute, shattered silence.

ACUTE STRESS DISORDER

Acute Stress Disorder (ASD) was introduced as a diagnostic category into the *DSM-IV* (APA, 1994), primarily to help identify those at risk of developing later PTSD. ASD is defined as a reaction to the traumatic stress that occurs within 4 weeks of the index trauma. Although ASD focuses more on dissociative symptoms than PTSD, it also includes symptoms of reexperiencing, avoidance, and hyperarousal. Preliminary prospective studies suggest that between 60% and 80% of individuals meeting criteria for ASD following a traumatic event will meet criteria for PTSD up to 2 years later.

The ASD diagnosis has been contentious since its inception. It has been criticized on the grounds of being conceptually and empirically redundant with PTSD, as well as pathologizing common symptoms of psychological distress in the immediate aftermath of trauma (Koch, Douglas, Nichols, & O'Neill, 2006). However, it recognizes that some patients may show traumatic reactions close in time to the injurious event, and it reinforces the importance of early treatment where ASD is clinically indicated. Early treatment is especially important for crime victims, for whom optimal clinical intervention begins from the initial moment of contact with the first responder (chapter 5).

PARTIAL AND ATYPICAL PTSD SYNDROMES

When fewer than the number of symptoms considered necessary to satisfy the full diagnostic criteria for PTSD can be assessed, some clinicians speak of subsyndromal or partial forms of this disorder (Stein, Walker, Hazen, & Forde, 1997). Thus, one patient may report only traumatic nightmares, while another may experience hyperarousal without numbing/avoidance or reexperiencing symptoms. Note that the actual number of symptoms need not correlate with severity of psychological disability: Even if not formally diagnosed with PTSD per se, a crime victim may be so psychologically disabled by crippling anxiety or sleep loss, he may develop secondary cognitive and emotional impairment sufficient to disrupt work and family life (chapter 3).

To account for psychological responses to trauma that do not fit neatly into the *DSM-IV* diagnostic formulation, Alarcon (1999) has proposed a PTSD typology to accommodate these unusual variants. Again, clinicians should be careful not to overlook other *DSM-IV* diagnoses that might fit these patients (Miller, 2002e; see chapters 3, 4).

The *depressive subtype* of PTSD presents with psychomotor retardation, social withdrawal, inability to deal with everyday occurrences, loss of interest, low self-esteem, self-criticism, guilt feelings, and suicidality. Differential diagnoses include major depressive disorder and adjustment disorder with depressed mood (chapter 3).

The *dissociative subtype* is characterized by a predominance of flashbacks, hallucinatory experiences, depersonalization, derealization, fugue-like amnesic behavior, and symptoms resembling multiple personality disorder. Differential diagnoses include dissociative identity disorder, borderline personality disorder, and temporal lobe epilepsy. However, as noted above, some degree of dissociation occurs during the traumatic event in some victims and this may be predictive of more serious PTSD later on.

The primary manifestation of the *somatomorphic subtype* is chronic pain or some other type of physical symptomatology, typically without clear localization or identifiable medical cause. Differential diagnoses include the somatoform disorders (chapter 4), as well as unrecognized organic injury or illness.

In the *psychotic-like subtype,* the patient shows distortions of consciousness, fantasizing, staring, inattentiveness, impaired motivation and volition, paranoia, and behavioral regression. Differential diagnoses include schizophrenia, schizoid, schizotypal, or paranoid personality disorders, or brain injury effects (chapter 3).

The *organic-like subtype* presents with impaired attention, concentration, learning, memory, and cognition, along with confusion, slowness in thought, speech, and behavior, and in some cases, a dementia-like clinical picture. Differential diagnoses include the postconcussion syndrome following traumatic brain injury, severe depression, or naturally occurring dementias in older patients (Miller, 1990, 1991a, 1993e; Parker, 2001; Wolfe & Charney, 1991).

The *neurotic-like subtype* is characterized by anxiety, phobic avoidance, restlessness, hypersensitivity, obsessionalism, and panic attacks. Differential diagnoses includes the anxiety disorders and some personality disorders (chapter 3).

CHILD-SPECIFIC PTSD SYMPTOMS

Certain PTSD symptoms seen in children following traumatic crime victimization may differ from those of the adult syndrome (James, 1989; Johnson, 1989; Miller, 1999d, 1999e; Quinn, 1995), and may include the following (also see chapters 8, 13).

> *Repetitive play.* Children may reenact the traumatic crime over and over again in play with dolls, toy soldiers, toy guns, and so on. This appears to be a behaviorally based equivalent of the more cognitively based intrusive thoughts and imagery of adults. Victimized adolescents may obsessively replay music, videos, or videogames that reflect themes of violence or retribution.
>
> *Self-blame.* Children, more so than adults, may fixate on what they might have done to bring the violence on themselves. Children are used to being chastised and blamed by adults in authority and may fantasize that the criminal assault was punishment for some imagined wrongdoing, or that they should have somehow done more to help their families who were victimized.
>
> *Foreshortened future.* Children may express the belief that they will "never grow up" and that there is little point in preparing for the future by continuing to go to school, to follow adult advice, or to make new friends.
>
> *Regression.* Children may stop developing, or regress cognitively, psychosocially, and emotionally. Developmental milestones that have been passed years ago may reappear. Older kids may wet the bed, play baby games, reacquire tastes for previously abandoned foods, or prefer to play with younger children. Cognitive regression may occur in the form of loss of acquired academic skills, more primitive handwriting, reversion to baby talk, or even complete mutism.
>
> *Atypical cognitive disturbance.* In addition to concentration and memory impairment that may affect schoolwork, some cases of global psychogenic amnesia for whole blocks of time may be seen following severe traumatic stress. In such extreme cases, virtually all memories for events contemporaneous with the traumatic incident, or even

memory for all prior childhood events, may be seemingly irretrievable. This psychologically self-protective mechanism may be misdiagnosed as brain damage, psychosis, or malingering.

Somatization. More than most adults (but see chapter 4), children tend to communicate with their bodies, and may therefore be likely to express their distress somatically, even while saying that things are fine. Virtually any organ system may be affected by stress, with headaches, heart palpitations, dizziness, stomach aches, and asthma-like breathing problems being especially common. Aside from representing increased physiological arousal, somatization in children may take on a symbolic form of communication, such as unexplained visual impairment in a child who witnessed the assault or homicide of a friend or family member, or repetitive vomiting in a child who wants to clean out his or her memory of experiencing or witnessing a violent crime.

PTSD IN ELDERLY PATIENTS

Patients now in their 70s, 80s, and 90s comprise the generation of the Great Depression, World War II, the Korean War, the button-down Eisenhower era, and the early days of the Cold War, when stoic endurance of adversity was part of the general American culture and their personal upbringing. Many of these elders survived civilian or military traumas in their youths that may barely have been acknowledged and certainly not worked through in that pretherapeutic era. Preoccupied and distracted by the daily struggles of adult job and family life, they could afford to put their painful memories on the psychological back burner until the relative quiescence of retirement had given their minds more free time to dwell on the past. Like mental shrapnel that lies dormant until an additional injury triggers a painful spasm, a superimposed trauma such as a criminal assault may summate with a long-buried event to produce a synergistically boosted psychopathological reaction (Solomon, Mikulincer, & Waysman, 1991).

Although I could find no studies that relate to crime victimization of elders per se, there have emerged several research reports and case studies of past trauma reawakened in elders under the press of a contemporary stressor. The original experiences mostly center around the WW II era, including battlefield traumas (Bonwick & Morris, 1996; Lipton & Schaffer, 1986; Nichols & Czirr, 1986), civilian internment (Potts, 1994), and the Holocaust (Robinson, Rappaport-Bar-Server, & Rappaport, 1994). The reemergence of decades-old intrusive recollections, nightmares, insomnia, and hypervigilance in response to a current stressor is a common feature of these cases. Age-related stress-ors, such as deterioration of physical health, retirement, and the death of loved ones, have all been identified as precipitants of latent PTSD symptoms (Bonwick & Morris, 1996).

Several of my own cases (Miller, 1999f) have corroborated the potential role of present victimization in the reevocation of latent PTSD in elderly pa-tients. The original experiences have ranged from WW II–battlefield traumas in the European and Pacific theaters, to the tribulations of Holocaust concen-tration camp survivors, to childhood sexual abuse by relatives (long before the time when such matters were even acknowledged, much less discussed), to the experience of prior criminal victimization as children or young adults.

In these cases, the patients were retired and living satisfactory lives when their criminal assaults occurred, usually muggings, purse-snatchings, or carjackings, most with minor or no physical injuries. A typical response is, "I haven't thought about that [the old trauma] in years." These old traumas are not described as re-pressed, per se, because they could be volitionally recalled at any time during the ensuing decades, as in occasional Memorial Day barbecue reminiscences with fellow veterans. Rather, these elders had managed, for the most part, to "put the bad memory behind them," or at least the disturbing emotional com-ponent of it, until a current criminal traumatization dragged the recollection to the forefront of consciousness (Miller, 1999f).

Harry was wounded at the Battle of the Bulge at the end of WW II, when a piece of hot metal from an exploding gun turret cut a gash in his right side and burned the right side of his face. He recalls the worst part of the ordeal as having to sit in the cold snow, in severe pain, not knowing if the medic was going to come or even if he'd be able to get himself out of there alive. At one point, he looked up and saw one of his squad buddies lying a few feet away. "At first, I figured he was sleeping or lying there wounded, but then I realized he was dead and I thought, oh shit, is that gonna be me?" Harry was eventu-ally evacuated to a field hospital then stateside and was honorably discharged toward the end of his tour.

After the service, Harry completed college on the GI Bill, earning a degree in finance. He tried his hand in the banking world, but "office life wasn't for me," and he went on to open two profitable pawn-shops in his local neighborhood in Philadelphia, which he operated for many years, eventually with the help of his two sons. One of the pawnshops was in a rough neighborhood and Harry was held up at gunpoint several times, all miraculously without injury. He and his wife eventually retired to sunny Florida but he soon grew bored with the daily routine of canasta games and early bird specials. Since his college days, he had always been fascinated by the law and so became a volunteer *guardian ad litem* for the local county juvenile court, drawing great satisfaction from helping children and their families negotiate the legal system.

Then, one day, a scuffle broke out in the courtroom where Harry was scheduled to give his testimony. One of the youths roughly pushed Harry aside as he tried to run out of the courtroom. Harry fell onto one knee, "and I knew something wasn't right, 'cause I heard the crack." An orthopedist recommended arthroscopic knee surgery and it was during his convalescence from this procedure that "I just went to pieces—a nervous breakdown or something." He began experiencing flashbacks from his war experience and from some of the holdups during his pawnshop days. "The crazy thing about it is I was more scared about the holdups sitting in a hospital bed in West Palm Beach 35 years later than I was looking down the gun barrel back in Philly."

In therapy, Harry was able to understand how the cumulative build-up of his so-called mental shrapnel, combined with the feelings of vulnerability and helplessness produced by the knee injury and his subsequent layup in the hospital, caused him to have an exaggerated reaction to the seemingly minor courtroom incident. "I guess it opened the dyke and everything came flooding back," Harry insightfully noted.

EVOLUTION OF THE TRAUMA RESPONSE

Crisis counselors know that the phenomenology of ASD and PTSD consists of more than a tabulation of index symptoms, and the reaction to a traumatic event can begin within the first few moments of the traumatic event. Hollywood portrayals to the contrary, during an immediate crisis, most people don't become overwhelmed or paralyzed by intense fear or shock; in the breach, many behave quite adaptively (Aldwin, 1994; Miller, 1998h, 2002d, 2003d, in press-b; Miller, Pirtle, & Bartlett, 1997; Weiner, 1992). Assault victims calculate their avenues of escape; passengers purposefully unstrap their seatbelts and climb out of the window of the burning plane or submerging automobile; office workers find the exit and file down the stairwell of the bombed building, even helping others in the process. The entire organism seems to go on automatic and is directed toward survival. A certain degree of adaptive depersonalization or dissociation (see above) may take place, an unnatural mental detachment from the surrounding events that enables the person to deal with the practical survival needs of the situation; this is often described in retrospect as "like being in a dream" or "happening in slow motion." Cinematic wild-eyed panic is extremely rare and disaster management experts frequently note how difficult it is to shake people out of their inertia and complacency during an emergency and get them to move at all (Miller, 1998h, in press-b; Miller et al., 1997). The same is true in many cases of criminal victimization.

After the event, the numbing depersonalization may continue for some time, leaving the survivor feeling confused and bewildered. It's as if the psychoanesthetic freeze elicited during the trauma incident needs time to thaw out in the more temperate affective climate of real life. Unfortunately, though, real life doesn't last very long, as the intrusive recollective and emotional gale rushes in at the weak chinks that begin to form in the crumbling psychic armor. Thus begins the wrenching emotional seesaw of painful intrusion alternating with numbing denial, along with many of the other posttraumatic stress symptoms described above.

In the majority of cases, especially where there is no persisting physical injury, the major symptoms and disturbances diminish in the course of weeks to months as the traumatic event becomes integrated into the life narrative and personal history of the crime victim. A more realistic awareness of individual vulnerability is built up, so that basic feelings of security and confidence are restored. However, in some cases, a number of mental roadblocks may stand in the way of the crime victim's making peace with himself and the world (Everstine & Everstine, 1993; Kushner, Riggs, Foa, & Miller, 1993; Matsakis, 1994; McCann & Pearlman, 1990; Miller, 1994b, 1998h).

One of these stumbling blocks involves guilt and stigma. Many crime victims believe that they could have somehow prevented the traumatic event from occurring; this is especially true for victims of sexual assault (chapter 10) and may be accentuated in the case of disenfranchised victims who are accused of asking for it by their dress, behavior, or overall lifestyle (Doka, 2002; Spungen, 1998). Others interpret the criminal assault as a kind of hard-knocks wake-up call for their poor judgment or as cosmic punishment for past misdeeds. Many survivors feel marked by fate, especially if this is not their first traumatic experience. Still others experience a violation of their bodily and territorial integrity. They feel fragmented and scattered, and the slightest upset makes them irritable and isolative. They may literally wince when touched or when others encroach upon their personal space, and they become panicky in rooms or in crowds where they are unable to negotiate a clear route of escape.

The criminal assault and its aftermath comprise a shattering existential experience. The crime victim is starkly confronted with his or her own vulnerability and mortality in a way that most of us manage to avoid by using the normal, adaptive denials of everyday life, of business as usual (Horowitz et al., 1997; Kushner et al., 1993). The victim's existential violation may be all the more painful if the trauma took place at the hands of a known and heretofore trusted person, such as a family member, friend, workmate, neighbor, doctor, or clergy member.

Being in a trauma mode is difficult to stop and can be hard to let go of. Many crime victims generalize the helplessness of the cognitive survival state to other aspects of their lives; they feel powerless to control even their own behavior or to influence the merest actions of others. Or they may impute domineering or retaliatory motives to anyone who tries to exert even the normal, socially appropriate influence or authority over them, such as bosses, doctors, parents, or spouses. In some cases, outright paranoia and projective hostility may develop: "You can't do that to me; you're all out to get me!"

Even after things seem to have calmed down, when the crime victim has achieved some measure of delicate equilibrium, the stresses of returning to the normal routines of work and family life may trigger PTSD reactions. Also, delayed PTSD reactions may crop up years or even decades after the event as illness or the aging process begin to deplete the individual's adaptive reserves (Miller, 1999f; see above).

In general, the more severe the trauma and the longer the trauma response persists, the more problematic the outcome. That's why it is important for all traumatic disability patients, including crime victims, to receive quick, effective treatment (Litz, 2004; Litz, Gray, Bryant, & Adler, 2002; Miller, 1998h). And even after a delay, or when the trauma syndrome takes time to surface, proper treatment can still have a significant impact, so no situation should ever be considered categorically hopeless.

NEUROPSYCHOLOGY OF PTSD

Peter Rabbit is happily hippity-hopping his way down a path in the woods, on his way to his favorite meadow of delicious marigolds for a festive and filling lunch. Although always reasonably cautious about his surroundings (as all rabbits have to be), he's taken this well-traveled route—under the hydrangea bush and past the maple tree—many times before without mishap. Today, however, a fox suddenly springs from behind the maple tree and grabs Peter by his hind leg. A desperate struggle ensues and it looks like it's the end for poor Peter, when, with a final agonized lurch, he breaks free of the fox's death grip and bounds into the neighboring underbrush where he hides for hours until finally limping his way home.

For the next few months, the other rabbits observe that Peter never goes near the marigold field; in fact, he doesn't even go on the same path to other meadows and is forced to scrounge for much less scrumptious fare in the already well-picked fields close to home. What is more baffling is that he cannot bear to come anywhere near hydrangea bushes or maple trees of any type, no matter where they are, because doing so makes him tremble and shake. "Stop worrying, already," the other rabbits tell him. "Fox ambushes are an occupational hazard we rabbits all face and we'll just have to be a little more careful, that's all. You can't put your whole life on hold just because of what *might* happen." They even have it on good authority, his fellow rabbits tell him, that the human hunters have recently dispatched the fox in question, so there is now really nothing to be afraid of. "Easy for you to say," retorts Peter, "You're not the ones who almost had your leg chewed off. Besides, you think there's only one fox in these woods? And what about hawks? And what if the human hunters come for us next? Nothing is safe anymore!"

What Peter never learned at rabbit school, however, is that Mother Nature has programmed his DNA to create a nervous system exquisitely sensitive to what is termed *one-trial fear avoidance learning,* or as Peter and his friends call it: "Once bit, twice shy." Nature can't depend on rabbits or other creatures to decide for themselves what behaviors have evolutionary survival value, so she makes sure that animals who narrowly escape a brush with death by a particular event and in a particular location come to categorically avoid anything even remotely associated with that event or locale—paths, bushes, trees, marigolds—even if that means a markedly limited lifestyle. At least that way, Peter will avoid potential danger in the future and he is more likely to meet the future Mrs. Peter and raise a brood who will inherit this inborn, genetically programmed, neurobiologically based skittishness and will, in turn, be more likely to let Peter someday play with his grandrabbits. Besides, who said marigolds were so great, anyway?

Human beings are not rabbits, but we retain a similar *limbic system*—the emotional and motivational brain network—to that of our fellow mammals, from mice to gorillas. In the last few years, advances in brain research (Dowden & Keltner, 2007; Lyons et al., 1993; McFarlane, 1997; McNally, 2007; Weiner, 1992; Weiss, 2007) have led to several theoretical models that describe the brain mechanisms that may account for the trauma response and the symptoms of PTSD and other traumatic disability syndromes (Miller, 1990, 1993d, 2007l, in press-a). While it is not essential to grasp these neurophysiological concepts in order to do effective crime trauma counseling and therapy, many patients gain increased reassurance from the fact that there is a known name and mechanism for their symptoms, that they are not just weak or crazy. They may not understand all the brain stuff you try to explain to them, but it's often comforting for them to know that *you* do.

Kolb's (1987) theory of PTSD takes as its starting point a concept that was first articulated by Freud (1920): A *cortical stimulus barrier* serves to protect the individual from being overwhelmed by excessive stimulation. Massive psychic trauma may overcome this stimulus barrier and, according to Kolb's hypothesis, produce synaptic changes by way of neurophysiological sensitization. If continued at high intensity and repeated frequently over time, those neural processes mediating discriminative perception and learning may become impaired, including the possibility of stress-induced neuronal death in the brain's hippocampus, which has a high number of stress-responsive glucocorticoid receptors (Sapolsky, Krey, & McEwen, 1984).

Parker (1990) points out that multiple afferent stress signals through sensory and emotional brain pathways lead to the adrenal gland's secretion of glucocorticoid hormones such as cortisol—the classic stress hormone. High levels of cortisol appear to depress neuronal functioning, especially in the hippocampus, which plays an important role in memory as well as an important feedback role in the modulation of the stress response. Oscillations in the brain's stress-memory system may account for the cycles of intrusion and avoidance seen in PTSD.

Decreased hippocampal volume in persons with PTSD is consistent with animal studies showing that glucocorticoids can damage hippocampal neurons (Sapolsky, 1996; Sapolsky, Uno, Rebert, & Finch, 1990), which suggests that trauma can have a direct toxic effect on the brain (Bremmer, 1999; Bremmer et al., 1993, 1995; van der Kolk, 1994; Weiss, 2007). However, structural changes in the brains of persons with PTSD might also be markers for vulnerability to trauma, reflecting individual differences that predate exposure (Paris, 2000; Yehuda, 1998, 1999, 2002).

Kolb (1987) identifies another limbic structure, the amygdala, as interacting with the hippocampal system in mediating stress effects. The amygdala functions as a sort of rapid-decision "good or bad" emotional evaluator of environmental stimuli. Stress overload in this system may force the individual into a state of hair-trigger hypersensitivity, in which a multitude of internal and external stimuli lead to continued heightened arousal. Recurrent intense emotional arousal further sensitizes and simultaneously disrupts those processes related to habituation and learning, leading to an exacerbation of PTSD symptoms, such as hypervigilance and flashbacks (Frewen & Lanius, 2006; Nutt & Malizia, 2004).

With excessive limbic sensitization and diminished capacity for adaptive information-processing by the cortical stimulus barrier, subcortical and brainstem structures escape from inhibitory cortical control and repeatedly reactivate the perceptual, cognitive, affective, and somatic clinical expressions related to the original trauma. These abnormally reactivated memory loops are projected into daytime consciousness as intrusive thoughts and images and into sleep as traumatic nightmares.

Cortical neuronal changes are responsible for impairment of perceptual discrimination, reduced impulse control, and affective blunting. Excessive activation or release of subcortical systems results in conditioned startle reactions, irritability, hyperalertness, intrusive thoughts, repetitive fearful nightmares, and psychophysiological symptoms such as heart palpitations, panic attacks, musculoskeletal pain, headache, and gastrointestinal disturbances. The repeated reminders of the traumatic event associated with somatic symptoms disrupt the patient's body-image and self-concept and are responsible for numbing and avoidance behaviors such as social withdrawal, alcohol and drug abuse, and compulsive risk-taking, as well as emotional disturbances that include depression, survivor guilt, shame, and suicidality.

Deitz's (1992) neuropsychological theory attempts to extend Kolb's (1987) formulation by conceptualizing a dual pathway of traumatic information processing in the brain. The first system links perceptual evaluation and emotional tone with the cognitive and language regions of the brain, allowing the individual to make sense of the experience, no matter how frightening or painful. A second, independent limbic system pathway bypasses the conscious evaluative system and feeds directly into the emotion-memory complex of the hypothalamus, hippocampus, and amygdala.

For survival purposes, it is critical that the amygdala-processed positive/negative, good/bad discrimination be made as fast as possible to allow time for the appropriate fight-or-flight or approach-avoidance response. In fact, in order to link the affective tone to neocortical processing—the conscious feeling and meaning connected to language and abstract thought—the second, phylogenetically newer pathway is needed. Where these two systems are out of sync, as in the case of severe trauma, the conscious cognitive-linguistic memory of the trauma may be repressed, while the emotional reaction persists in response to stimuli the person may not even recognize. In fact, the specific neurophysiological and behavioral response to crime-induced trauma appear to be influenced by the victim's relationship to the perpetrator (Yehuda, 2002).

Charney, Deutsch, Krystal, Southwick, and Davis (1993) have elaborated a psychobiological model of PTSD that appeals to limbic sensitization. According to this model, sensitization by fear associated with traumatic stress results in a change in excitability of amygdala neurons. This in turn influences the functioning of a variety of limbic and brainstem structures involved in the somatic and autonomic expression of fear and anxiety. For example, a reduced activation threshold of the locus coeruleus in the brainstem results in a surge of arousal-enhancing norepinephrine at many sites throughout the brain. In addition, functioning in mesocortical dopaminergic neurons is elevated, heightening the propensity for quick action (van der Kolk, 2003; Weiss, 2007).

Stress-induced impairment of long-term potentiation, mediated in part by excitatory amino acid, noradrenergic, and opioid receptor systems, may be responsible for the development of the learning and memory deficits observed in PTSD. Because extinction appears to involve an active learning process—an idea that goes back to Pavlov (1927; also see McNally, 2007)—deficits in learning may impair normal extinction in patients with PTSD, leading to the abnormal persistence of emotional memories. This may partially explain the paradox of learning and memory deficits coexisting with abnormally intense intrusive recollections in PTSD.

Further, locus coeruleus activation of the amygdala enhances memory retrieval. This memory-enhancing effect of increased noradrenergic activity may be mediated by beta-adrenergic receptors within the amygdaloid complex. By this mechanism, some of the acute neurobiological responses to trauma may facilitate the extra-strong encoding of traumatic memories, leading patients, like Peter Rabbit, to exclaim, "I can't forget it."

In both rabbits and patients with PTSD, specific sensory phenomena, such as sights, sounds, and smells circumstantially related to the traumatic event, persistently produce a reoccurrence of traumatic memories and flashbacks (Yehuda, 2002). The brain regions mediating these processes include the amygdala, locus coeruleus, hippocampus, and sensory cortex. Most of the evidence points to the amygdala as particularly important in the conditioning and extinction of sensory and cognitive associations to the original trauma and subsequent activation of traumatic memories. N-methyl-D-aspartate (NMDA) receptors on the amygdala are inferred to be involved in these processes because NMDA antagonists applied to the amygdala and NMDA lesions of the amygdala prevent the development of fear-conditioning responses and the extinction of fear-precipitated startle.

Thus, the amygdala functions to attach fearful or anxious affect to neutral stimuli associated with the trauma. The functional interchange between the amygdala and the sensory cortices, where memories of each sense are stored, may be critical for the ability of specific sensory inputs to elicit traumatic memories. In addition, activation of the amygdala may also be responsible for the highly correlated set of behaviors associated with traumatic memories.

The continued revivification of traumatic memories associated with a painful injurious event may thereby act as both trigger and reinforcer of chronic pain as a coping response to trauma.

What all of these neurophysiological theories share in common is a conceptualization of brain mechanisms involved in perception, emotion, memory, thought, and symbolic language, all coordinating the response to traumatic stress and all susceptible to disruptions in their functioning that are responsible for the symptoms of PTSD. But this is not all theoretical. From a practical treatment perspective, it has been shown that early application of arousal-reducing pharmacological agents, such as beta-blockers, following psychological trauma can significantly reduce the extent and severity of later PTSD reactions. What is more important from our point of view, however, is that behavioral treatment modalities, such as relaxation training (chapter 6) applied early, can have a similar trauma-mitigating effect (Charney et al., 1993; McNally, 2007).

Research also indicates that selective serotonin reuptake inhibitor (SSRI) mood stabilizing medication may reverse stress-induced hippocampal damage and improve memory functioning (Bremmer, 2006; Javitt, 2004). Again, however, what is perhaps most exciting from this book's perspective is the evidence that psychotherapy itself may be able to reverse the neurophysiological changes associated with traumatic memories and enhance renewed synaptic growth, leading to better symptom resolution and improved cognitive and emotional functioning (Centonze, Siracusano, Calabresi, & Bernardi, 2005; Cozolino, 2002; Etkin, Pittenger, Polan, & Kandel, 2005; Farrow et al., 2005). This highlights the vital role of counselors and therapists in both immediate (chapters 5 and 6) and longer term (chapter 7) treatment of traumatized crime victims.

Readers who are by now wondering what biology class they mistakenly wandered into may be relieved to note that these neuropsychological models are also compatible with cognitive-behavioral conceptualizations of PTSD (Ehlers & Clark, 2000; McNally, 2007; Taylor, 2006). In this model, PTSD occurs when individuals cognitively process the event and/or its effects in a way that colors other current or impending threats. Unlike Peter Rabbit, most humans who recover naturally from a traumatic incident tend to view it as a time- and circumstance-limited event with little spillover into their normal lives. However, poor Peter and his fellow persistent PTSD sufferers tend to perceive the traumatic incident as having made an indelible, negative change in their lives: "I'm scarred forever; my life will never be the same again." Victims of persistent PTSD also tend to overgeneralize their fear from the traumatic event to normal life events, thus coming to perceive more and more everyday situations as potentially threatening: "Why even go out of my hole in the ground? Life is just one fox after another." They also may tend to personalize the events and thereby overestimate the likelihood of being harmed again: "I'm a marked bunny; no matter what I do or where I go, there'll be a fox with my name on it."

Thus, a crucial role of trauma therapy after crime victimization is to break these vicious cognitive cycles and help the patient achieve a sense of reality-grounded safety and self-efficacy. As noted above, by changing minds, we also change brains, but from the practical point of view, our actions are primary; the theories afford a certain guidance and rationale, but it all comes down to what we do that makes our healing efforts effective.

RISK FACTORS FOR PTSD

Clinicians who work with crime victims and victims of other kinds of trauma are often impressed with the wide range of individual response patterns to seemingly similar traumas by decidedly dissimilar patients. That's why I take so much space to delineate the individualities and idiosyncrasies of crime victim responses: A one-size-fits-all approach to treating these patients is no more appropriate than for any other area of medical or psychological practice. Researchers and clinicians alike have endeavored to discern the factors that contribute to some trauma survivors developing disabling traumatic disability syndromes, while others fare far better (Kilpatrick & Resnick, 1993; Norris, 1992; Paris, 2000).

A number of risk factors for PTSD have been identified in the literature (Basoglu et al., 2005; Brewin, Andrews, & Valentine, 2000; Carlier, Lamberts, & Gersons, 1997; Green & Berlin, 1987; Hoge, Austin, & Pollack, 2007; Kessler et al., 1999; King, King, Fairbank, Keane, & Adams, 1998; Marmar et al., 1994; Orr et al., 1990) and include pretrauma, peritrauma, and posttrauma variables.

Pretraumatic vulnerability variables exist before the trauma occurs. Examples include lower educational level, lower intelligence, neurodevelopmental delays, such as delayed onset of walking and speech, as well as learning disabilities, a previous history of mental disorders, and female gender.

Peritraumatic vulnerability variables are those that are present at the time of the trauma itself and include the sheer magnitude of the stressor—sometimes referred to as the *dose-response effect*—and immediate reactions to the stressor, such as fear of threats to one's safety, or dissociation.

Posttraumatic vulnerability variables occur after the traumatic event; they include perceived level of social support, subsequent life events, and ongoing threat to safety, such as fear of retribution by criminal associates of an assailant the witness must testify against (see chapter 16).

Wohlfarth, Winkel, and van den Brink (2002) identified four risk factors in crime victims that, when combined, predicted a significantly high rate of PTSD: (a) being the victim of a violent crime, (b) knowing the perpetrator, (c) experiencing the results of the crime as worse than was expected, and (d) blaming oneself for the event. Other predictors, such as dissociation and anxiety at the time of the traumatic event, were also strongly associated with PTSD but did not substantially improve the prediction over the four primary items.

Genetic and biological factors have been shown to contribute strongly to how sensitive individuals are to trauma, and they have also been shown to influence how frequently certain individuals are exposed to adverse life events through their contribution to the traits of impulsivity, poor judgment, and insufficient consideration of consequences (Kendler & Eaves, 1986; Kendler, Neale, Kessler, Heath, & Eaves, 1993; Lyons et al., 1993; Paris, 2000; Thapar & McGuffin, 1996). A reaction of defeat in response to trauma has been associated with cortisol-related memory impairment and symptoms of avoidance, amnesia, and dissociation, whereas a defensive posture is related to increased epinephrine and norepinephrine, which is associated with hyperarousal, hypervigilance, and flashbacks (Elzinga & Bremmer, 2002).

An important trait underlying vulnerability to PTSD has been termed *neuroticism* (Costa & McCrae, 1988; Eysenck, 1990; McCrae & Costa, 1990), which describes a tendency to react to adverse events with especially strong emotion, and which seems to be a stable trait over the adult life span. These individuals are more sensitive to stress because they react more rapidly, more intensely, and they are slower to return to baseline than others. Conversely, those who are lower on trait neuroticism find it easier to shake off stressful events. In line with the above discussion, variations in this dimension may reflect levels of activation in the amygdala (LeDoux, 1996).

Another biogenetically influenced factor that may be involved in some or many cases of PTSD is *impulsivity*. This trait mediates exposure to stress (Kendler & Eaves, 1986; Kendler et al., 1993), in that individuals who act more quickly and take greater risks are more likely to be exposed to potentially traumatic experiences than those who are more cautious.

So what kind of person is likely to develop PTSD after exposure to trauma? A combination of trait neuroticism, impulsivity, and heightened exposure to adversity seems to be a particularly vulnerable combination. Indeed, as discussed in the last chapter, inhabitants of certain communities seem to experience more than the national average of adverse life events. This complexity of etiology argues for multimodal treatment of crime victims (Paris, 2000), which will be elaborated in later chapters.

PROTECTIVE FACTORS FOR PTSD

In addition to *risk factors* that contribute to the likelihood that some crime victims will be more likely to develop traumatic disability syndromes, it is just as important to consider *protective factors*—that is, traits and characteristics that make some people more resilient and resistant to traumatic stress effects (Bowman, 1997, 1999; Hoge et al., 2007; Miller, 1998b, 2007m). When conducting counseling and psychotherapy interventions of all types, it is always important to be searching for these positive personal resources that can be capitalized on in treatment and recovery efforts.

Traits and Patterns of Resilience to Stress and Trauma

Traits associated with *resilience* to adverse life events in children and adults (Bifulco, Brown, & Harris, 1987; Brewin et al., 2000; Garmezy, 1993; Garmezy, Masten, & Tellegen, 1984; Luthar, 1991; Rubenstein, Heeren, Houseman, Rubin, & Stechler, 1989; Rutter, 1985, 1987; Rutter, Tizard, Yule, Graham, & Whitmore, 1976; Werner, 1989; Werner & Smith, 1982; Zimrin, 1986) include the following:

- Good cognitive skills and intelligence, especially verbal intelligence, and good verbal communication skills
- Self-mastery, an internal locus of control, good problem-solving skills, and the ability to plan and anticipate consequences
- An easy temperament, not overly reactive emotional style, good sociability, and positive response to and from others
- A warm, close relationship with at least one caring adult or mentor, other types of family and community ties and support systems, and a sense of social cohesion as being part of a larger group or community

Indeed, on close inspection, these appear to be virtually the opposite of the traits of impulsivity, neuroticism, and poor social connection and support that characterize those most vulnerable to trauma. Although the above positive traits of resiliency may occur naturally in some people (Miller, 1998b), they can be developed and strengthened in your patients by proper training, encouragement, and modeling.

Kobasa (1979a, 1979b; Kobasa, Maddi, & Kahn, 1982) introduced the concept of *hardiness*, which has been defined as a stable personality resource consisting of three psychological attitudes and cognitions (Maddi & Khoshaba, 1994):

- *Commitment* refers to an ability to turn events into something meaningful and important, something worth working for and seeing through.

- *Control* refers to the belief that, with effort, individuals can influence the course of events around them, that they are not helpless, but effective influencers of their fate and the responses of others.
- *Challenge* refers to a belief that fulfillment in life results from the growth and wisdom gained from difficult or challenging experiences, a realistically confident but not reckless bring-'em-on attitude.

Similarly, Antonovsky (1979, 1987, 1990) has proposed a stress/health-mediating personality construct termed *sense of coherence,* or SOC, which is expressed in the form of three component orientations or beliefs (theorists, apparently, like to work in threes):

- *Comprehensibility* refers to the events deriving from a person's internal and external environments in the course of living that are structured, predictable, and explicable. Things make sense and therefore are less overwhelming.
- *Manageability* refers to the idea that the individual possesses the resources to meet the demands posed by the adverse events. The person feels realistically in control, not helplessly adrift.
- *Meaningfulness* refers to the idea that the person conceptualizes the adversity as a challenge worthy of his or her investment and engagement. There is an intellectual and emotional satisfaction in tackling a tough problem and seeing it through to the conclusion.

The higher a person's SOC, the better able he or she will be to clarify the nature of a particular stressor, select the resources appropriate to that specific situation, and be open to feedback that allows the adaptive modification of behavior when necessary.

The Psychobiology of Mental Toughness

More recent research has revealed that resilience to stress may depend on how graded and nuanced the person's psychophysiological stress response is, a characteristic which varies among individuals. Dienstbier (1989, 1991) has used the term *toughness* to refer to a distinct reaction pattern to stressful events—mental, emotional, and physiological—that characterizes animals and humans who cope effectively with stress (Miller, 1989b, 1990, 1998b). Two main physiological systems underlie the toughness response.

The first involves a pathway from the brain's hypothalamus to the sympathetic branch of the autonomic nervous system, and from there to the adrenal medulla. The sympathetic nervous system, or SNS, is responsible for the heart-pounding, fight-or-flight response that mobilizes body and mind to deal with challenging situations. As part of this response, the adrenal gland releases its main hormone, adrenalin.

The second system involved in the toughness response also begins with the hypothalamus but acts through the pituitary gland which in turn stimulates the adrenal cortex to release cortisol—the main hormone involved in the physiological stress response, as discussed earlier. Together, the pattern of SNS–adrenal medulla and pituitary–adrenal cortex responses to stressful challenges characterizes the nature of the toughness trait.

It is the flexibility and gradedness of the response of these two interrelated systems that defines an individual's physiological resilience or toughness. In resiliently tough organisms—Peter Rabbit or you and me—the normal, everyday activity of the two systems is low and modulated: Tough individuals are at relative ease under most ordinary circumstances, and their physiological responses reflect this natural quiescence. But when faced with a stressful challenge or threat, the SNS–adrenal medulla system springs into action quickly and efficiently, while the pituitary–adrenal cortex system remains relatively stable. As soon as the emergency is over, the adrenalin response returns quickly to normal, while the cortisol response stays low. The smoothness and efficiency of the physiological arousal pattern is what characterizes the psychophysiological toughness response—a response that has important aftereffects on the brain. Such a restrained reaction prevents depletion of catecholamines, important brain neurotransmitters that affect mood and motivation.

Not so with the untough. The physiological reactions of less resilient individuals tend to be excessive and longer lasting, even in the face of everyday hassles. The result is more intense and disorganizing arousal, less effective coping, and faster depletion of brain catecholamines, which can lead to helplessness and depression. With each tribulation, major or minor, less resilient individuals tend to overrespond, their arousal levels overwhelming them and rendering them unable to do much about the current situation, leading to progressively deteriorating confidence in their future ability to cope.

That's where the real psychological significance of psychophysiological toughness comes in. Humans can do one thing Peter Rabbit can't: We can reflect on our own thoughts, feelings, and actions, conceptualize our responses in terms of what kind of person that makes us, and thereby anticipate how we'll react to future challenges. Dienstbier (1989, 1991) points out that the toughness response—or its absence—interacts with a person's psychological appraisal of his or her own ability to cope with challenge. This in turn contributes to the person's self-image as an effective master of adversity or a helpless reactor—a self-assessment that in turn influences later psychophysiological reactions to stress.

CONCLUSIONS

This, then, is the psychophysiological rationale of many of the therapeutic techniques to be described in this book: By learning to control their perceptions, feelings, thoughts, and reactions through progressive practice and rehearsal, crime victims may come to develop and enhance a core of resilient toughness that will enable them to cope with the aftermath of the crime, the criminal justice system, and life ahead. You can forget the biology lesson if you want to. The important thing to remember is that, although individuals differ naturally in their innate resilience, you can help virtually any crime victim to reinforce his or her resilient coping skills to make a difference between survival and progress versus capitulation and despair.

CHAPTER 3

Psychological Disorders Associated With Crime Victimization

$\mathbf{A}$ttorneys who handle personal injury cases (see chapter 16) speak of some of their clients as being "thin eggshells." That is, a given injury, physical or psychological, happens to an individual with a unique and individual history and the law says that "we take our victim as we find him." What's true in the legal arena applies to clinical psychology and psychotherapy as well. As we've just seen (chapter 2), there are a variety of risk and protective factors that can influence a patient's response to crime victimization. Although the bulk of clinical and research attention has been given to PTSD, many other psychological reactions can occur in the wake of crime victim trauma and will usually be superimposed upon, and commingled with, the victim's preexisting personality and coexisting psychological traits and syndromes (Falsetti, Resnick, Dansky, Lydiard, & Kilpatrick, 1995; Kilpatrick & Acierno, 2003). Proper treatment of these patients requires knowledge of, and sensitivity to, these individual differences. Indeed, only by understanding these syndromes can clinicians steer clear of two major pitfalls: either (a) assuming the patient's unusual presentation is solely due to crime trauma–related PTSD and thereby ignoring preexisting or coexisting personality and psychopathology factors, or (b) the opposite mistake of attributing everything to the premorbid pattern and thereby ignoring or downplaying the traumatization effects.

ANXIETY DISORDERS

For most of us, our normal mood is neither especially happy or sad, angry or loving, agitated or calm, but just a steady sense of what might be called *provisional well-being:* the overall feeling that life has its difficulties but everything is basically okay and we hope for better days. It's like the feeling between meals when we are neither hungry nor full, when, in fact, we're too preoccupied with what we're presently doing to pay conscious attention to our gastronomical—or emotional—states at all. All healthy people show a range of moods, becoming periodically happier, sadder, angrier, calmer, and so on, in response to various life circumstances. Some people, however, seem to be dispositionally predisposed to either the cheerier or more dour side of the mood spectrum. Like any trait or syndrome, it is the *extremes* of mood that characterize a disorder, especially when these mood disturbances impair healthy life functioning or produce unreasonable conflict with others.

Anxiety disorders are characterized by heightened worry, fear, and arousal and are classified into several main types.

Generalized Anxiety Disorder

Generalized anxiety disorder (GAD) involves a pervasive feeling of anxiety that is not necessarily tied to any specific event or circumstance, sometimes referred to as *free-floating anxiety.* These individuals are always anxious about something, although the level of anxiety may wax and wane in response to different situations. Others may perceive these individuals as never being able to relax or be at peace. This sense of generalized agitation and unease can only be expected to increase after a criminal victimization, and it is important for clinicians to recognize that recovery from crime-induced traumatization may never entail complete cessation of anxiety because that was never this patient's baseline to begin with. Instead, the modest therapeutic goal of return to a manageable anxiety level may be more realistic. In the best cases, treatment of the crime-related traumatic anxiety can actually serve as a catalyst for mastery of more general anxiety, that is, the patient can learn to apply the strategies and insights gained in therapy for coping with the symptoms of traumatic victimization (chapter 6) to the preexisting GAD and broader life issues as well.

> Always skittish by nature, it had taken all the guts she could muster to apply and interview for the bank teller's job, and Sharon had only been working there a week when the holdup occurred. Although she was not directly threatened—the teller two windows down was the one who actually had the gun stuck in his face—Sharon was so shaken by this event that she could not bring herself to go back into the bank long after her coworkers had returned to work. Over the next few weeks, her therapist was able to work with her, in conjunction with her psychiatrist who prescribed medication, so that she could get back to a tolerable level of anxiety sufficient to allow her to function at her job.

Panic Disorder

Some individuals with GAD may suffer from *panic disorder,* which involves brief episodes of extremely elevated physiological arousal and fear. Or panic disorder may exist as a sole syndrome, which may be all the more disconcerting, as the attacks often seem to come out of nowhere. During a panic attack, the individual may experience a racing, pounding heart, profuse sweating, rapid, shallow breathing, numbness and tingling in the face and extremities, and faintness or lightheadedness—all the hallmarks of sheer terror. Many subjects fear they will faint or pass out during an attack, although this is extremely rare. The attacks may occur in response to certain events, or they may happen randomly out of the blue. Panic attacks are also likely to occur in the context of depression (see below), often in response to perceived abandonment or loss of support. Interestingly, a number of crime victims have related that, during the attack, the fear and terror they experienced were actually familiar to them from previous panic episodes they've endured. Still, the frequency and intensity of these attacks may be expected to rise following criminal victimization, and the clinician should try to capitalize on what has previously proven effective in treating past attacks.

> Rafi could remember a few isolated episodes of anxiety attacks when he was in high school and college, but these seemed to go away after he had achieved his career goal in the computer field, gotten married, and started a family. Then, one night, he was mugged on the subway coming home from work. "Now, I'm getting these attacks, like two or three times a day. I understand intellectually that they're just a physical reaction, but they freak me out so much, I'm afraid to go out of my house." Through a combination of lowered-arousal training and cognitive restructuring (chapter 6), he and his therapist were able to reduce the frequency and severity of the attacks to a manageable level where Rafi could ride out those remaining episodes he couldn't actually prevent or abort.

Phobias

If the anxiety and panic are associated with particular places or situations, the individual may develop one or more *phobias,* which are irrational extreme fears of particular persons, places, or things. Note that these are not delusions (see below), because the person usually recognizes that the fear is irrational, yet he or she feels powerless to control it and must avoid the feared situation to forestall panic. It is also questionable whether they can truly be called irrational if they arise following exposure to a certain traumatic stressor: Remember, "Once bit, twice shy." Nevertheless, sufferers often feel demoralized and out of control at not being able to will themselves out of these disturbing fears. Phobias may be generalized, involving fears of a wide variety of people, places, or things that are usually related or have some elements in common, or they may be quite specific. In fact, it is quite common for crime victims to develop phobias to specific people or places associated with the traumatic victimization.

For example, victims may shun certain streets, stores, or buildings, or they may develop a fear of being near certain types of people who resemble their attacker. In fact, many victims have bemoaned the fact that "I've become a racist" when it comes to a certain group of people that the attacker was a member of. Prior prejudices aside, this is not racism per se, as much as a case of Pavlovian fear conditioning—the Peter Rabbit principle applied to a certain class of people—and it can often be successfully addressed in therapy.

> "This is the part I hate to admit," Rafi went on. "The guys that pushed me down in the subway were black and now I get nervous any time I'm around black people, even friends at work I've known for years. It's even worse for me to feel this way, because I'm originally from the East End of London where the white kids used to fight with the Pakistani kids all the time, and I swore to myself I'd never be like that. But it's not that I hate these black people, it's just, like, I don't want to be around them. One time, I was standing in queue at the cafeteria and big Frankie was standing behind me and I went into one of my panics. I was able to keep it together, but I think a few people knew something was up because they were giving me funny looks. What am I supposed to do now?"

> Fortunately, Rafi's therapist was able to guide him in using a form of systematic desensitization (chapter 6) to help Rafi tolerate being with black people without the conditioned anxiety. We also appealed to his logical mind ("the two rational brain cells I have left," he joked) to facilitate his use of self-talk (chapter 6) to remind himself that his aversion was just a symptom and that he could work through it. The therapist also advised him to find areas of relative safety, like an open hallway, to begin to purposefully engage the black coworkers he already knew in pleasant conversation, as a form of *in vivo* desensitization (chapter 6) to complement the work he and his therapist did in session.

Posttraumatic stress disorder is classified as one of the anxiety disorders, and this syndrome has been described in detail in chapter 2.

MOOD DISORDERS

Mood disorders are generally classified into unipolar and bipolar types, depending on whether the extreme changes in mood are in one direction (down-depressed) or both directions (down-depressed and up-elated or up-angry).

Major Depressive Disorder

Major depressive disorder is characterized by episodes of depressed mood that may last for days, weeks, or months at a time. In severe cases, the individual may be virtually immobilized. More characteristically, subjects feel dejected, demoralized, helpless, and hopeless. Sleep and appetite may be impaired; alternatively, some individuals become hypersomnic (sleep virtually all the time) or hyperphagic (binge eat). Concentration and memory may be affected to the point where individuals feel they are becoming demented. Gone is any motivation or enthusiasm for work, play, or family activities. Accompanying emotions may include anxiety, panic, irritability, or anger. The disorder usually occurs in cycles over the life span, and fortunately, in most cases, is very responsive to treatment.

As with most syndromes, depression will likely be exacerbated by criminal victimization. The sense of helplessness and hopelessness that characterizes the cognitive component of depression may come to assimilate the ruminations about the crime, which may then become one of the cognitive themes of the patient's depressive narrative. On the positive side, this may sometimes serve to crystallize the otherwise amorphous depressed cognitive style of the depressed patient and can thereby provide a well-defined gateway into treatment.

> April had wrestled with her "black cloud," as she called it, since high school. Things would be going okay, but then, over the course of several weeks or months, her motivation for school or friends would deteriorate, she'd start to lose weight, her sleep would become "light and choppy," and life would take on a cold, gray cast where "nothing seemed to matter." On a few occasions, she scared her parents by talking about how "the world wouldn't miss me if I weren't here," and they took her to a psychiatrist, who prescribed an antidepressant. This seemed to help a great deal because, while she still got some down moods, she no longer suffered the bouts of incapacitating depression that had messed up her school work and social life. She graduated high school and attended a university in another city.

Then, one night she came back to her dorm and was surprised to see a figure running out of her room as she entered. On closer inspection, she discovered that the room had been ransacked. "I immediately went into a tailspin" and she stopped going to class. The campus police later caught the burglar, who had broken into several dorm rooms, but April just couldn't get back to a normal routine. A campus counselor told her she was "traumatized" by the burglary and by having her "personal space violated," but that eventually she'd "get past it." But what the counselor didn't understand, April said, was that, "this was just my usual depression, only it was kicked off this time by being scared by the break-in guy. I thought I was over these bad depressions and the fact that it could come back like this made me even more depressed."

Dysthymic Disorder

Dysthymic disorder is a more stable and persistent, but less severe, mood disorder. These individuals mentally limp through their daily activities, able to perform sufficiently to get by at work or at home, but they experience little pleasure or excitement from life—they are the walking wounded, leading a drab, joyless existence. Many of these individuals will deny being depressed, per se, but report that they've never known what it feels like to be actually happy. Some individuals with major depression will recover from their severe episodes, but only to the bland baseline state of dysthymia, rarely experiencing anything that could be called a happy or even normal mood. Thus, trying to get a premorbidly dysthymic crime victim to appreciate life's blessings in existential psychotherapy (chapter 7) may be a misguided clinical goal. Rather, more practically focusing on developing a sense of mastery for daily tasks will hopefully give the patient a sufficient sense of self-efficacy to continue functioning in spite of the traumatic event.

"I guess I've always been a glass-half-empty kind of guy," Franz said. "So when those sonsabitches threw me down and stole my car, I figured, 'Great—another shitty episode in my shitty life.' Since it happened in my company's parking lot, their EAP sent me for some counseling and the lady there said I was showing 'posttraumatic blurring' or 'blunting' or something like that. But it was just my usual blah mood and personality. She asked me if I wanted a referral to a psychiatrist for medication, and I just said, 'What's the point?' I think that freaked her out a little because she just sat there for a while giving me this funny look. I never went back there and just decided to take care of the car business and move on."

Bipolar Disorder

Bipolar disorder, also known as *manic-depressive illness,* is characterized by extreme shifts in mood, from elation to depression, usually with an absence of normal mood in between: For such individuals, there are only highs and lows, nothing in the emotional middle. The manic phase typically begins with the individual feeling energized and overconfident—pumped. He becomes hyperactive and grandiose, spinning all kinds of half-baked, unrealistic ideas and plans, but being increasingly impulsive and distractible. Thinking and speech become rapid and forced. Need for sleep decreases and the individual may be hypersexual; all appetites are on sensory overdrive. The overall impression is that of someone on stimulant drugs, and indeed, such individuals may abuse amphetamines, cocaine, or alcohol to enhance the natural high and try to keep it going.

At the beginning of the manic phase, the individual may appear quite engaging and entertaining in a gonzo-comic kind of way, but as the manic phase progresses, he becomes increasingly short-tempered, irritable, anxious, and paranoid. Inevitably, the crash comes as the individual begins to cycle into the depressed phase. At this point, if he's into drugs, he may increase his use of stimulants to try to prolong the high, but eventually even this isn't enough to stave off the depressive avalanche. Suicide is a distinct risk at this stage. In other bipolar patients, the manic phases do not involve elation so much as they are characterized mainly by irritability, anger, and paranoia, and these symptoms may be misdiagnosed as schizophrenia.

Crime victims who have previously suffered from bipolar disorder may be expected to incorporate the traumatic imagery, thought, and emotionality into their manic and depressed episodes. Remember that mood swings can be a prominent symptom of PTSD following crime victimization (chapter 2), so a thorough clinical history is essential in differentiating new from prior symptoms and developing an appropriate treatment plan. Following a traumatic victimization, and facing legal hassles ahead, many bipolar patients may be at increased risk of substance abuse (also see below), so clinicians should monitor this as carefully as possible.

> Hank was trying to score some coke one Saturday night and was beaten and robbed for his efforts. Over the next several days, he became increasingly hypervigilant and paranoid, slept little, and eventually walked into a police station and told them he was being stalked and threatened by both the DEA and the Columbian drug cartel. The police took him to a local emergency room, where the attending psychiatrist diagnosed paranoid schizophrenia. Hank was

transferred to a local psychiatric facility, where the diagnosis became bipolar disorder, manic phase. When his assault victim history was related to the staff, the differential diagnostic rule-out became acute stress disorder with psychotic features. Eventually, he signed himself out of the hospital AMA (against medical advice) and was lost to follow-up.

SCHIZOPHRENIA AND OTHER PSYCHOTIC DISORDERS

Psychotic disorders comprise a group of syndromes, the main commonality of which is a significant break with reality, characterized by severe disturbances of mood, thought, and goal-directed action.

Schizophrenia

The most common form of psychotic disorder is *schizophrenia,* which is a progressive syndrome, usually first presenting in adolescence or early adulthood (although childhood forms occur), and characterized by *delusions* (disturbances of thought and belief) and *hallucinations* (disturbances of perception), which are typically auditory (hearing voices), and more rarely, visual (seeing things). Untreated schizophrenics may suffer episodic bouts of delusional and hallucinatory psychosis, between which they may appear simply odd or weird, unable to maintain any consistent work activity or social connection. Many of these individuals swell the ranks of the street people found in any major municipality. Even if not homeless per se, individuals with schizophrenia are at extremely high risk for criminal victimization and are also highly likely to be arrested, usually for misdemeanor crimes such as vagrancy, panhandling, public urination, shoplifting, simple assault (annoying and harassing passersby), and drug crimes.

Although diagnostic overlap is common, schizophrenia is typically classified into four major types:

- The *paranoid* type is characterized mainly by delusions of persecution and accusatory hallucinations.
- The *disorganized* type is characterized by general aimlessness and lack of contact with reality.
- The *catatonic* type is more commonly seen in institutional settings because of their near-immobility and lack of responsiveness to outside stimulation.

- The *undifferentiated* type may comprise features of the other three classifications and/or show additional symptoms.

Treating schizophrenic victims of crime will usually be difficult for all the reasons that schizophrenic patients are difficult to treat in general: poor interpersonal relatedness, lack of engagement, unreliable and inconsistent behavior, and poor medication compliance. As victims, law enforcement and criminal justice authorities are likely to take them less seriously than other citizens because of their poor cooperation and because of what most officials perceive as their continued cycling through the so-called revolving doors of the mental health and criminal justice systems.

Delusional Disorders

Delusional disorders are distinguished clinically from schizophrenia by the fact that the affected individuals may function adequately in most life areas, despite the presence of isolated, fixed ideas, which are nevertheless sufficiently out of sync with reality to qualify as delusions. Examples of the main types of delusional disorders include the following:

- An *erotomanic* type of delusional disorder would describe a movie fan convinced that a starlet he has never met is nevertheless in love with him.
- A *grandiose* type of delusional disorder would involve the belief that one has the true secret for world peace, if only he could get on national television and tell everyone.
- A *persecutory* delusional disorder would characterize the individual who believes that "they" (whoever they are) are after him (often for the purpose of stealing or silencing his grandiose idea).
- A *jealous* type of delusional disorder would apply to the husband who is absolutely convinced that his wife is having an affair, despite no shred of hard evidence.
- A *somatic* type of delusional disorder would describe the person who believes that his body is decaying from within, shrinking or expanding, or that radio waves are changing his skin color or brain patterns.

When individuals with delusional disorders or outright schizophrenia become crime victims, the events of the crime may be incorporated into the delusional framework or, alternatively, the criminal assault may remain peripheral to the core delusion, seeming more like a distraction to the patient from his or her "real" concerns. Recalling the adage, "Just because you're paranoid doesn't mean they're *not* out to get you," the clinician should try to ascertain whether what seem like grandiose or persecutory delusions may, in fact, have some basis in reality. For example, some disenfranchised victims may be correctly perceiving that they're being taken less seriously than other solid citizens. Or a victim or witness may legitimately fear retaliation from the cohorts of a criminal he or she is scheduled to testify against.

> "Jake's been a regular around here for a while," said Officer Ortiz. "Usually, he's harmless, occasionally he panhandles the citizens, but he moves away when we tell him. He mostly stays away from the other homeless guys and shows up at the shelter pretty steady, especially when it gets cold. The other day, we found Jake lying on the sidewalk, bleeding, busted up pretty bad. We took him over to County General and they got him stable, then we tried to question him about what happened and who did this, but all he kept saying was that it 'wasn't hardly nothing' and that he 'had to get back to the compound,' whatever the hell that meant. We couldn't get anything coherent out of him to work the case, so we just let the hospital patch him up and they let him go."

PERSONALITY: TRAITS, TYPES, AND DISORDERS

We all have different personality traits, which contribute to our psychological uniqueness as human beings. But when these personal quirks begin to grate harmfully on others or significantly derail our own success, psychologists speak of having a *personality disorder,* which is defined as "an enduring pattern of inner experience and behavior that deviates markedly from the expectations of the individual's culture, is pervasive and inflexible, has an onset in adolescence or early adulthood, is stable over time, and leads to distress or impairment" (APA, 2000, p. 629).

Seriously personality-disordered individuals often show little insight into their own behavior and have similarly poor understanding of the adverse impact they have on themselves and others. They characteristically justify their self-defeating or offensive behavior as someone else's fault or being due to uncontrollable fate. It is the *extremes* of their self-perception and conduct toward others that distinguish personality disordered individuals from those with more moderate personality traits and styles (Miller, 1990, 2003a, 2003b, 2004b, 2006b; Millon & Davis, 2000; Sperry, 1995, 1999). This may have implications for crime victimization, as many types of personality disorders carry a heightened risk for exposure to dangerous situations in general, including being the victim of crime, while others may show exaggeratedly pathological responses to such victimization.

Histrionic Personality

Histrionic personality is a pattern of excessive emotionality, attention seeking, need for excitement, flamboyant theatricality in speech and behavior, an impressionistic and impulsive cognitive style, and use of exaggeration to maintain relationships for the purpose of getting emotional needs met by being admired and cared for by others. These victims will describe their crime experience in dramatic tones, as if they were the only ones that such a thing has ever happened to. Their overemotionality and difficulty staying on topic will make it difficult for law enforcement officers, attorneys, and mental health clinicians to conduct a coherent interview. Craving attention, they may try to ingratiate themselves with the authorities by virtue of their wit and charm; there may be a creepily inappropriate coquettishness or seductiveness to their demeanor that seems out of place for someone who's just been victimized. Correspondingly, professionals who are able to project an attitude of empathic concern will probably find these subjects more than willing to cooperate. The problem is that, in their desire to please, they may often change their story to suit what they believe the listener wants to hear. This is usually not deliberate deception, but a largely unconscious and instinctive strategy to put themselves in the best possible light and get their interlocutor to like them. Careful, gentle probing of inconsistencies may be necessary to get at the facts of a given case. In therapy, they will typically be preoccupied with how much the therapist likes and approves of them, which may make it difficult to adhere to treatment goals.

> The seasoned detective had questioned some pretty tough perps in his day, but few were as difficult to pin down to a straight story as Caroline—and she was the victim! Tissues flew as she sobbed out her story of being accosted in her apartment building hallway until neighbors scared the would-be assailant away. "But the more we try to get her to give us a description, the more the story keeps changing," the detective complained. "It's almost as if she's making it up as she goes along. I even started to wonder if this was a false report situation, but she did have some cuts and bruises that looked real. But how are we supposed to follow up on this?"

> Caroline fared little better with two therapists she saw soon after her assault. Both were frustrated by the difficulty getting a coherent clinical history. "Every time I ask a question, she moves her answer

in the direction of that question," said one. Finally, a third counselor took a more open-ended approach. She put aside the structured interview and let Caroline tell her own story as it emerged over several sessions, without probing or questioning, and was eventually able to piece together a picture of events that seemed to conform to the facts. The clinician was also able to marshall the proper degree of empathic attunement so that Caroline felt engaged and understood, without the need to impress the therapist with emotional or narrative embellishment.

Borderline Personality

Borderline personality is a pattern of instability in interpersonal relationships, fragile self-image, and labile emotional swings. These individuals may exhibit a pattern of erratic and intense relationships, alternating between over-idealization and devaluation of others. They may show self-damaging impulsiveness in the form of risky activities, substance abuse, and explosions of grief and rage. Signs of emotional instability include inappropriately intense anger and/or depressive mood swings and possible suicidality. Persistent identity disruption may manifest itself as disturbances in self-image, blurred interpersonal boundaries and relationships, confused goals and values, and a chronic feeling of emptiness that may propel the quest for stimulation via substance abuse or provocation of confrontational incidents.

Given this description, it is not surprising that borderline individuals frequently find themselves on both ends of the criminal victimization spectrum—as victims and perpetrators. These individuals are commonly encountered by police officers on domestic disturbance calls or in workplace disputes (chapters 11, 12), since their most intense conflicts involve those with whom they've had some kind of previous close relationship. Extremely sensitive to rejection or betrayal, they may respond to any slight with intense anger, which may escalate to violence. As crime victims in treatment, they are likely to be preoccupied with how they've been wronged by the evil perpetrator and how they can achieve retribution, which they will justify in terms of righteous justice. Any hint that the therapist isn't wholly and completely on their side will be met by fierce resistance, so setting realistic therapeutic goals is likely to be challenging. One strategy is to utilize calming techniques and active listening (chapter 6) to convey a sense of sincere concern, backed by no-nonsense resoluteness that you will support the patient but that retributive violence or self-destructive behavior won't be tolerated.

"I want that bastard in jail," Janine told the arriving officers, "he's hurt me for the last time." This wasn't the first domestic disturbance at this residence that the local cops had responded to, but, on this occasion, both Janine and her husband looked like a truck had run them over. It became a dispute over who hit who first, but clearly, each had taken a beating from the other. Under the state guidelines, the police had no choice but to arrest both of them. A few days later, the court-ordered psychological examiner was surprised to hear Janine say of her husband, "He's the most important thing in my life. I love him so much. I couldn't live without him."

Narcissistic Personality

Narcissistic personality is a pattern of grandiosity, sense of entitlement, arrogance, need for admiration, and lack of empathy for others' feelings or opinions. Individuals with this pattern typically get in trouble because they believe that rules are for other people and that they are allowed to bend, twist, or shatter those rules because of their special entitlement and unique powers of perception, insight, and judgment. They expect others to appreciate, admire, and defer to them, and they will become irritated or rageful when they don't get the respect they feel they naturally deserve. Not surprisingly, this attitude tends to irritate and antagonize other people and this may occasionally impel others to assault them.

Both criminal justice and mental health professionals can expect two kinds of reactions from narcissistic crime victims. The first is an over-familiar, back-slapping camaraderie that implies that he and you are really of equal status or have a common bond: "It's okay, officer, I understand all about police procedure—my uncle's a cop in Atlanta," or, "I get what you're doing, doc—I took a lot of psych courses in college. This is that paradoxical kind of therapy, right?"

You can use this to your advantage by allowing the subject to take your side and emphasize how what you're asking him to do is of mutual benefit: "I'm glad you have an understanding of law enforcement protocol [or] clinical mental health procedure, Mr. Newman. That's why I know you'll appreciate how important it is to get through these questions one at a time."

The other reaction (sometimes after the first reaction has failed to get the anticipated response) is outrage at not being regarded as a special case: "I'm not just some junkie that got bopped on the head—I'm an important man in this community and I expect my case to be taken seriously!" Or, "What do you mean you can't schedule a few extra therapy appointments for me this week after work? Didn't I explain to you how I'm suffering here?"

In these situations, verbally disarm the subject by being somewhat deferential, but at the same time maintaining the need for your actions: "We understand, sir, and we are taking your case seriously. We've assigned an investigator to it as we do with all high-priority violent crimes. We do appreciate your patience and cooperation." Or, "I don't have anything after 6:30 pm this week, but if you can be flexible with your work schedule, we can carve out an extra early-morning slot first thing on Monday."

Similar to the case of the histrionic personality, interviewing the narcissistic personality crime victim is likely to elicit some degree of mood incongruity and looseness of content.

> Despite having been pretty seriously stabbed a few months earlier ("They say the knife lacerated my liver and missed my aorta by a few millimeters"), Freddy was all smiles as he sauntered into the therapist's office, plopped into the chair, opened his mouth, and started talking—and was still at it an hour later when it was time for the session to end. In fact, after about 3 minutes of clinical history relating to the criminal assault itself, Freddy spent the rest of the session educating the clinician about his illustrious business career, the fortunes he'd won and lost, the travels he'd taken, the important people he knew, and other highlights of his exciting life. The overall impression was that the crime itself—even though it had literally nearly cost Freddy his life—was but a minor detail in the illustrious autobiography he felt compelled to grace his counselor with, and the clinician later recalled thinking how this gave new meaning to the term *free association*.

Avoidant Personality

Avoidant personality is a pattern of social inhibition, feelings of inadequacy, and hypersensitivity to criticism. Even relatively neutral interpersonal interactions or confrontations are approached with trepidation and these individuals are often comorbid for anxiety or mood disorders (see above). A violent crime is likely to shock these individuals into a state of hermit-like withdrawal. When questioned by law enforcement, their extreme nervousness may lead the investigator to suspect that they've got something to hide, thus prompting a more extensive search and questioning, further agitating the subject. In therapy, they will often choke on their words, anxiety inhibiting their ability to give a coherent narrative of events or description of their feelings.

In interacting with these crime victims, a collaborative and supportive clinical interview style will be the most productive approach. In the beginning, you may want to utilize a more gently directive, structured, question-and-answer format of the interview protocol, which may actually make it easier for avoidant types to reveal what they know in piecemeal fashion. Later, if and when they become more comfortable, you can probe for a more free-recall type of narrative. Therapeutically, these patients may respond well to calming and arousal-control strategies (chapter 6), once a basic level of trust has been established.

> Artie's supervisor at the car dealership said he was a good mechanic at the repair bay, got his orders, did his work, and didn't waste time. Most of the other guys basically liked Artie, although they admitted they didn't know much about him, since he pretty much kept to himself. But they all felt bad when one new employee, who turned out to be a little crazy, started picking on Artie for no reason and then one day just hauled off and hit him. The attacker was fired and arrested, but Artie took a leave of absence and hasn't been back to work yet.

Dependent Personality

Dependent personality is a pattern of submissive and clinging behavior stemming from an excessive need for care and nurturance. Whereas avoidant subjects fear people and prefer to be away from them, dependent personalities cling to people for guidance and support and fear only their rejection and abandonment. Even more so than avoidant personalities, dependent types will respond well to a supportive, collaborative approach to clinical interviewing. The danger is that, in their eagerness to please, they may be apt to tell you what they think you want to hear, so follow up your open-ended questions with a few close-ended queries to nail down the details. Be careful, however, not to give the impression that you don't believe or trust the patient, which he or she will take as a mortal wound, and which may close off any further productive therapeutic communication. For both avoidant and dependent personalities who have been victimized, don't necessarily mollycoddle them, but be careful about using therapeutic strategies that too quickly jar them out of their comfort zones, and be prepared to offer a lot of encouragement and support.

> "Be careful what you wish for," Robin's therapist told me in supervision, only half-jokingly. Robin had sought therapy following a date-rape episode and the clinician had begun training her to use self-calming and cognitive restructuring techniques (chapter 6), with considerable success. "You can call me in between sessions if you need a little guidance getting through some of the exercises," the therapist helpfully told Robin. What she probably should have

added, however, is, "but not twenty times a day." Robin kept phoning the therapist to make sure she was "doing everything right" and "not making any mistakes." We conjectured that what Robin really needed was some additional contact and support in her emotionally vulnerable state, so the therapist scheduled an extra session a week for the next few weeks. That seemed to be reassuring to Robin, and the between-session calls dropped to a manageable frequency.

Schizoid and Schizotypal Personalities

The central characteristics of both schizoid and schizotypal personalities include avoidance of others, severe deficiencies in social skills, generalized withdrawal from life, and sometimes impairment in perceptual and cognitive capacities. *Schizoid personality* is a pattern of aloof detachment from social interaction, with a restricted range of emotional expression. These are people who don't need people and are perfectly happy being left to themselves (as opposed to avoidant personalities who actually fear people). *Schizotypal personality* involves more serious disturbances of thinking, more bizarre behavior, and possibly delusions. It is thought that these two personality disorders really represent points on a continuum from schizoid to schizotypal to outright schizophrenia, the latter characterized by severe distortions of thought, perception, and action, including delusions and hallucinations (see above). In fact, schizoid and schizotypal personality disorders may episodically decompensate into schizophrenic-like psychotic states, especially under conditions of stress.

The flat, nonengaged interpersonal style of the schizoid crime victim may be mistaken for the affective blunting of PTSD. In fact, a number of schizoid and schizotypal victims seem to react less strongly than others to violence by virtue of their internal preoccupation with more important idiosyncratic concerns. These subjects may seem detached and disinterested during a law enforcement encounter, criminal justice proceeding, or clinical interview, not because they're ignoring or disrespecting the interviewer, but because of their internal preoccupations or because human interaction is of little interest to them to begin with. Any real distress may be masked by their relatively nonresponsive style, so a careful clinical history is still imperative. In most cases, their blank, far-away facial expression and attitude will be quite noticeable.

Even when they do communicate, the sometimes bizarre and delusional nature of the information these subjects provide may compromise its validity and usefulness. For both law enforcement investigative and clinical therapeutic purposes, encouraging a free narrative will likely yield either an incoherently rambling stream-of-consciousness oration or a rigidly obsessive reiteration of key ideas or phrases. Instead, it will be more effective to use a firm and directive approach to focus the schizoid subject's attention on simple, precise questions. These queries should be designed to yield specific, tangible bits of information that can then be painstakingly fitted together to create a coherent narrative of useful information. Standard forms of psychotherapy will usually be difficult, but a number of these individuals are able to form limited attachments with a trusted therapist who takes care not to overtly challenge the patient's idiosyncratic belief system and who can encourage him or her to utilize selective therapeutic techniques that can lessen the traumatic impact.

> For someone who'd just had a gun held to his head, Ben seemed strangely unconcerned about the jewelry store robbery. His main question was, "When can I go back to work?" A police department on-scene trauma counselor thought Ben might be suffering from posttraumatic numbing, so he referred him for mental health counseling. But over the first few sessions, it emerged that this flat, minimally responsive presentation was pretty much Ben's normal mood and demeanor, so he was discharged with an invitation to come back if he wanted to.

Antisocial Personality Disorder

Subjects with *antisocial personality disorder* are more often encountered within the criminal justice system as perpetrators than as victims, but in many social settings, both roles commonly alternate as these individuals, also sometimes termed *psychopaths,* are characterized by a completely self-centered worldview, lack of empathy for others, and a craving for immediate gratification, with little or no frustration tolerance. They have an excessive need for stimulation and excitement, and their behavior is impulsive, erratic, and markedly deficient in sustaining any long-term goal-directed behavior. More so than other offenders, punishment seems to have little effect on them, a feature that has both been noted behaviorally and documented neurophysiologically (Raine, 1993). Commonly, there is a long history of substance abuse and criminal activity, dating from childhood, at which age the syndrome is known as *conduct disorder* (APA, 2000; Mandel, 1997; Miller, 1988).

   In their youth, antisocial personalities typically have done poorly in academics, especially verbal subjects, although they may possess contrastingly high mechanical skill and athletic prowess. If big and strong enough, they were probably bullies since grade school. When older, they tend to be unreliable workers. They may perform poorly on formal IQ tests, again especially in the verbal areas, yet they typically possess a very keen social intelligence that they use to manipulate and exploit others for their own ends. They can be glibly persuasive, seductive, or threatening with facile ease, often in the same conversation. They are the classic con artists who can turn on the charm or flare into fury if that's what it takes to get what they want from others. Human beings, in their minds, are just objects to use and throw away, and there is no true sense of loyalty or friendship. People who value such human traits as love, honesty, commitment, or honor are seen by antisocial personalities as fools and suckers who deserve what they get.

Their frequent confrontations with others usually mean that they get a lot of people mad at them, so sooner or later somebody decides it's payback time. As crime victims, antisocial personalities are less likely to be concerned with recovering or becoming healthy, productive citizens again, because they were never these things to begin with. More likely, they'll attempt to use the criminal justice and mental health systems for their own aims, for example, to get money, favors, drugs, or special privileges. Nevertheless, they may experience classic posttraumatic symptoms in response to severe trauma and are very likely to use drugs and alcohol to self-medicate.

Probably, the first guideline for law enforcement and mental health interaction with these individuals relates to the old adage of not trying to outcon a con man. Any intervention that is perceived or misinterpreted as a ploy will be countermanipulated and exploited by the subject. Police officers, attorneys, and clinicians should all be alert to the cunning-conning dimension of the antisocial personality: Many of those who deal with these characters often find themselves "liking this guy too much." Lubit (2004) speaks of the "intense, emotionless gaze" that many antisocial personalities fix on their interlocutors, their attention seeming to be riveted on you in a kind of sham active listening posture, but their facial expression reveals no particular genuine feeling state because there isn't any—they're just searching for an angle to exploit.

Often, in dealing with these characters, their overpolite, deferential, and friendly demeanor may give you the distinct impression that you're being greased, or they may be so smooth that you can't even tell. For clinicians, there may come the crushing blow that all those months of intense therapy, when you really, really felt you were the only one who was reaching this patient, is abruptly revealed to be pointless when the patient doesn't need you anymore and lams out—maybe stealing something from your office as a memento, or covering the remaining bill with a bounced check.

The best approach is the most direct. Be firm, polite, and civil, and take nothing the antisocial subject says at face value. You'll be entreated, cajoled, and, in some cases, subtly or overtly threatened to do special favors for this patient, like writing letters on his behalf or even lending him money. It should be clear from the outset that any illegal activity will be immediately reported.

If this patient has been assigned to you by the court or other agency, bide your time until he cycles through the system. Minimize the use of therapeutic self-disclosure, which he will file away as ammunition to get back at you if he wants to. Your overall attitude should be authoritative: not abrasive, which may impel him to try to save face by becoming belligerently confrontational, but not too friendly, either, which will invariably be seized upon as a weakness to exploit.

Remember that the one thing antisocial personalities do respect is power, and if you provide this patient a face-saving means of ensuring compliance with your requests, and firmly present yourself as a reasonable but no-nonsense authority figure, the antisocial patient may grudgingly comply. If he isn't getting what he wants from the treatment process and there is no external compulsion for him to be there, he will soon eventually just leave.

> "They beat me pretty bad, Doc. I coulda died. I think God was giv-ing me a message to change my ways. Maybe you're the guy who can help me do that." Flattery will get you nowhere, Chico's therapist recalls thinking as his patient related his poignant, almost cinematic, tale of sin and redemption. Although seeming to make superficial sense, Chico's account of what happened to him never really added up. "And, by the way, Doc, the pain from my injuries is getting worse every day, but those other doctors won't give me any more Perco-cets. Do you think you could write them a letter or something?"

> Fortunately, Chico's psychologist was a tough cookie himself. He calmly but firmly laid down the rules of engagement, listened to Chico's numerous objections, repeated the rules again, and invited Chico to stay in treatment or—since this was not court-mandated treatment—to do whatever he felt was right for him. Chico said he'd think about it and was never heard from again.

ALCOHOL AND DRUG INTOXICATION

Drug and alcohol use is a risk factor for both committing a crime and being a victim of crime (Miller, 1985, in press-d; Schmalleger, 2007; Siegel, 2003). Thus, mental health clinicians who work with crime victims can expect to have to deal with substance abuse issues in some or many of their patients.

Signs of *alcohol intoxication* are familiar to anyone who has ever been to a New Year's Eve party: slurred speech, unbalanced posture, impaired coordi-nation, and so on. It is possible, however, for many drinkers who are legally intoxicated to act fairly normally, for example, when trying to impress a parole officer or mental health clinician with their intactness. Alcohol has varying effects, depending on the particular user, with some inebriated drinkers becoming more mellow and tractable, others becoming angry and agitated. In general, alcohol and most other drugs lower inhibitions and self-control, so any intoxicated person has to be approached with caution in any clinical or law enforcement encounter.

Less common, but potentially more serious, are signs and symptoms of *alcohol withdrawal* in subjects who are physiologically addicted to alcohol. This usually presents as an agitated state with tremors (the shakes). In severe cases, this can be accompanied by hallucinations and/or seizures. An acute state of agitated delirium, characterized by intense fear and tactile and visual hallucinations of vermin crawling on the skin, is called *delirium tremens* (the DTs). Typically, such individuals will be so clearly impaired that the need for transport to a medical facility is obvious. Years of long-term heavy abuse of alcohol can also lead to *alcoholic dementia,* but these patients are likely to be confined to institutions and not typically encountered in clinical practice.

A rare, but more dangerous, syndrome is *pathological intoxication,* where even small amounts of alcohol trigger violent rages in susceptible individuals, which is thought to be due to an electrophysiological disturbance in sensitive limbic areas of the brain (see chapter 2). Witnesses will describe an explosion of rage in which the subject's actions appear to be "on automatic" or "like a runaway train," fueled by adrenalin, and capable of inflicting severe damage to anyone who gets in his way. These episodes typically last only a few minutes, and there is usually at least some recall of the incident by the subject, who may also subsequently express regret at losing control. During these brief episodes, it is useless to try to talk the subject out of his aggressive actions. The only effective strategy is to use appropriate physical restraint by qualified authorities to keep him from harming others. Understandably, such a combative individual is at high risk for being counterattacked and injured.

Other substances of abuse have different effects on behavior, depending on their biochemical action within the nervous system. *Stimulants* (uppers), such as cocaine and amphetamine, produce a racing kind of high, with rapid thought and speech, erratic and impulsive behavior, and a turbo-charged energy level. Such individuals may occasionally become violent, but more commonly, they will present as simply annoying and raucous, quite similar to the manic state described earlier; in fact, many manic subjects deliberately use stimulants to enhance and extend their natural high. Danger may arise when their overconfidence and impulsivity leads to confrontations that may get them beat up, shot, stabbed, or arrested.

Central nervous system *depressants* (downers), such as barbiturates (e.g., Quaaludes) or benzodiazepines (e.g., Valium, Xanax), have effects similar to alcohol, which include a calming effect, but this tranquilization can be accompanied by a loosening of inhibitions, which may lead to impulsive and dangerous actions. Most encounters with medical or law enforcement services for these users tend to be due to their passing out unconscious in a public place, in which case they may be robbed or beaten, but they may become combative if they are still confused and disoriented when aroused from their stupor.

The effects of *hallucinogens,* such as marijuana, LSD, or angel dust, may range from mellow loopiness to violent delirium. *Organic hydrocarbons,* such as the glue and paint thinner enjoyed by sniffers or huffers, tend to produce a toxic delirious state; these latter substances are also extremely injurious to brain tissue and can produce long-term cognitive impairment.

Especially if this has been their previous pattern, crime victims who have been habitual substance users will continue or escalate their use post-victimization, now with the added justification that they're doing it to deal with the stress of their ordeal, which may at least partly be true. Tricky differential diagnostic questions may arise in cases where substance abuse, PTSD, and other syndromes all coexist and feed off one another. Then, the clinician may then be faced with complex treatment issues. For example, it may be unrealistic to try to enforce a sobriety or abstinence policy in a habitually drug-using or drinking crime victim who's only way of feeling in control is to numb herself with her drug of choice. The counselor may have to wait until some degree of emotional and behavioral control have been achieved before broaching the subject of tackling the substance issue. These clinical situations are best handled on a case-by-case basis.

> "Treatment? What do you mean, treatment?" Marcy told her victim advocate. "Every time I go to one of those counselors, they ask me if I'm using drugs and if I say yeah, then they're all like, 'Oh, well, we got to get you into a program.' I don't need any program, I just need something to help these nightmares and bad memories go away, and the beer and the pot are the only things that even help a little. They sent me to a psychiatrist for medication and he said he couldn't prescribe anything till I got detoxed. So what am I supposed to do?"

TRAUMATIC BRAIN INJURY AND THE POSTCONCUSSION SYNDROME

In the United States, an estimated 400,000 people are admitted to hospitals with traumatic brain injuries (TBIs) every year, and about one million suffer from head injury effects at any given time. The constellation of somatic, cognitive, and behavioral symptoms seen after TBI was first termed the *postconcussion syndrome* by Strauss and Savitsky (1934), and many of the symptoms described in that original report are psychological in nature: irritability, poor concentration, loss of confidence, anxiety, depression, and hypersensitivity to light and noise. Today, the postconcussion syndrome describes a cluster of symptoms that occur following a closed head injury—frequently a mild head injury—and it continues to be a source of clinical and forensic controversy (Miller, 1991a, 1993e; Miller & Magier, 1993; Parker, 1990, 2001).

Despite the fact that many criminal assaults involve physical trauma to the head and face, when crime victims are medically treated, the focus is typically on observable injuries and often overlooks mild postconcussive symptoms, especially when there are few or no objective signs, or more commonly, when these have been insufficiently explored (Miller, 1993e; Parker, 2001). Conversely, crime victims treated by mental health clinicians may report an array of postconcussion symptoms that may be misdiagnosed as anxiety, depression, PTSD, or even malingering (Miller, 1998f, 1998g; also see chapter 4). To compound matters, several of these syndromes may coexist with the postconcussion syndrome; indeed, a particularly common cluster of syndromes in criminal or accidental traumatic injuries of many types involves the triad of postconcussion syndrome, chronic pain, and PTSD (Miller, 1993d, 1993e, 1998a, 1999i), all of which must be recognized and treated appropriately.

Commonly reported postconcussive symptoms include headache, dizziness, fatigue, slowness and inefficiency of thought and action, impaired concentration and memory, irritability, anxiety, depression, impaired sleep pattern, heightened somatic concern, hypersensitivity to noise and light, blurred or double vision, problems in judgment, and altered sex drive (Miller, 1993e; Parker, 2001). Postconcussive symptoms that may become the focus of particular diagnostic confusion in the context of criminal victimization include the following:

Difficulties in attention and concentration. Patients have trouble following directions, keeping on track with daily schedules, maintaining continuity of activities in the face of distractions, or remembering the sequence of steps of various activities. They are slow to focus on tasks or figure out what to do next. A typical complaint is that "I'm not as sharp as I used to be." Others may describe them as "space cadets." In a clinical session, their attention may seem to wander, and this may be mistaken for disinterest or posttraumatic numbing and withdrawal. In the legal context, these subjects may have trouble focusing on the interviewer's questions, which may be misinterpreted as evasiveness.

Learning and memory problems. These include difficulty retaining material heard or read, forgetting names or faces of both new and familiar people, confusing one person with another, having trouble recalling information "that I know I used to know," and struggling to remember things that used to be learned easily. In general, it is harder for new information to get processed, and what does get in seems to be forgotten more quickly. Clinicians may grow frustrated that so little of what transpires in the therapy sessions seems to stick, and this may be misinterpreted as posttraumatic memory impairment or lack of motivation on the patient's part. Criminal investigators may grow suspicious that the crime victim's story seems to change or that he seems to be unable to recall certain aspects of the crime, yet is crystal clear about others.

Slowness and inefficiency. Tasks take longer to do and they may have to be done over and over again. In many cases, the basic skills and knowledge necessary to perform a task may be essentially preserved, but the quickness and efficiency with which those abilities are applied to the problem at hand have been impaired. This may be mistaken for willful noncooperation or passive-aggressive sabotage of treatment goals.

Concreteness. Postconcussion patients generally do better with tasks and in situations that are familiar rather than novel, structured rather than open-ended, and specific rather than ambiguous. Because of frontal lobe egocentricity, patients may not appreciate jokes that involve shifting or reversing one's point of view, and they may have difficulty perceiving more than one side of an argument (their own) or putting themselves in another person's shoes—which is often interpreted by others as shallowness or selfishness. Be aware, however, that traumatic stress can also cause people to become very concrete, as can the blunted affect of a number of psychological syndromes described in this chapter.

Depression and mood swings. Patients may show a Jekyll-and-Hyde lability of emotional responsiveness over the course of minutes, hours, or days. Irritable outbursts or crying spells may occur with minimal provocation. Manic highs may alternate with depressive lows, and family members may report feeling yoked to the patient's emotional rollercoaster. Always vigilant of victim's abrupt mood swings, family members may feel incapable of relaxing, which tends to put everybody on edge. Mood swings can also be a feature of the alternating intrusion–numbing cycle of PTSD (chapter 2) and can occur as a feature of other syndromes described in this chapter. In many cases, postconcussion symptoms and other symptoms aggravate one another in a vicious cycle.

Impaired sex drive. Although this is an expectable feature of the aftermath of sexual assault (chapter 10) and some other crimes, sexual inhibition and, more rarely, heightened sex drive, may be seen in cases of traumatic brain injury that affects hypothalamic, limbic, and/or frontal lobe functioning. As always, a good clinical history and knowledge of differential diagnostic alternatives are the main clinical tools to guard against misdiagnosis and mistreatment.

Agitation, irritability, paranoia, and rage. Problems with emotional control may most prominently affect anger. A smoldering edginess may be seen, and persistent carping, complaining, and hostility on the patient's part may strain relationships with friends, family, workmates, and some clinicians. Many postconcussion patients seem to have developed a short fuse that at intervals flares into aggression and rage, in part fueled by the increased suspiciousness and paranoia that sometimes additionally develop after TBI. The latter may stem from reduced ability to process incoming information: missing certain pieces of what people say or what's going on around him, the patient may interpret this as others deliberately trying to trick him. In cases of crime victimization, the patient may have every reason to be mistrustful, and his reduced cognitive processing capacities only heighten this paranoia, leading to a vicious cycle.

Impulsivity and inertia. Patients may alternate between mute inactivity and frenetic running about, starting and leaving unfinished all sorts of tasks and projects, taking dangerous physical and social risks at home or at work, and generally showing little foresight or judgment. This type of syndrome may be especially associated with damage to the brain's frontal lobes, the executive control system for modulating thought, feeling, and action. Lack of appreciation of postconcussive effects may lead clinicians to interpret these behaviors as symptoms of bipolar disorder, personality disorder, posttraumatic despair, willful obstructionism, or "just not giving a damn about her own recovery."

"I must have served that guy a hundred times and today he decides to clock me," Katie said. "I don't even remember the tray cracking over my head—the whole thing is still fuzzy." Katie was waitressing at a local, upscale health food restaurant, when a patron, who had always seemed a little weird but harmless, suddenly picked up a heavy metal tray and struck Katie from behind. The next thing she remembers is sitting on a chair with another waiter holding a towel to her bleeding head. Nobody saw her actually pass out, but she was dazed for a couple of seconds. The attacker ran out of the restaurant but was later arrested by the police. Paramedics were called and Katie was taken to a local ER, where she received a single stitch for the cut on her scalp and was released with instructions to follow up with her doctor.

Over the weekend, the worst consequence of the attack was scalp pain at the suture site, but Katie felt well enough to return to work on Monday: "Besides, I needed the money." However, over the next few days, she began making "stupid mistakes," mixing up orders, forgetting to refill drinks, going to the wrong tables, putting phone callers on hold and not coming back, and struggling to recall the names of regular patrons who had been coming in for years. She started feeling like a "moron." She still felt a little twinge of fear when she waited on the table where the angry wacko attacked her but not enough to account for her state of confusion.

After a day or two of this, the restaurant manager asked Katie if she wanted to use some of her sick days to take more time off. Since it was already Friday again, she decided to take the following Monday and Tuesday off for doctors' visits. One of the appointments was with a therapist who also happened to be a neuropsychologist. He explained to her the nature of the postconcussion syndrome and gave her some literature on it that she could share with her workmates if she wanted to. She and the psychologist devised a plan to pace her activities at the restaurant so that she could begin by working shorter shifts at less peak times and then gradually work her way up to her former full schedule. Fortunately, her manager was cooperative and, within a few weeks, Katie was back to her regular routine.

CONCLUSIONS

"The first step to making a diagnosis is to think of it" (Thibault, 1992). Thick or thin, the eggshell that is our patient is the one we have to deal with, and the better we understand the unique and complex dynamics that influence his or her reaction to a criminal victimization, the better we will be able to encourage their inner healing resources and teach others that he or she can climb the psychological ladder back to an optimum state of health. But this also sometimes means confronting the clinical mimics and masquerades that can confound the diagnostic and treatment process with victims of crime.

CHAPTER 4

Crime Victim Trauma

Confounding Symptoms and Syndromes

A person is attacked and injured, physically and/or psychologically. We want to help, so we automatically assume that the victim's distress is caused by the attack in question. But, as discussed in the last chapter, sometimes we have to understand that the distress experienced by crime victims may be related to syndromes that don't necessarily directly reflect the effects of the criminal victimization. This is not to blame the victim, but to recognize the reality that many of our patients may exaggerate, distort, or fabricate their posttraumatic symptoms for reasons that may range from the psychodynamic to the utilitarian. Being able to recognize these so-called shadow syndromes is essential, to either treat them effectively or to direct the crime victim to other services that might be more appropriate.

SOMATOFORM DISORDERS

The common feature of the *somatoform disorders* is the presence of subjective physical symptoms that suggest a medical illness or syndrome but that are not fully explainable by, or attributable to, a general medical condition, substance abuse, or other type of mental disorder (Miller, 1984). Needless to say, a thorough medical workup is necessary to rule out actual physical illness or injury, and there is no clinical rule that says that somatizing patients can't develop real illnesses or sustain real injuries. Indeed, otherwise minor injuries sustained in the criminal assault may become the nidus for one or more somatoform disorders. In the current classification of *DSM-IV-TR* (APA,

2000), somatoform disorders include several subtypes. Although these tend to be relatively consistent from patient to patient, it should be recognized that patients may show more than one subtype, a combination of subtypes, or alternation between several subtypes as a continuum of coping style (van der Kolk, 1994).

Somatization Disorder

Somatization disorder, formerly referred to as Briquet's syndrome or just hysteria, involves a history of multiple unexplained physical symptoms and complaints, beginning before age 30, and often traced to childhood and adolescence. Outbreaks of numerous and varied symptoms may occur in clusters that wax and wane over time, often in response to interpersonal, vocational, and other stressors. Associated features include anxiety, depression, impulsivity, relationship problems, psychosocial discord, and possibly substance abuse.

Symptoms in somatization disorder may closely mimic standard traumatic disability syndromes, or they may be atypical or frankly bizarre in quality, location, or duration. The patients typically describe their symptoms in exaggerated, florid terms, and several physicians may be consulted concurrently, leading to secondary problems associated with medication abuse and unnecessary surgical treatment. Forensic psychological examiners or treating clinicians who carefully review medical records of these crime victims will typically be impressed by the sheer number and variety of past injuries, illnesses, and unexplained symptoms, covering a wide range of organ systems and medical diagnoses.

From the point of view of crime victim treatment, clinicians should try to determine whether the present symptoms are related to the aftermath of the criminal assault or fall into a prior long-standing pattern and history of multiple symptoms and complaints. In pure somatization disorder the patient genuinely believes that he or she is ill or impaired and, most probably, that all or most of the disability is related to the criminal assault. The underlying motivation is frequently inferred to be a quest for support and reassurance, or manipulation of the affection of a significant other. The psychodynamic goal is the satisfaction of dependency needs by reliance on caretakers or on the protective role of medical and/or judicial authority. In such cases, being a "victim" can have multiple meanings, including the need to be treated with extra special care, consideration, and love.

Jean, a 53-year-old female office manager, had undergone numerous diagnostic tests and treatments for headaches, dizziness, anxiety attacks, and gastrointestinal symptoms since her early 20s. Over the years, she frequently voiced fears of having a brain tumor or a "silent stroke," despite the lack of medical evidence. Two years ago, she sustained a mild closed-head injury when she was knocked to the ground in a purse-snatching incident.

Since then, her headaches and dizziness worsened, accompanied by hypersensitivity to light and noise, tinnitus, anxiety attacks, and severe "forgetfulness." Six months later, brain MRI, EEG, and other tests were all within normal limits, and neuropsychological testing showed mild, equivocal findings. She is now concerned about permanent brain damage and continues to seek consultations. In addition, she has developed cardiac palpitations and intestinal spasms.

Conversion Disorder

The essential feature of *conversion disorder* is the presence of sensory or motor deficits that appear to suggest a neurological or medical illness or injury. In conversion disorder, the patient is almost always unshakably convinced of the disability, and the underlying motivation typically involves the attempted resolution of psychological conflicts, such as those involving dependency wishes, by channeling them into physical impairment. Alternatively, there may be an actual symbolic conversion of a particular psychological conflict into a representative somatic expression, as in psychogenic paralysis of an arm in a crime victim who wishes to repudiate a hostile retaliation fantasy that makes him "feel like a bad person" or severe, incapacitating back pain in a worker who believes that "I was a *stand-up guy,* but my *spineless* company didn't *back me up* when my coworker attacked me and knocked me *flat on my back.*"

Other examples of symbolic conversion symptoms seen in crime victims include visual or auditory impairment ("I can't stand to look at what he's done to me," "I don't want to hear any more about this case"); genitourinary and sexual dysfunction, most frequently seen in victims of sexual assault; disturbances in consciousness or cognition, such as impaired memory ("What happened is all a big blank to me"); and psychogenic seizures, or fainting spells. Unlike the anxious, agitated, angry, or depressed emotional state of many injured crime or accident victims, conversion patients may display a phenomenon known as *la belle indifférence,* a bland, almost nonchalant demeanor that seems to suggest that the conviction of physical impairment is of little concern to the patient, despite his or her protests of catastrophic ruin.

Exacerbations are typically precipitated by psychosocial stresses including the ordeal of the crime itself, as well as resulting personal, family, job, and legal hassles. A common psychodynamic force in men who feel they were sneakily coldcocked, or otherwise overcome unfairly in a physical confrontation, is a combination of anger and derailment of overcompensated masculinity that had previously been utilized as a defense against unconscious dependency wishes (Ford, 1977–1978).

> Willie, a 36-year-old male prison guard, was jumped by a group of inmates during a carelessly carried-out cell search conducted by several of his coworkers. He sustained a low back injury, resulting in a mildly herniated lumbar disk and some soft tissue sprain-strain injury, along with a few scrapes and bruises. But the fatal injury was to his self-image. He had always prided himself on being a very hardworking, independent, and capable man, holding two jobs and supporting his wife and children, plus his wife's mother. Tall, physically imposing, but with a calm, authoritative, no-nonsense demeanor, he had built a reputation at the prison of being the guy who could talk down any situation. "But these guys were on me before I knew what happened and they beat my ass till the other guards pulled them off."

> Over the course of several weeks, as he was scheduled to return to work, Willie's low back pain worsened and was accompanied by progressive weakness and numbness in his legs. Eventually, his right leg "gave out," and soon he was walking with crutches. He is now convinced of his total incapacity for work and is claiming total permanent disability, despite the lack of medical evidence of serious injury, and even in the face of his insurance company's threatened termination of benefits because of his noncompliance with treatment. When queried, he exudes an eerie calm and says, "This is what they've done to me, but I've learned to accept my fate. I'll just have to live with the fact that I can't go back to being a guard."

Pain Disorder

The essential feature of *pain disorder* is chronic pain that causes significant distress or impairment in social, occupational, or other important areas of functioning, and in which psychological factors are judged to play a significant role in the onset, severity, exacerbation, or maintenance of the pain. The pain is not intentionally produced or feigned as in malingering or factitious disorder (see below), but rather it expresses, represents, or disguises an unconscious need, fear, or conflict, closer to somatization disorder. In addition, pain caused by documented physical injury can be exacerbated by real-life external stressors, setting up a vicious cycle, which may partly explain the etiology of such syndromes as fibromyalgia. In many cases, no legitimate medical explanation for the degree of severity and/or length of persistence of the pain can be discovered, and patients make the rounds from doctor to doctor until they are eventually shunted into the mental health system or rejected outright from further treatment (Miller, 1993b, 1998h).

In many cases, the chronic pain syndrome has a characteristic evolution and course (Hendler, 1982) that I have observed in both cases of accidental injury and crime victimization. The problem typically begins with some type of physical injury during the assault which causes an expectable degree of acute pain requiring medical treatment. In a certain proportion of these patients, the pain and disability never seem to get better, and in fact are reported by the patient to worsen with time. Various medical strategies are tried but nothing seems to work. Excessive physical disability related to sleep and appetite disturbance complicate the picture and are often exacerbated by the side effects of excessive and varied medication.

The patient's ongoing struggle with continual pain results in depression, obsessive somatic preoccupation, and a tendency to increasingly conceptualize most life events, activities, and problems solely in terms of how much pain it will cause, leading to a vicious cycle of hopelessness, helplessness, and despair. Each new treatment or physician may briefly inspire hope, which is then dashed by disappointment when the procedure fails to cure or significantly relieve the pain. Resentment and bitterness grow toward the medical profession, and this antipathy is reciprocated, as doctors come to dread visits by the "crock."

Pain now becomes the central focus of the crime victim's life, overshadowing the psychological aftermath of the assault itself. The victim progressively withdraws from family and social activities, and interpersonal interactions are fraught with tension and anger. Sometimes the patient develops a symbiotic alliance with a close family member or sympathetic clinician who becomes the patient's advocate and champion, further fueling a sense of martyred victimhood. In addition to the criminal trial, civil attorneys seeking compensatory damages (see chapter 16) may become involved in this support network, entrenching an adversarial relationship among patient, family, doctors, and the legal system.

Problems with medication and with alcohol and drug abuse may compound the problem by producing toxicity and addiction. Pain behavior now becomes the sole coping mechanism, progressively allowing the patient to avoid any kind of stressful task or issue. After considerable passage of time, even the patient's own doctors and attorneys begin to lose patience and subtly or overtly urge the patient to "give it up." In the worst case scenario, this leads to further incapacitation and the inexorable decline toward total invalidism.

Michelle was sexually assaulted at a drunken frat party while she was a sophomore at a local college. In her struggle, she sustained a right tear to the rotator cuff of her right shoulder, requiring surgery and several weeks of convalescence, followed by several more weeks of physical therapy. Finally, her orthopedist declared her to be well, but Michelle couldn't go back to class: Her right shoulder and arm still hurt too much to sit in a chair and write notes. Once a popular, outgoing young woman, she began to spend most of her time alone, refusing invitations to socialize because "I'm too sick."

As her grades declined and friends drifted away, Michelle began to spend more and more of her time going to doctors and alternative medicine practitioners, seeking relief from the pain that was ruining her life. When her physicians wouldn't prescribe any more pain medication, she fumed that it was because, "They're men—what do you expect? Men don't care about women, we're just things for them to use."

Hypochondriasis

The conviction that one has a serious illness or injury, in the face of numerous medical pronouncements to the contrary, is the defining characteristic of *hypochondriasis*. Patients are preoccupied with the fear of pathology, injury, disease, or deterioration, and tend to misinterpret normal bodily signals as signs of dire illness or injury. Unlike the varied and changing clinical presentations of somatization disorder, hypochondriacs tend to focus on one or a few specific symptoms and remain preoccupied with them, although the focus may shift over time from one symptom or disorder to another—for example, from memory impairment, to dizziness, to headaches, to back pain—and the associated anxiety may wax and wane over time. Unlike conversion disorder, there may be no actual observed or experienced impairment per se: It is the *fear* of insidious damage that is the problem. Examples seen after crime victimization include fear of undiagnosed brain damage "that will cause me to just stroke out in my car one day," or preoccupation with having contracted a sexually transmitted disease following a rape, even though multiple tests have yielded a clean bill of health.

The unconscious motivation in hypochondriasis typically involves a deflection of anxiety away from broader issues surrounding the implications of the crime for the victim's future safety and quality of life. This is achieved psychodynamically by focusing the anxiety on a more delimited, and hence controllable, source of concern in the form of a somatic symptom or feared illness. These tortured souls search endlessly for the one enlightened medical expert or miracle diagnostic technique that will either conclusively validate or rule out their worst fears. Yet with each reassurance, more fears arise because no one can actually prove they are well.

Ahmed, a 27-year-old male convenience store clerk, was involved in a late-night robbery attempt in which the thieves locked the three employees on duty in a storage closet, ransacked the place, and then set the store on fire. He recalls the smell of the acrid smoke in his nostrils as he tried to bang down the door to escape. All three workers got out with minor injuries, but the robbers were never caught.

Ahmed subsequently became preoccupied with the fear that he had been exposed to toxic fumes during the fire: "We have plastics and other materials that burned." He complained of subjective disturbances in breathing, including shortness of breath, painful inhalation, gasping and wheezing, hyperventilation, and other symptoms, all focused on the respiratory system, and he consulted cardiologists, pulmonologists, and other specialists and underwent numerous tests. Repeatedly, no medical abnormalities could be determined; besides, his coworkers, who were also exposed to the smoke, were doing comparatively well.

Finally, one of the medical doctors referred him for a psych consult. Clinical history revealed that at age 11, Ahmed had witnessed his grandfather gravely ill with congestive heart failure, and the boy had subsequently become obsessed with heart problems, spending a good portion of his adolescence and early adulthood fearing sudden cardiac death and undergoing many unrevealing diagnostic workups. The preoccupation with respiratory symptoms following his exposure to fumes appears to have been one form of extension and redirection of those fears.

Body Dysmorphic Disorder

Many criminal assaults leave victims physically injured and, in some cases, temporarily or permanently disfigured. Diagnostically, *body dysmorphic disorder* involves a preoccupation with an imagined defect in appearance, or overconcern with a minor defect that has resulted in some degree of disfigurement or loss of function that impacts the patient's self-image. More broadly, such overvalued impairments may include lost physical prowess, reduced work capacity, or weight changes due to immobility after an orthopedic injury. It may also present itself as a form of *cognitive dysmorphic disorder* associated with the postconcussion syndrome (chapter 3) following a traumatic brain injury (Miller, 1993e), in which diminished intellectual skills, interpersonal functioning, or employment status is the main source of self-deprecation.

Unconsciously, the motivation for such preoccupation with self-perceived ugliness or worthlessness may involve deep-seated and long-standing feelings of self-loathing, which are now, postinjury, projected onto a more objectifiable physical or mental impairment that serves as the new focus of the patient's self-perceived "badness." Alternatively, the physical disfigurement may come to represent a concrete, physical symbolization of the more amorphous existential fear and loathing that the crime victim is struggling with. Focusing one's attention on an "ugly face" may actually be less threatening than confronting the prospects of an "ugly life." A physical injury or disfigurement is a permanent reminder of what has happened to the crime victim and assails the victim every time he or she looks in the mirror.

Note that the formal diagnosis of body dysmorphic disorder implies that the perception of, and reaction to, the defect is beyond what is considered the normal for that feature. However, the line between pathological preoccupation with minor defects and realistic concern for actual, significant disfigurement may sometimes be a touchy clinical issue. For example, a scarred chin on a middle-aged businessman is likely to have a completely different meaning than the same blemish on a young fashion model. Clearly, a traumatic reaction to a real disfigurement should not be regarded as a pathological reaction without careful attention to the context of the injury and the effects on the victim's life.

The human face, especially, is the uniquely individualized expressive medium for our thoughts, feelings, moods, personality, and identity. Our face is us. Unwanted alteration of the face may therefore have a greater psychologically jarring effect than even more severe injuries to other parts of the body and may thus pose unique challenges to the treatment of crime victims. Indeed, an emerging body of research indicates that violence-related facial injury may put victims at an increased risk for PTSD, depression, and other traumatic disability syndromes (Bisson, Shepherd, & Dhutia, 1997; Fukunishi, 1999; Jaycox, Marshall, & Schell, 2004; Levine, Degutis, Pruzinsky, Shin, & Persing, 2005; Roccia, Dell'Acqua, Angelini, & Berrone, 2005; Wong et al., 2007).

> Mandy, a 40-year-old female high school teacher in the midst of a contentious divorce, was assaulted by a student who hit her in the face with a canvas backpack. She was momentarily dazed and sustained a mild cervical sprain-strain (whiplash) injury, which subsequently resolved. However, she also sustained several scratches and bruises on her face, which, although healed and virtually invisible to the close inspection of doctors and friends alike, continued to

plague Mandy every time she looked in the mirror. In addition, she became convinced that the neck injury had caused her head to tilt at an ugly angle and that she now "looked like a gimp." She was about to undergo cosmetic surgery, but the plastic surgeon hesitated when he reviewed the history and subsequently requested a psychological consultation.

FACTITIOUS DISORDER

Factitious disorder is defined as the deliberate production, manipulation, or feigning of physical or psychological signs and symptoms to satisfy psychological needs, rather than for material gain. Because the intentionality of symptom production is conscious and deliberate, it is diagnostically separated from the somatoform disorders. However, unlike malingering (see below), where the evaluator can often discern a utilitarian motive for the deception, the motive in factitious disorder is primarily to assume the sick role, with all the attendant care, solicitous concern, and relief from the responsibilities of normal life that this entails, even at the price of substantial cost in money, health, or freedom—that is, the motive would be viewed by most people as senseless in terms of significant practical gain. In many cases, the patient also appears to derive satisfaction, perhaps only partly unconscious, from manipulating the medical system and fooling the experts.

Historically, factitious disorder was referred to as *Munchausen's syndrome,* and the manifestations of this disorder are limited only by the imagination and ingenuity of the patient. Medically sophisticated patients, such as nurses or mental health clinicians, may be quite clever in feigning credible medical and psychiatric illnesses and injuries by the surreptitious use of chemical substances or medical apparatus, or by displaying realistic physical or psychiatric symptoms. Less knowledgeable patients may resort to cruder methods such as drinking toxic concoctions, bruising or cutting themselves to simulate injuries, or acting like their imagined version of a brain-damaged or crazy person. Crime victims may incorporate their new status into their existing life-long "victim" role by exaggerating symptoms and impairments and presenting themselves as a uniquely challenging (and therefore special) case to clinicians and criminal justice personnel alike.

> Cassandra had her pocketbook and a bracelet stolen by a group of two or three young thugs who were marauding through an amusement park, preying on customers. She was roughly pushed into the wall of one of the concession stands but was otherwise seemingly unhurt. Her 6-year-old son was on one of the rides at the time and was

oblivious to the whole episode. A few days later, Cassandra called in to work sick and subsequently appeared at the office of her physician, requesting medication for "deep trauma." It was discovered that her blood pressure was abnormally low and Cassandra said that this had led to fainting spells and that she was afraid to drive. She had to quit her job, she told the doctor, and now her husband "takes care of me every minute he's not at work."

She subsequently began spending most of her days in bed, receiving solicitous visitors who sympathized with her plight. One of these supporters even set her up to be interviewed by a local reporter who was doing a story on crime victim trauma. She tearfully informed the camera that "the thought that my son could have been killed is too much for me to take." She was told by two lawyers she consulted that there was no basis for a legal case against the amusement park, and her extended absence from work had long since used up her sick time and was starting to affect the family's finances.

Her mysterious drop in blood pressure and frequent fainting spells remained a mystery and she was about to be scheduled for a battery of medical tests. Even her once-devoted husband was starting to lose his patience with her endless bids for care and attention. The last straw came when he discovered a bottle of propranolol, a beta-blocker medication used for high blood pressure, hidden in one of Cassandra's drawers. Further investigation revealed that she had been ordering great quantities of this drug on the Internet and had been overdosing herself daily.

MALINGERING

Malingering is not classified as a true psychiatric disorder per se, but rather is defined as the conscious and intentional simulation of illness or impairment for the purpose of obtaining financial compensation or other reward; evading duty, responsibility, or obligation; or getting relief from the consequences of one's criminal actions or other illicit behavior. In other words, there is a practical and sensible—albeit ill-intended—motive for the subterfuge and therefore it does not represent a true symptom of psychopathology, although malingering patients may have comorbid psychological syndromes and personality disorders.

The incidence of malingering differs across clinical and forensic settings and populations, with estimates ranging from 1% to 50% (Resnick, 1988; Schretlen, 1988). Many experts view malingering in terms of a continuum, based on the degree to which the subject is consciously aware of his actual motivation (Nies & Sweet, 1994; Travin & Potter, 1984), although such a fuzzy conceptualization of intentionality may blur the diagnostic distinction between true malingering and the other syndromes discussed above. In crime victims, malingering typically occurs in cases where the crime has led to a civil suit for monetary damages against a third party and, consequently, the more impaired the plaintiff appears, the greater the anticipated award. Alternatively, aggrieved victims may consciously fabricate or exaggerate impairment to get back at the perpetrator by trying to influence the court to impose a harsher sentence (see chapter 16).

Based on Lipman's (1962) typology, I have categorized malingering into four main categories (Miller, 1998f, 1998g, 1999a, 1999j, 2000e, 2002e, 2008), which I have summarized by the mnemonic acronym, FEEM, for Fabrication, Exaggeration, Extension, and Misattribution:

Fabrication. The patient has no symptoms or impairments resulting from the crime, but fraudulently represents that he has. Symptoms may be atypical, inconsistent, or bizarre, or they may be perfect "textbook" replicas of real syndromes. In common clinical practice, this wholesale invention of an impairment syndrome out of thin air is the rarest form of malingering.

Michael was held up in the parking lot of an all-night drugstore. One of the robbers roughly bent him over the hood of his car while rifling through his pockets for his wallet and keys. Then the crooks quickly fled. Other than fear and embarrassment, Michael was uninjured and immediately filed a police report. He recalls one of the cops saying something like, "You should be more careful," which irritated Michael. Also, the drugstore manager "acted like this was no big deal," Michael said. A few weeks later, Michael filed a lawsuit against the drugstore chain for negligent safety, claiming he was incapacitated from work due to severe back injury sustained during the robbery. On independent medical examination by the store's insurance company doctor, Michael was noted to show "inconsistent and nonphysiological symptoms" and was referred for a psych exam.

Exaggeration. The patient has real symptoms or impairments caused by the injury but represents them to be far worse than they really are. This is probably the most common form of malingering in clinical and forensic practice.

On Friday night, Janie was jostled by her new boyfriend while fending off an unwanted amorous advance. He quickly backed off but, in the course of the brief struggle, she twisted her neck. She broke up with the creep and, by Sunday, her neck was feeling better. She returned to work on Monday, still fuming to herself about her bad choices in men. The erstwhile paramour phoned her a few times during the week and, when she refused to go out with him again, verbally pelted her with unflattering names and hung up. On Friday, Janie filed a police report of sexual assault. The next Monday, she appeared for an orthopedist appointment wearing a cervical collar, and reported unrelenting, excruciating headaches and severe shoulder and arm weakness that precluded her from working. She also filed a civil suit against lover-boy.

Extension. The patient has experienced real symptoms or impairments caused by the injury, and these have now recovered or improved, but he falsely represents them as continuing unabated, or even as having worsened over time.

Freddy was beat up at his high school by a group of punks, who were subsequently expelled. For several weeks, he was unable to return to school, too fearful of even walking on the grounds. He was seen by a mental health clinician who diagnosed ASD and PTSD (chapter 2) and recommended home schooling for the rest of the spring semester. By the summer, Freddy was feeling back to his old self, but he had come to enjoy the convenience and freedom of being home, so when the fall semester loomed in August, he returned to the therapist, claiming that all the old fears had come "rushing back" and that "all the old trauma and anxiety is still with me—there's no way I can go back to that school."

Misattribution. The patient has symptoms or impairments that preceded, postdated, or are otherwise unrelated to the criminal assault, but he fraudulently attributes them to that event.

Talk about bad timing. Robert was just walking into the bank when the robber came rushing out. In his haste to escape, the crook pushed Robert out of his way, smacking Robert's leg into the wall. Robert is suing the bank for negligence because he now has difficulty standing or walking; the affected leg frequently "gives out," causing him to fall; and he has had to borrow crutches from a neighbor just to get around. However, further historical exploration revealed that Robert sustained a prior injury to the knee in a college football mishap, as well as a second injury to the same leg less than a year ago in a motorcycle accident while intoxicated.

As noted above, malingered exaggeration of existing symptoms is more frequent than pure fabrication of totally nonexistent illnesses or injuries. Also, more than one category of malingering may be observed in the same patient at the same or different times. To compound matters further, more than one syndrome may be the subject of different types or degrees of malingering, for example, postconcussion syndrome, chronic pain, anxiety, depression, PTSD, or others. Finally, malingering can co-occur with other psychological syndromes, such as the somatoform disorders or personality disorders. In many cases, malingering is suspected when patients exaggerate impairment beyond the level of clinical believability, or when they are observed (e.g., on insurance company surveillance) to be performing activities that they are supposedly incapable of doing. It is here that the clinician's knowledge of typical and atypical traumatic disability syndromes is crucially important in making the correct diagnosis and appropriate clinical or forensic recommendations (Miller, 1998h, 2002e, 2008).

CONCLUSIONS

Just as it would be clinically irresponsible to miss an important diagnosis of crime-related PTSD or other psychological syndrome, it would be equally unfortunate to overattribute a patient's distress to the criminal victimization and overlook crucial factors that might complicate his or her response to the trauma or impede recovery. As the past two chapters have illustrated, knowledgeable clinicians need to take into account the crime victim's personality, comorbid psychopathology, social environment, and cultural factors for treatment to be effective. In the chapters that follow, think about how to apply the principles and techniques of effective crime victim therapy to the diverse syndromes we've just discussed and that may frequently arise in your own caseload.

PART II

Foundations of Practical and Clinical Strategies for Crime Victims

CHAPTER 5

On-Scene Crisis Intervention

Guidelines for Law Enforcement, Emergency Services, and Mental Health Responders

As noted throughout this book, effective mental health intervention for crime victims begins the moment the first responders arrive. For most crimes, this will consist of police and paramedics, sometimes accompanied by a special mental health trauma clinician; indeed, many police departments are establishing *crisis intervention teams,* or CITs, composed of law enforcement and mental health personnel, to respond to crises (Miller, 2006m). In other cases, the first mental health contact will occur in the emergency room if the victim is taken to a hospital.

Whoever the first responders are, they should be aware that they are in a unique position to help crime victims deal with the impact of their ordeal, to help restore a sense of safety and control to an otherwise fearful and overwhelming situation. How police officers respond to victims from the first moments of contact can have a tremendous impact on how a subsequent criminal investigation is handled and in the confidence—or lack of it—that victims, their families, and the larger community have in their law enforcement agency's ability to protect them. The way paramedics deal with victims' emotional states while treating their physical injuries can influence how they will respond to subsequent medical intervention. And the quality of initial mental health contact will influence whether this modality will subsequently prove to be a help or a hindrance in the crime victim's recovery and restabilization.

First responders themselves may not even be aware of the tremendous impact they have on crime victims, but those victims often report that the

treatment they received in the immediate aftermath of the crime greatly influenced their future perceptions of, and interactions with, law enforcement, the
medical establishment, and the mental health system, as well as their ability to
move on with their lives. Victims who receive the support they need—starting
with first responders—not only recover more quickly, but will be more in-
clined to fully cooperate with the subsequent investigation and prosecution
of the crime (chapter 16). They are also more likely to work with the police
officers in their neighborhoods in other, more general, aspects of crime control and community policing. In short, properly supported victims become
more effective and more willing participants in the criminal justice system
(Herman, 2002; Miller, 2006m).

Yet many officers and even some clinicians feel somewhat uncomfortable
dealing with crime victims on-scene, partly as a result of individual factors and
partly due to lack of training. With regard to the latter, this chapter will offer
some practical guidelines. Many of these recommendations apply directly to
police officers who are most likely to be the first responders to crime scenes.
However, mental health clinicians should be knowledgeable in these strategies because: (a) occasionally, they themselves are among the first responders;
(b) they may be in an advisory role to law enforcement agencies and even
involved in training these personnel; and (c) the basic principles of crisis intervention that underlie these recommendations have broad application in
many aspects of mental health treatment (Gilliland & James, 1993; Kleespies,
1998; Miller, 1998h).

EFFECTS OF CRIME ON VICTIMS AND SURVIVORS

First responders may face a confusing scenario when arriving at a crime scene
(Herman, 2002; Miller, 1998e, 1998h, 1999i, 2000b, 2003f, 2006m). Traumatized victims may be in a state of shock and disorientation during the initial
stage of the crisis reaction. The crime victim has just endured an experience
totally beyond his or her control and will most likely feel helpless, vulnerable, and frightened. Other victims will be in a state of flight-or-fight panic,
and some may actually try to flee the scene of the crime. Some victims may
be confrontational or combative with arriving police or paramedics, adding
to the confusion as to who is the victim and who is the offender; this is most
likely to occur in cases of barroom brawls, domestic disturbances, or neighbor
disputes. In some instances, virtual physical and emotional paralysis occurs,
rendering the victim unable to make rational decisions, speak coherently,
or even move purposefully, much less seek medical attention or report the
incident to the police.

As we've seen, long-term psychological effects of crime victimization include persisting anxiety, depression, phobic avoidance, physical symptoms, substance abuse, PTSD, shattered sense of safety and security, mean world syndrome, cynicism, and distrust. Victims may be unable to function normally at their jobs or in family life. Again, much of the lasting impact of crime victimization may depend on the actions of first responders in the immediate postimpact minutes, hours, and days.

WHAT CRIME VICTIMS SAY THEY NEED
FROM FIRST RESPONDERS

As I've emphasized elsewhere, police officers are "practical psychologists" who daily utilize principles and practices of human behavior in the course of their work (Miller, 2006m). This type of practical psychological approach is especially important in the immediate response to a traumatized crime victim.

Yet, police officers, and occasionally paramedics, mental health clinicians, and other first responders, often complain that when they try to help crime victims at the scene, their efforts are misinterpreted or unappreciated. In a study of crime victims' feelings, perceptions, and wishes with regard to police interactions at the scene, Herman (2002) found that most of these victims are actually quite clear about what they feel they most need from the initial police contact at the crime scene. Their responses tend to cluster in three categories.

Regaining a sense of safety and control. Crime victims want the responding officer to interview them in a safe, quiet location, preferably away from the immediate scene of the crime. They want to be reassured of their safety, that the immediate crisis is over and that the perpetrator can't harm them again. They would like the officer to speak in a calm, reassuring voice, not pepper them with questions in a brusque, staccato tone. They especially don't want officers stating or implying judgments about what the victim could or should have done before, during, or after the crime; victims feel bad enough without these recriminations.

Being allowed to vent. Victims want time to talk about their experience. For most victims, this is the most horrible thing that's ever happened to them, and they need the opportunity to describe the event at their own pace and in their own way. This may prove frustrating to investigators who are eager to get the facts as quickly as possible. Although some gentle prodding and guiding may be appropriate to keep the narrative on track, officers should try to hold their questions or comments until the victims have finished telling their story. The presentation may be emotional and rambling, as it often is with individuals under extreme stress, but ultimately, officers will get a more complete picture if they let the victim tell it her way. What officers can and should do is reassure, normalize, and validate the victim's experiences and reactions so that she does not feel even more stigmatized by thinking she's acting crazy or being a crybaby for expressing her feelings.

Knowing how to access additional support. Officers or other first responders should describe the upcoming steps in the criminal investigation and legal proceedings. Without further frightening the victim, they should inform her of the possibility that emotional delayed reactions may occur over the next few days and, importantly, new memories of the crime may emerge, in which case officers want her to feel confident enough in them that she'll be willing to call them with such additional information. Indeed, victims themselves say they'd like officers to make the first move in encouraging further contact with law enforcement, since victims often feel embarrassed or intimidated to call on their own; some don't want to be seen as a pest.

Being referred to community services. Finally, victims are frightened, confused, and in pain, and most of them understand that there's a limit to what the responding officer can do in his or her law enforcement role. So victims want information about community services and other agencies that are set up for crime victim assistance. Taking the time to ensure that the victim knows what comes next and what to do about it can be a positive step in the direction of improved police-victim and police-community relationships.

"There were two cops who showed up pretty fast after I dialed 911," said Rachel, "and they were, like, total opposites. The first, a little guy, was all businesslike, asking questions, what did the attacker look like, was he short or tall, and so on, and I started getting confused and started crying, and the cop just gives me this look, like 'what's wrong with you?' So then, the other cop, the bigger one, asks the first guy to go get something from their car, like I think I wasn't supposed to know that this was their way of letting the other guy take over without embarrassing the first guy. But, anyway, the big cop was more patient, he let me say what I wanted to say, told me how I could get home, or did I want to go to the hospital, or need a ride home, like giving me a choice, you know? It was more the way he said it than anything else that made me feel he was really trying to help me, not just get the whole thing over with, like the first guy, the little cop."

ON-SCENE CRISIS INTERVENTION

As we've seen, the first point of contact between police officers or other first responders and crime victims is often at the crime scene itself, although this contact may take place in an ambulance or emergency room if the victim is already receiving medical care. Here, the responder is confronted with a victim whose emotional behavior may run the gamut from numbed unresponsiveness to raw panic. Aside from providing medical and psychological first aid, a frequent practical task of the first responder is to obtain as much information as possible from the victim about the crime itself in order to maximize the possibility of apprehending the perpetrator(s), preventing further violence, and planning for aid to other potential victims. Balancing concern for victim welfare and the need to obtain detailed information is thus a delicate dance and requires some degree of interpersonal skill on the part of the interviewer. The following are some practical recommendations for first responders who have to deal with crime victims on-scene (Clark, 1988; Frederick, 1986; Miller, 1998e, 2006m; Silbert, 1976).

Introduce Yourself

As soon as you arrive, identify yourself by name and full title to the victim and bystanders. Even if you are in uniform, have a picture ID tag, or clearly look like a police officer, paramedic, or mental health clinician, the victim may be too distraught to understand who you are. You may need to repeat the introduction several times. Remember that victims who are still in shock may respond to you as if you are the criminal, especially if you arrived quickly on the scene. Children traumatized by adults may respond with fear to any new adult in their environment.

Apply Medical First Aid

The first priority is to make sure any physical injuries get treated. In fact, with serious injuries, any further law enforcement questioning or mental health intervention may have to be deferred to the hospital setting after the victim's medical condition has been stabilized. Yet a substantial number of crime victims may have few or no significant physical injuries, at least not ones that are immediately detectable. If the direct victim is the child or other family member of the interviewee, the parent or relative may be physically untouched, but emotionally in shock at the attack on their loved one.

It is typically the job of paramedics to render emergency medical care. But even if you are a police officer or mental health clinician, as the first responder on the scene, you may sometimes have to be the one to apply first aid until further medical help arrives. Whoever carries out this task, calmly explain to the crime victim what you're doing, especially when you are touching the victim or doing an otherwise intimate procedure, such as applying a breathing mask or removing clothing. If possible, let the victim help you treat her if she wants. This may be as simple as having her hold a bandage on her arm or letting her undo her own clothing, but it can offer a much-needed quick restoration of control in a situation where the victim is otherwise reeling in a state of helpless disorientation. In particular, many children respond well to this helping maneuver. Other victims may be so paralyzed with fear that they forget how to do simple things like untying shoelaces or unbuttoning a shirt.

Respect the Victim's Wishes

Similar to the above, this principle is more generally related to restoration of the victim's sense of control and should be followed whenever reasonable. If, for example, the victim wants a family member or friend to remain with her during treatment or questioning, let that person stay. Don't take offense if the victim refuses to let you touch, treat, or even talk to her: You may look, act, speak, smell, or have the same name as the perpetrator. Child victims are often unable to express their fears and may just flail or shout for you to get away. Perhaps another member of the law enforcement or emergency medical team can interview or treat the victim more comfortably.

Validate the Victim's Reactions

Always try to validate the traumatic ordeal the victim has been through and, as realistically as possible, reinforce his or her resilience and coping efforts thus far. In general, build on the victim's own resources to increase his or her feelings of self-efficacy and control: "I can see this must have been a terrible experience for you. Most people would be feeling pretty much like you are under these circumstances. But I'm glad to see you're handling it as well as you are."

Investigate Sensibly and Sensitively

After ascertaining that the victim is physically intact and in sufficient emotional shape to have a conversation, briefly verify essential details of the criminal incident: "Please tell me what happened to you. Did it happen here or in another location?" Police officers should do whatever they can to secure the crime scene while calling for appropriate backup, if necessary. If possible, remove the victim from the scene to a safer or more neutral location. Be sensitive and tactful with onlookers and media, and cooperate with paramedics and other vital responders. Mental health clinicians who are on-scene can assist and advise law enforcement personnel in these actions.

Avoid even unintentional accusatory or incriminatory statements such as "What were you doing in that building so late at night?" These not only needlessly upset and retraumatize the victim but also erode trust, making further interview and treatment attempts extremely difficult. Try not to overuse platitudes such as "Everything will be all right," which will doubtless sound hollow and insincere to a victim whose world has just been shattered. More helpful are simple, supportive, concrete statements such as, "It's okay now. We're going to go to a safe place so you can tell us what happened."

Avoid statements or implications indicating to an adolescent or young adult victim that you think he or she should "act your age." Most people don't behave like their normal selves right after they've been severely traumatized and many crime victims may regress to a childlike, dependent mental state immediately after the incident. In such cases, simple, nonjudgmental statements such as "I can understand why you're upset" or "What can I do to help?" can ease the victim's distress.

Even the most hard-boiled investigator or no-nonsense medic should understand that a sympathetic, supportive, and nonjudgmental approach can do much to restore the crime victim's trust and confidence and thereby facilitate all aspects of criminal investigation and medical treatment. So listen to the victim if she wants to talk, even if she digresses, rambles, or strays off topic. Let her express emotion if she has to "get it all out." At the other extreme, tolerate silence without feeling compelled to jump in with a question or comment. At this stage, don't press for more detail than necessary for purposes of immediate treatment or case investigation—crime victims will be forced to tell their stories again and again at multiple points in the criminal process.

When necessary, use a combination of open-ended and closed-ended questioning: "Can you remember what your attacker looked like? Tell me. About what age was he? What race do you think he was? Was he taller than me? Was he thin or stocky? What else can you remember? That's all right— take your time."

If the victim seems to be getting more and more agitated, disoriented, or panicked during his narrative, employ *diversionary reality questions*. These serve to defocus the victim's attention from the most horrifying aspects of the event, while keeping the topic related to the subject in question, for example:

VICTIM: The guy who jumped me in the clothing department was a new hire. I never saw it coming. He just started beating me. They never check the background of these new guys. We're all going to be killed here. We're all dead sooner or later.

OFFICER: How many people work here?

VICTIM: About thirty.

OFFICER: Okay, was there anything different about the guy who jumped you? How long has he worked here?

Present a Plan

Related to the issue of restoring control is having some kind of *clear plan* to provide further structure and order to an otherwise overwhelming situation. You don't have to feel bound to follow the plan to the letter if contingencies change, but some structure is almost always better than none. It's also useful to back up this plan with concrete suggestions for action: "We're going to move to a safe area, have the medics take care of these cuts, then I'm going to ask you a couple of questions, if that's all right. After I'm done, I'm going to explain what happens next in the police process and legal area, then I'll give you a card with some phone numbers of victim's assistance agencies you can contact. I'm also going to give you my card, and you can contact me at any time for any reason. Do you understand? Do you have any questions?"

Employ Humor Judiciously

A well-placed witticism may put some perspective on the crisis and ease an otherwise tense situation, but traumatized people tend to become very literal and concrete under stress, and well-meaning humor may be mistaken for mocking or lack of serious concern. As with all such recommendations, use your judgment.

Utilize Interpersonal Calming and Coping Techniques

Never overlook the interpersonal power of a reassuring presence, both verbally and physically. Project a model of composure for the victim to emulate. Eye contact should be neither a detached glance nor a fixed glare but more of a concerned, connected gaze. Stand close enough to the victim to provide proximal contact comfort, but don't crowd or intimidate by invading the victim's personal space. Use physical touch carefully. Sometimes a brief pat on the shoulder or comforting grasp of the hand can be very reassuring, but it may frighten a victim who has just been physically assaulted. Take your cue from the victim.

One technique I've found useful on-scene for both victims of crime and distressed responders during critical incidents is what I call the *therapeutic hand-clasp* (Miller, 2006m), which can be adapted to a regular handshake for both men and women, or a more supportive handhold, usually for female victims. For a subject who feels like, or looks like, he or she losing control, ask that person to squeeze your hand and mentally transfer the overwhelming emotions into this physical activity: "Okay, just squeeze my hand, put the fear into my hand, just hold on and let it drain into my hand like an electric current, like you're discharging a battery. Feel yourself relax as the fear drains away. That's it, all the excess fear and tension is flowing out of you: You can handle this, you're getting stronger, you'll make it, you'll be okay. All right, take a deep breath, and let go slowly when you're ready."

At subsequent intervals during the critical incident, this technique can be repeated silently and unobtrusively when necessary, appearing like a normal handshake. With practice, it can be internalized so all the subject has to do is think about it, or clench his or her own fist to reevoke the tension-reducing feeling. The technique is simple to use and relies on the basic therapeutic principles of psychological suggestion, human physical contact, and interpersonal support.

Other kinds of body activity can be therapeutic. To break the sense of physical and mental paralysis that often accompanies posttraumatic numbing, have the victim take a little walk with you, let him get a drink of water, or give him some simple but useful task to perform. Just being able to move one's body around in a productive way can sometimes restore a feeling of efficacy and control: "See, my legs still work, I can move my hands, I'm not a complete basket case." Even where there has been a limiting physical injury, there is almost always some activity or body function that the victim can perform. Anything that will show the victim that there's some shred of normality left, that something still works, contributes to a sense of safety and hope.

With extremely distraught, disoriented, regressed, or psychologically immobilized victims, you may have to provide a *breakthrough stimulus* to capture the person's attention. This may involve shouting, making a loud noise, or gently shaking the severely traumatized victim to break the numbing spell of dissociation that he or she is entombed in (Everstine & Everstine, 1993). This technique should be reserved for situations where it is an emergency matter to get the subject's attention and cooperation, such as getting out of a dangerous area quickly. Otherwise, you may risk further traumatizing an already overfrightened victim. Forget about slapping the victim's face: that's for the movies and almost never works in real life; besides, you could risk further injury, not to mention a lawsuit. No cold water in the face, either—but giving the victim a sip of a cold drink often helps.

For a victim's own protection or the protection of others, sometimes you may have to physically restrain a victim who has been severely traumatized, who is under the influence of drugs or alcohol, or who is in the throes of a psychotic episode (chapter 3). Here, however, you should think more in terms of *supportive containment* than restraint per se. Sometimes people who are out of control can derive a primitive sense of safety and peace by being enveloped in a cocoon of benevolent external containment. Use the minimum amount of force and restraint necessary, for example, wrapping the distraught victim in a blanket as opposed to pinning his arms. Again, remember that if the subject is not actually being arrested, physical restraint should be used only as a last resort, and only in the interest of the subject's own safety and of those around him.

Another technique that often works with severely traumatized victims is referred to as *augmented behavioral mirroring*. For example, you may encounter a victim sitting on a curb or on a hospital cot, rocking rhythmically back and forth, humming to herself. Gradually imitate and replicate her movements, until both of you are in a comfortable rhythm, and then augment with the repeated phrase, "It's all right, you're safe. It's all right, you're safe," or some equivalent phrase (Everstine & Everstine, 1993). Once again, these types of specialized techniques should be reserved for extreme situations.

ACTIVE LISTENING SKILLS

Active listening techniques comprise the fundamental skill set for any kind of crisis intervention. They are multipurpose communication tools that can be effectively applied to a variety of both emergency and routine clinical and law enforcement settings, and they have reached perhaps their greatest degree of refinement and sophistication in the field of hostage negotiation, where life and death can literally hinge on the tone of a voice or the turn of a phrase (Call, 2003; Lanceley, 1999; McMains, 2002; McMains & Mullins, 1996; Miller, 2005c, 2006m, 2007b; Noesner, 1999; Noesner & Webster, 1997; Rogan, Donohoe, & Lyles, 1990; Rogan & Hammer, 1995; Slatkin, 1996, 2005). I have found many of these techniques to be useful for on-scene crisis intervention with crime victims, as well as for phone interventions and in-office contacts with distressed and distraught patients. Often, during a crisis, these forms of intervention serve the dual purpose of calming the victim and allowing the gathering of further information for law enforcement investigation and/or clinical treatment.

Emotion Labeling

Emotion labeling helps the subject clarify what he's feeling. It contributes to a state of calmness by reducing internal confusion. Sometimes, just giving an intense feeling a name shows that the emotion is understood and that the subject is less out of control than he might have thought. Also, by focusing on the crime victim's emotions, you allow a break from discussing frightening events and fears about the future, and at the same time you let the victim know you're interested in how he feels about things, not just what kind of information you may want from him about the crime.

Indeed, with a disturbed or incoherent victim, it may not be immediately apparent what he wants—in fact, he may hardly be clear about this himself. In such cases, the initial step may be to clarify what he's thinking and feeling. In general, respond first to emotion, not content. That is, address yourself to the victim's emotional state, while sidestepping any fearful words or imagery. But be careful not to convey the impression that you're ignoring or discounting his issues if that's what he really wants to discuss. The important thing is to demonstrate to the victim that you are tuned in, that he has your undivided attention, either by an "um-hmm"-type interjection or by encouraging him to go on. Utilize emotion-labeling phrases, such as: "You sound . . . ," "You seem . . . ," "I hear . . . ," and so on.

VICTIM: What if the guy's still here? Did they catch him yet? He's gonna find me. We have to get out of here or I'm gonna die.

RESPONDER: You sound like you're feeling really frightened.

Paraphrasing

Paraphrasing is basically recasting the victim's statement in your own words. This accomplishes several things. First, it reinforces empathy and rapport by saying to the victim, in effect, that if I can restate your meaning in my own words, then I must have a pretty good understanding of what you're experiencing; in this way, paraphrasing can convey to the victim that "I'm really hearing you." Second, effective paraphrasing actually clarifies what the victim is saying: Think of it as the clarification-of-content partner of the clarification-of-feelings that occurs with emotion labeling. Third, it encourages the victim to slow down and listen, which may have a calming effect of its own. It also promotes a verbal give-and-take that does not automatically put the victim on the defensive. Finally, just hearing one's own thoughts spoken aloud by someone else can provide clarification and a feeling of being heard and understood.

When paraphrasing, summarize in your own words what the subject has just told you.

VICTIM: What if the guy's still here? Did they catch him yet? He's gonna find me. We have to get out of here or I'm gonna die.

RESPONDER: Sounds like you think you're still in danger.

The responder should be careful not to add or embellish, as in: "I understand it's never easy to know when you're completely safe. We live in a dangerous world, so a lot of people are scared. . . ." This is not an effective response because it may serve to further frighten the victim. Remember, the overall goal of the on-scene intervention is to calm things down, not stir them up.

Structure paraphrases in a way that solicits confirmation of the victim's thoughts and feelings. This can be explicit, like interjecting "right?" at the end of your paraphrase. Or it can be more subtle, such as leaving your paraphrase dangling by the intonation of your voice, or following your restatement with silence, creating a verbal vacuum for the victim to fill. Paraphrasing wordings can include: "Are you telling me . . . ?" "What I hear you saying is . . . ," "Let me see if I have this right . . . ," "So . . . ," and similar phrases.

As always, if you are not sure what the victim just said or meant, ask him to repeat it: "I don't know if I got all that, Andrew. Could you say it again, please. I want to make sure I understand exactly what you're telling me."

Reflecting/Mirroring

Here, the responder repeats the last word or phrase, or the main word or phrase, of the subject's statement in the form of a question, thereby soliciting more input without actually asking for it. It also allows the responder to buy time if he or she cannot immediately think of an appropriate emotional label or paraphrase, while still encouraging the victim to focus on what he or she has just said. Early in the encounter, it allows information to be gleaned in a nonthreatening, nonconfrontational way and is a generally good initial rapport builder.

VICTIM: What if the guy's still here? Did they catch him yet? He's gonna find me. We have to get out of here or I'm gonna die.

RESPONDER: We have to get out?

VICTIM: Yeah, the guy might still be around, waiting to attack me.

RESPONDER: You think he might still be here, huh?

Minimal Encouragers

Minimal encouragers are nothing more than the little conversational speech fillers we all use to indicate that we're paying attention to someone during a conversation. In the on-scene crime victim crisis intervention context, these consist of short utterances and questions that let the victim know that the responder is listening but that don't interfere with the victim's narrative flow. Indeed, the purpose is to encourage the victim to keep talking. Examples include: "Oh?" "I see." "Yeah." "Uh-huh." "When?" "And?" "Really?" "You do?" "He did?"

Silence and Pauses

Aside from just buying time, silence can be used strategically. For one thing, in a relatively active conversation, your silence encourages the victim to fill in the gaps, which keeps him talking. Following a statement by silence is also a way of emphasizing a point you've just made:

RESPONDER: I know this looks like it's gotten out of control, but not everything that starts bad, ends bad. It doesn't have to end bad [pause].

You can also use silence to frame the victim's point or to encourage elaboration:

VICTIM: I'm trying to think positive about this, but what am I supposed to do, just take your word for it that I'll be safe?

RESPONDER: [stays silent].

VICTIM: I guess you wouldn't lie to me about something like that, would you? I mean what would be the point?

Like all active listening techniques, silence and pauses are best used in combination with other techniques and may be particularly effective when used in conjunction with minimal encouragers. Be careful about too much silence, however, because you don't want the victim to think she is being ignored or has been forgotten about. Again, try to understand the victim's perspective as well as possible and fine-tune your approach accordingly.

"I" Statements

People under extreme stress often become suspicious and defensive, and any comments or statements that are too directive may sound like an insult or attack. In such circumstances, "Maybe you ought to . . ." will be interpreted as "You better, or else. . . ." To keep potentially accusatory-sounding "you's" out of the conversation, use "I" statements to clue the subject in on what effect she's having on the responder's perception, while at the same time allowing for some subjectivity and personalization of the responder; victims will generally respond better to a responder whom they regard as a flesh-and-blood human being who cares, instead of some cop or doc who's barking orders. The basic model is "I feel . . . when you . . . because. . . ."

This technique may help defuse intense emotions and may help refocus the victim during an emotional crisis.

VICTIM: You don't care about me—all you want is to get your damn information so you can solve your case. You're just like that first cop who was here—you guys are all alike.

RESPONDER: When you're yelling like that, it's hard for me to focus on what we're talking about.

Or:

RESPONDER: I don't know about anybody else, but all I want to do is hear what you have to say.

Open-Ended Questions

This technique has wide applicability in both law enforcement and clinical crisis intervention work, from police interview and interrogation to suicide prevention and on-scene intervention with crime victims. Here, the responder asks questions that cannot be answered with a simple yes or no. This encourages the victim to say more without the responder actually directing the conversation. This technique may be used in combination with other active listening techniques, such as minimal encouragers, reflecting/mirroring, and silence. In addition, open-ended questions can be followed or combined with closed-ended queries:

VICTIM: I know I'll never get over this. My whole life's gonna be ruined now.

RESPONDER: How?

VICTIM: What do you mean, "how?" Everything's ruined, nothing'll ever be the same. It's all screwed up.

RESPONDER: I really want to understand this. Can you give me an example?

CONCLUSIONS

Like virtually all of the therapeutic intervention strategies in this book—as in the real world of clinical practice—there is no strict dividing line between short-term and long-term approaches to crisis intervention. Each type of intervention approach may blend into the next and cycle back to previous ones as clinical needs dictate. The important thing is for the counselor to be familiar with as wide a range of intervention options as possible in order to be able to intervene quickly in a comprehensive and flexible way.

CHAPTER 6

Symptom Management
and Short-Term Mental
Health Stabilization

Clinicians often wonder, "When does crisis intervention end and 'real' psychotherapy begin?" However, as discussed earlier, the border between short- and long-term therapies is a fluid one. Furthermore, so is the line between so-called superficial and deep therapies. Much depends on the patient. For example, what could be more profoundly life-altering—deep in the truest sense of the word—than helping a victim of sexual assault regain control of her bodily reactions and feel like an effective person again by utilizing some of the simple behavioral medicine low-arousal techniques to be described below? And what could be more superficially time-wasting than attempting the psychodynamic exploration of the deep roots of a traumatic reaction to crime in a patient whose adaptive insight only extends to the immediately practical goal of feeling safe? As always, take your cue from the patient and have a sufficient number and variety of tools in your therapeutic kit box to address a wide range of problems.

EDUCATIVE AND SUPPORTIVE MEASURES

Physical injuries are taken very seriously by the medical profession. If you've ever been treated for an injury in a hospital ER, or by paramedics at an accident scene, or even in a doctor's office, you've probably been impressed with the judicious care given even to what you would commonly consider a scratch worthy of no more than a quick rinse and a Band-Aid. But in the medical setting, the little laceration or abrasion is carefully cleaned and dressed as if it were a battle wound. Okay, you say, better to overtreat than undertreat.

But when it comes to psychological injury, even severe levels of distress are often disregarded and dismissed by medical professionals, probably because these clinicians never have been adequately trained to treat psychological trauma, and therefore it makes them uncomfortable to feel ignorant and ineffectual. So rather than appear stupid, they consider the psych stuff to not be real, and they concentrate on the physical. Added to this is the idea, endorsed by many medical professionals, that coddling injured patients will reinforce their psychological disability (strange that they don't seem to think that putting a massive field dressing on a hangnail will coddle and reinforce physical disability). But as discussed in chapters 1 and 8, such disenfranchised suffering only serves to entrench disability and impede recovery.

Thus, the first step in effective clinical intervention is to treat crime victim traumatic stress syndromes with the respect they deserve. Indeed, research and clinical experience show that early, intensive, and appropriate treatment within the first weeks and months of any physically or psychologically injurious event improves the prognosis for all kinds of traumatic disability syndromes (Miller, 1998h). Accordingly, far from coddling patients into permanent invalidism, appropriately solicitous clinical attention and a reasonable interval of convalescence can actually prevent the development of subsequent persistent traumatic disability (Modlin, 1983).

The initial approach to a traumatized crime victim is twofold. First, the therapist demonstrates her understanding of what the victim is going through by asking questions that elicit the nature of the common posttraumatic symptoms, giving the patient an "Aha-she-gets-it" feeling. The therapist then reinforces this bond of understanding by offering a comprehensible explanatory model that emphasizes the universality and normality of the stress response and its manifestations. This process is replicated in each session, either explicitly or subtly. The patient may not completely grasp the psychological explanation, but what he does hear is that the therapist understands what he has gone through, that she believes the patient has a legitimate clinical syndrome with a name and a causal explanation, and that the clinician knows what to do about it.

Therapists like to do therapy and sometimes feel that it's somehow not real clinical work to provide concrete, practical help to patients, but the importance of this assistance cannot be overestimated (Brom & Kleber, 1989; Werman, 1984). These practical measures may involve referrals to law enforcement, legal, and social service agencies. Patients at first may refuse these recommendations and, unless clinically or legally necessary, therapists should refrain from forcing the issue, so as to give the patient some sense of autonomy

and control over what happens to him, all the while continuing to provide realistic reassurance (Matsakis, 1994). But gentle encouragement of the patient
to act on his own behalf should continue to be provided at intervals during
the course of treatment.

In the acute trauma stage, the patient's concept of reality is often profoundly altered. Accordingly, in the first phase of contact, the therapist should
try to bring structure to the experiences of the crime victim in an adaptive,
reality-oriented manner. This is done by first following the narrative of the
patient and then identifying the emotions as they are expressed. During this
initial stage, the therapist encourages the crime victim in only a limited way to
explore his feelings further or deeper, as a prematurely intense discussion of
emotions may increase confusion and contribute to an atmosphere of crisis.
As time passes and the patient begins to recapture a sense of fundamental
safety and control, he will need this structuring form of support less and less.
The therapist can then adopt a more probing and challenging approach that
incorporates confrontation and reality-testing, although the atmosphere of
understanding and trust remains the most important basis of the therapeutic relationship (Brom & Kleber, 1989; Everstine & Everstine, 1993; Hamblen, Gibson, Mueser, & Norris, 2006; Rudofossi, 2007; Shalev, Galai, & Eth,
1993).

Gard and Ruzek (2006) enumerate what they term the *eight core actions and
goals of psychological first aid* for victims during a community crisis, and these
can equally be applied to intervention with crime victims.

1. *Contact and engagement.* As much as humanly possible, be available to
   respond to the crime victim. At times, when he or she doesn't seem to
   want to speak to anyone, you may have to initiate contact in a nonin-
   trusive, compassionate, and helpful manner. But respect the victim's
   wishes for privacy, where appropriate. Allowing her to decide when
   and how to initiate contact can also be a form of helping her regain
   empowerment.
2. *Safety and comfort.* Provide an immediate and ongoing sense of safety
   and emotional support. Let your therapeutic meeting place be a fortress of refuge. Many crime victims have commented that they feel
   better "just walking into this room."
3. *Stabilization.* Provide a calming presence and corrective emotional orientation to the distraught and overwhelmed crime victim. Do this through your words, actions, demeanor, tone, and
   body language. Show that you can absorb and neutralize some of
   the patient's emotional toxin without becoming poisoned yourself
   (McCann & Pearlman, 1990).

4. *Information gathering.* Identify the victim's immediate needs and concerns, gather additional information, and tailor psychological first aid interventions to the victim's immediate needs.

5. *Practical assistance.* Offer reasonable practical help to the crime victim in addressing immediate needs and concerns regarding safety, housing, money, medical care, legal aid, and so on.

6. *Connection with social supports.* Isolation can be paralyzing and debilitating. Avoidant coping strategies have been found to be predictive of a heightened risk of immediate and chronic posttraumatic psychopathology (Bowman, 1997; Harvey & Bryant, 1998; Hobfoll, 1989; McFarlane, 1988a, 1988b). Therefore, help the crime victim initiate and maintain contacts with primary support persons, including family members, friends, and community helping resources. Show the victim how to access these individuals in manageable doses, so that he or she experiences them as supportive, not overwhelming, and respect the victim's need to balance human interaction with the option of temporarily withdrawing from interpersonal demands when they become overwhelming (Litz et al., 2002).

7. *Information on coping support.* Ignorance is harmful. Provide the victim with authoritative information about stress reactions and coping patterns that may help him or her deal with the event and its aftermath. This can be in the form of books, CDs and DVDs, Web sites, or anything that will provide accurate, authoritative information in an understandable and nonthreatening format.

8. *Linkage with collaborative services.* Help survivors hook up with services and inform them about services that may be needed in the future.

TREATING POSTTRAUMATIC SYMPTOMS

For many crime victims, the frightening and disorienting symptoms of PTSD and other traumatic disability syndromes (chapters 2, 3) are the most disabling part of the experience. For these victims, achieving a measure of control over disturbing symptoms is the first step toward allowing themselves to believe they can recover from the trauma. For others, even a cursory attempt to deal with symptoms must await the achievement of some degree of confidence and stability. For many patients, this is a reciprocal cycle, with small increments in confidence and equanimity permitting small steps toward symptom control, which in turn produce greater confidence and further attempts at mastery, and so on. In still other cases, patients may come to understand that while symptoms may be managed and controlled, they may never completely disappear but can be relegated to the background of consciousness, like mental shrapnel that only aches on occasion (Everstine & Everstine, 1993; Matsakis, 1994; Miller, 1994b, 1998h).

The following sections represent a menu of symptom-control techniques that I have culled from diverse areas of practice and have utilized with diverse clinical populations, including crime victims, accident victims, law enforcement critical incident stress, military psychology, sports psychology, and others (Miller, 1989a, 1989b, 1994a, 2006a, 2006m, 2007m). The techniques in this chapter should be thought of as a flexible menu of clinical options for treating patients with different personalities and life experiences (chapter 3). Some combinations of techniques will work better for some patients than others and, even for the same patient, some strategies may work better at different phases in the course of treatment. Again, this argues for a flexible, empirical, and clinically informed approach to psychological treatment of traumatized crime victims.

MODULATING AROUSAL

As we saw in chapter 2, the inability of traumatized crime victims to control their own physical and emotional arousal states can be among the most destabilizing of consequences, since patients come to avoid a growing number of situations for fear of being overcome with stress and then losing it.

The Optimum Arousal Level

Arousal, in and of itself, is neither good nor bad. And like virtually all psychological states, arousal must be maintained at the appropriate level for a given task in order for one's activity to be adaptive for that task. Arousal can be thought of as existing on a continuum. The optimum state of arousal in any situation, whether routine or emergency, is that which energizes the subject for proper action but does not distract or impede him from carrying out the task.

For most active tasks, too little arousal results in flagging motivation, drifting attention, and a lackadaisical, inefficient approach to the task, like sitting through a boring classroom lecture and trying to catch what the instructor is droning on about. Too much arousal, on the other hand, sends the subject into adrenalin overdrive, and she becomes scattered, panicked, and again unable to complete the task effectively, like suddenly having the final exam thrown on your desk without preparation. Psychologists will recognize this as the famous *Yerkes-Dodson law,* or inverted-U graph, where too little arousal bogs down task efficiency and too much derails it. After a traumatic event like a crime, this curve becomes asymmetrically shifted to the extreme side of arousal dimension; the victim becomes unable to calm down sufficiently on her own.

The goal of arousal control training, then, is to strive for a state of neither blissful repose nor wide-eyed panic but to help the crime victim induce or regain an *optimum arousal level* (OAL) that is appropriate for a given task or situation. Some circumstances may require ramping up one's arousal level to deal with a threat or challenge, while in other cases it may be necessary to calm oneself down so that extraneous arousal does not distract and disrupt daily life activities. Elite athletes, military personnel, performance artists, and peak performers in every field seem to learn to control their level of arousal so that they can generate the necessary OAL for specific situations (Asken, 1993; Doss, 2007; Flin, 1996; Hays & Brown, 2004; Klein, 1996; Rodgers, 2006). For the crime victim who is struggling with posttraumatic symptoms, keeping the level of arousal at a comfortable level is usually a prerequisite for dealing with other challenging issues in the course of treatment.

Relaxation Techniques

For more than half a century, the technique of *progressive muscle relaxation* (Jacobson, 1938) has been the standard recipe of stress management and is by now so well known that it will only be summarized here. The basic rationale is that much of what we experience as uncomfortably heightened arousal arises out of feedback from tensed muscles and other bodily signals of arousal. Essentially, then, the progressive relaxation exercise focuses on one muscle group or body area at a time and guides the subject through an alternate tense-and-relax sequence until all major muscle groups are in a state of relative physiological quiescence. This is typically combined with slow, steady, diaphragmatic breathing (deep stomach breathing as opposed to shallow chest breathing) and one or more mental cuing or imagery techniques (see below) to further induce a state of psychophysiological calm.

The key to successfully utilizing relaxation, as with any of these techniques, is their automaticity and portability. That is, one of the features of effective, practical low-arousal techniques that makes them useful in the patient's natural environment is the ability to utilize them quickly under adverse circumstances. Accordingly, the technique is first practiced in a peaceful, stress-free environment, such as in the therapist's office or stress-management class, guided by the clinician's or instructor's soothing words or by the use of a commercially prepared or custom-made relaxation tape or CD.

Later, with continued practice in a variety of settings and conditions, the traumatized crime victim should be able to self-induce the relaxed state on his own, in his natural environment, without external prompting, and without having to go through the whole tense-and-relax sequence each time. For example, someone who finds himself tensing up in traffic or in a business office might be able to quickly and unobtrusively induce a more relaxed, yet alert, state while sitting behind the wheel or at his desk.

Cued Relaxation

Once the progressive relaxation procedure has been practiced and mastered, many individuals are able to employ a kind of instant relaxation, or *cued relaxation* technique. By voluntarily reducing muscular tension, taking a calming breath, and using a cue word, the subject learns to immediately lower his or her physiological arousal and thereby induce a more calm and focused mental state. The *cue word or phrase* may range from the spiritual ("God is with me"; "Om") to the mundane ("Chill"; "Okay, I'm good"), and is basically any word or phrase that you have trained the subject to pair frequently with the full relaxation response and that he can now say to himself to signal his body to relax.

Similarly, a *cue image* is any mental scene the subject can invoke that has a calming effect, especially by virtue of having been paired with the initial relaxation response practice. Have your patient pick the modality or technique that works best for her: The key is to invoke some cue that enables the patient to quickly and voluntarily lower her arousal level to a degree that is appropriate for the situation she's in (Hays & Brown, 2004; Miller, 1994a, 2007m).

Centering

Centering (Asken, 1993) is a technique derived from Eastern meditation that involves combining diaphragmatic breathing with a *centering cue image*. The instruction to the patient is as follows:

> Begin by taking a slow, deep diaphragmatic breath. As you breathe out, slowly let your eyes close (or remain open if this is more comfortable for you) and focus your awareness on some internal or external point, such as your lower abdomen or an imaginary spot on the wall. Repeat this process until you feel yourself becoming calmer.

Mindfulness

For some people, trying to relax is a contradiction in terms: The more they try to force themselves to relax, the more tense they get. That's because, by definition, relaxation is something you have to learn to *let* happen, not something you can *make* happen, and some individuals are just too challenged by the process to allow this to take place comfortably.

In *mindfulness* training (Kabat-Zinn, 1994, 2003; Marra, 2005), the individual makes no conscious effort to relax, but simply allows him- or herself to take in the sensations and images in the surrounding environment. Eventually, by taking the demand element out of the process, relaxation will usually occur as a beneficial side effect. This technique may be especially useful with crime victims who already have enough to feel ashamed about without having to face the prospect of failing a relaxation assignment. Mindfulness training allows productive engagement with a therapeutic exercise that has as little demand as possible, thus allowing whatever small progress that occurs to be counted as a step in the right direction.

External Cues

These are any external cues or stimuli that can be utilized to tone down arousal level. These include calming *selective association,* which is essentially encouraging the patient to spend his or her time with people or in situations that lead to states of calm, not agitation. The more internal and external arousal control techniques you can cobble together for use by a particular patient (e.g., combining soft music with centering and cue-controlled imagery while taking a quiet walk on the beach), the greater will be the overall synergistic effect. Indeed, recent clinical research and practice have been moving away from an overreliance on structured breathing and muscle relaxation techniques in favor of more naturalistic strategies (Huppert & Baker-Morissette, 2003; Marra, 2005; Miller, 1994a; Schmid et al., 2000).

MULTISENSORY IMAGERY

The ability to use imagery to mentally project oneself into a different mind-set or state of being is a time-honored psychological technique for improving skills in sports and the performing arts (Hays & Brown, 2004), and enhancing law enforcement training for dealing with stress (Doss, 2006, 2007; Miller, 2006m, 2007m). I have found that the same principles can be applied to the treatment of traumatized crime victims in allowing them to gain greater control of their psychophysiological responses.

Imagery training is sometimes referred to as *visualization* training (Olson, 1998), but I agree with other authors (Asken, 1993; Hays & Brown, 2004) that *imagery* is the preferable term because such training should ideally involve sensory images in all modalities, not just vision. Like any skill, the use of effective imagery requires practice, general at first, but ultimately focused on the type of imagery that most closely replicates the actual event the crime victim is seeking mastery of. For example, the businessman who was car-jacked in his office building parking lot should ultimately be able to image himself successfully getting in and out of his car without fear or panic.

Note that I use *image* as a verb. That's because the more commonly used term, *imagine,* too often connotes fantasy and daydreaming ("Imagine yourself on a sandy beach . . ."). The imagery exercises described in this chapter are grounded in reality—the reality of whatever traumatic event has happened to that particular crime victim. I might also point out that the term *daydreaming* does in fact imply the powerful use of imagery, often combined with a state of rapt absorption and concentration. However, the difference is that, in day-dreaming, the dream leads the dreamer: What makes the process so enjoyable for most people is that there's relatively little conscious effort involved; that is, we passively experience the story as it unfolds in our own mind.

For traumatized crime victims, however, the intrusive imagery is a kind of malevolent daydreaming: The toxic images capture attention and won't let go. So the kind of healing imagery used to counteract them requires a precise kind of focused, effortful, volitional guidance, because the victim is purpose-fully trying to turn the tide of noxious thought and emotion to regain a sense of mastery and empowerment.

Visual-Motor Behavior Rehearsal

Developed by Suinn (1972, 1984, 1985) in the domain of sports psychol-ogy and adapted by Asken (1993) to the needs of emergency service work-ers, *visual-motor behavior rehearsal* (VMBR) combines the relaxation response with multisensory imagery to mentally rehearse and enhance skills for peak performance. It is an extension of mental imagery, in that it combines the internal act of generating a mental image with feedback from the real-world performance of a practical skill (Lane, 1980). This method has been used successfully for enhancing skills in a number of sports (Behncke, 2006), and it can also be used to enhance mastery of feared and avoided situations by traumatized crime victims.

As typically practiced, VMBR involves three phases. First, *inducing an appropriate arousal level* provides the psychophysiological background state that will be most conducive to the proper mental imagery, which involves utilizing the relaxation and arousal control skills described above.

"At first," said Sam, "every time I even thought of going back to that shopping mall, I'd break a sweat, get nauseous, and almost throw up. Then I'd start to breathe real fast and feel like I was going to pass out. My therapist taught me how to use my muscles and breathing to calm myself down and, when I got pretty good at it, she showed me how to gradually mentally put myself back into the mall scene, first from a mental distance and then like I was really standing there."

Second, *visualizing performance through various imagery techniques* allows a kind of internal rehearsal.

"We started out slow, first visualizing the mall from a distance, like one of those computer-generated aerial maps that you keep zooming in on with each frame. Every time I'd get a little closer, I'd feel some of the anxiety coming back, so I kicked in one of the relaxation exercises 'till the anxiety got manageable. Sometimes, I went too fast and I had to scale back a frame or two. But eventually I was able to get to the point where I could put myself in a vivid mental image of standing in the mall, hearing the people around me, even smelling the food court, without feeling like I was going to panic."

Third, *performing the actual skill under realistic conditions* reinforces the training link between the imagery exercises and the real-life skill. A particularly useful application of VMBR is to have the patient employ the mastery imagery at the same time as he's going back to the scene itself. Repeating this process with the target skill during training reinforces the feedback connection between the mental imagery exercise and the actual performance. In that way, adjustments in both the real-life skill and the imagery process can be maintained in parallel and in real time. Thus, the rationale behind VMBR is to keep mental imagery and skill performance closely linked in training, which should result in an enhancement of overall performance because the individual can fine-tune both processes simultaneously (Lane, 1980; Behncke, 2006).

"Okay, so now it was time for the big enchilada, actually going to the mall. Obviously, I couldn't zoom in from above like in the imagery map exercise, so I started by getting progressively closer to the actual location, street by street. When I'd get the queasies, I'd do the relaxation and imagery exercises, right there in the car. I have to admit, it took a while before I could actually park the car and walk into the courtyard, but one day, there I was standing in the mall. I still avoid the actual spot where I was attacked, but at least I can do my shopping there—just in time for Christmas."

Crime victims often find themselves caught in a seemingly endless cycle of what-if ruminations. "What if I had taken the stairs instead of the elevator?" "What if I had checked to see if my car door was locked?" "What if I had taken the longer route home that didn't involve the short-cut through the empty lot?" As noted in chapter 2, crime victims will often assume blame for their victimization even when others clearly point out that it wasn't their fault. That's because self-blame allows at least some measure of potential future control: "If I did something wrong this time, then if I do it right the next time, this bad thing won't happen." Appeals to logic go only so far in refuting these beliefs. But it can be a powerful exercise in self-efficacy to mentally rewind the tape and develop practical, if implicit, strategies for doing it "better" next time through the VMBR technique. The patient can tell himself that he really has learned from the experience and can protect himself in the future.

For such an internal error-correction exercise, first have the patient mentally replay himself going through the original crime experience. Of course, this should be done only after sufficient desensitization has been achieved so that the patient doesn't retraumatize himself. Then, ask him to mentally rewind the tape and image himself behaving the way he would now that he has additional data and insight. Have him rewind to the beginning of the situation and image himself mentally preparing for it. Tell him to fast-forward and image himself feeling competent and confident after successfully completing the sequence of events. Then, have him splice the parts together and mentally play the scenario in real-time sequence as many times as necessary until it feels natural and unforced.

> "The one thing that still bothered me, though," Sam went on, "was, how do I know this won't happen again in the future? Logically, we discussed in the therapy sessions all the ways I could avoid going past the mall movie theater when the late show lets out and the rough kids are running into the mall, but that only seemed to help up to a point. So the therapist had me use the imagery and relaxation technique again, this time putting myself in the mall, but taking the actual steps—in my head, for now—of using a different route to get from the store area to the main courtyard, steering clear of the movie entrance. Then, one day, I actually went back there and did it. I know there's no iron-clad guarantee against bad things happening to anyone, but at least now I feel confident that I can avoid the kinds of trouble that are avoidable."

USING THOUGHT AND LANGUAGE

Human beings are unique among creatures precisely because we can think, reflect, plan, anticipate, and transmit our ideas in the form of spoken and written language. Unlike Peter Rabbit in chapter 2, we can communicate our thoughts and emotions to others, and, just as importantly, we can articulate our thoughts and feelings to ourselves. Thinking and language are recursive and mutually reinforcing: Our words express what we want to convey and, in the telling, often reinforce the very thoughts and feelings that gave rise to them in the first place.

The upside is that rational thought and language allow us to avoid danger by anticipating consequences and permit us to analyze our own thoughts, feelings, and actions to gain greater insight and self-understanding. The downside is that we can just as easily think and talk ourselves into delusion and despair. Indeed, natural variations in the use of thought and language comprise further elements of cognitive style and personality that distinguish individuals from one another (Miller, 1990). The goal of this section is to introduce the clinician to a variety of cognitively based techniques that can help crime victims master their traumatic reactions by helping them utilize cognitive processes in their favor.

Thought Stopping

Sometimes, the best thing you can do with a dysfunctional thought or distressing internal dialog is to interdict it and banish it from consciousness. Everyone has had the experience of talking themselves into trouble. There is ample evidence from both practical experience and empirical research that negative, self-defeating statements and thoughts have a deleterious effect on a person's mental state and adaptive behavior (Hardy, Jones, & Gould, 1996). Being able to stop nonproductive thoughts and develop an internal dialog containing positive countermeasures has been repeatedly demonstrated to improve mastery and adaptive functioning (Van Raalte & Brewer, 2002). Thoughts thus jettisoned may float around in the mental shallows and later wash back up to pollute the shoreline of the patient's recovering psyche; if so, you'll deal with them as necessary in psychotherapy (chapter 7). But many dysfunctional thoughts, once set adrift, bob into the sunset never to return, and this leaves the patient with greater resources to tackle those that stubbornly return to tar the beach.

Thought stopping is not as strange or diabolical as it sounds, and in fact it is only a systematic application of something we all do when we need to keep unproductive ruminating thoughts from clogging our cognitive channels (Asken, 1993). As we saw in chapter 2, the combination of high internal arousal and poor attentional control may propel cycling loops of negative thoughts and images that prevent the crime victim from taking his mind off it and being able to utilize one's brain for making important life decisions and taking adaptive action.

You can conceptualize thought stopping to patients as the Ctrl+Alt+Del sequence of their cognitive keyboard that can clear their mental screen when it freezes up (older patients may relate better to the metaphor of tapping a phonograph needle to get a broken record unstuck). Thought stopping can also be used to keep negative ruminations from sapping one's motivation and determination or to prevent pointless, unproductive second-guessing or self-criticism that can keep patients from developing foresight and adaptive plans for the future.

Thought stopping is not an instant cure-all for negativity in general and it is not an excuse for failing to confront real-life challenges that require more complex and more long-term solutions. It is not self-deception or self-delusion. In fact, if maladaptive repression and denial are impeding the patient's recovery, you will eventually need to help her resolve the circumstances and mind-sets that generate the negative thoughts and dysfunctional behaviors in the first place. But the middle of a panic attack or disabling flashback is not the time to deal with underlying issues, it's a time for rapid, effective relief. And, in fact, achieving some measure of control over symptoms will ultimately give the patient greater confidence in eventually tackling these issues—highlighting the interrelationship between supposedly short-term and long-term therapies and so-called behavioral and psychodynamic approaches.

Thought stopping can be combined with imagery and with cognitive restructuring (see below) to clear the mind and enhance performance (Asken, 1993). The first step is to train the patient to monitor her consciousness for the presence of negative thoughts. Usually, finding these little demons will be the least of her problems, since they may be screaming louder than anything else in the patient's head.

Inez described her experience since she got into the fender-bender accident with her 5-year-old son that turned into a criminal assault: "I may have stopped short because I was trying to read the street sign, but that white car was too close and those guys bumped me from behind and started honking. Okay, I was pissed and I may have given them the finger and said something, but then four big guys jumped out and started to beat on my car. One of them picked up something and broke my side window and I got cut.

"They were about to reach in and grab me, but something must have scared them off, because they got back in their car and drove off. I was so freaked, I peed in my pants. I thought they were going to pull us from my car and rape me and kill me and Kevin. He was paralyzed for days from the whole incident, and he still can't ride in a car without covering his eyes.

"Since then, the worst part is that I can't stop thinking how it was my fault things got out of hand because I shouldn't have started up with those guys with the finger and everything—I should have been more responsible because my son was in the car. Since then, all I hear in my head is, 'It's your fault, it's your fault.' I just can't talk myself out of it."

To halt an unproductive negative thought, have the patient forcefully tell herself "No!" or "Stop!" Or have her visualize a flashing STOP sign or neon slash-in-circle symbol. Encourage her to be as creative as she wants to be and have her utilize whatever phrase or image works best for her (many of the examples cited by my patients are unprintable). She can say them aloud if necessary, of course being mindful of the sensibilities of others around her, or she can say them to herself. If a word or image doesn't do it for her, have her try some other stimulus: a sharp breath, a pinch on her arm, a riff or lyric from a favorite song—basically, any cue she can give herself that will be jarring enough to abort the negative thought.

But, like nature, the human mind abhors a vacuum, so to keep the negative thought from sneaking or barging back in, encourage the patient to insert something into her consciousness to take its place, something that is diametrically opposed to, and incompatible with, the negative thought. This would be the place to slide in a confidence-building affirmation, positive mental image, or instructional cue. Then, have the patient actually perform some productive activity to the best of her ability so that her constructive actions occupy her mind and her real-world success becomes the basis for future positive thoughts.

"I spent a lot of time working with my therapist on how, yeah, I might have gotten a little pissed at them and mouthed off, but it wasn't my 'fault' that these criminals smashed up my car," Inez went on. "But just knowing and accepting that didn't get the 'it's-your-fault' loop out of my head. So my therapist, who's kind of a funny guy, suggested I use my bird-flipping finger to good advantage and that, every time I get the lousy thought in my head, I flip the thought and say, 'It's *not* my fault we got attacked.' Obviously, I don't do this in public, I just visualize it and say it to myself, but it stops the thought for a little while and it also puts a little humor into it, which helps. Meanwhile, I still want to keep something like this from getting out of hand again 'cause I don't want to find myself in that position, you know? So now I'm also working on ways to deal with my road rage so I at least don't have to worry about that aspect of it again."

Cognitive Restructuring

This mechanical-sounding mental technique actually helps the patient break out of certain rigid thinking traps that jam his cognitive gears, and it can help him utilize more flexible decision-making and problem-solving strategies to cope with the traumatic crime victimization. In *cognitive restructuring,* you are training your patients to use their *metacognition,* or observing ego, to make a command decision about what thoughts they will permit to dominate their thinking. Cognitive restructuring is aimed at unjamming and retuning repetitive thoughts or cognitive distortions that have built up in the wake of the traumatic event and that get in the way of clear, adaptive thinking. More than just an attitude adjustment, it is a realignment of the crime victim's whole way of perceiving and conceptualizing the challenges he confronts.

Patients can be taught to use thought stopping to interrupt a repetitive loop of toxic self-statements, then evoke imagery and utilize cognitive restructuring to give themselves a more realistically hopeful perspective and motivation for action. As always, the more creative ways you can combine different techniques and gear them to the needs of your particular patient, the more effective the therapy will be.

Hamblen et al. (2006) describe six basic steps of cognitive restructuring, used for prolonged disaster distress, that I have adapted to the treatment of crime victims. For such purposes, these should be thought of not necessarily as a rigid sequence but as a flexible menu of options.

> *Describe the situation.* "I was assaulted coming out of the elevator in my office building after working there late one night."
>
> *Identify the negative feeling.* "I feel helpless to protect myself and scared to go back in the building."
>
> *Identify the automatic thought related to the feeling.* "I must be a real idiot not to be able to protect myself."
>
> *Challenge the thought.* "There was no way I could have predicted this. The security in this building is usually top-notch. I've worked later than this many times without a problem."
>
> *Make a decision as to whether the evidence supports the thought or belief.* "I still should have checked before I came out of the elevator instead of talking on my cell phone."
>
> *Develop an action plan.* "Okay, from now on, I'm going to be a little more aware of my surroundings if I'm working in the building during off-hours. For starters, no phone; I'll keep my eyes and ears open until I'm safely out of the building and in my car."

Challenging Automatic Thoughts

There are several main types of *automatic thoughts* that can plague crime victims, with various solutions for dealing with them (Asken, 1993).

All-or-nothing thinking. Here, things are either black or white, never shades of gray. In crime victims, this expresses itself in two main ways: (a) "if I didn't do everything possible to prevent the attack, then it must have been my fault"; and (b) "if I'm not getting over this right away, I must be a sick or weak person."

> "If I'd given that angry customer his refund right away, he wouldn't have hit me."

> "It's been 2 weeks since the attack in the store. I shouldn't still be feeling this bad."

Because human nature is normally risk averse, we tend to pay more attention to negatives than to positives, which is nature's way of keeping us alert to danger and one step ahead of trouble. Under ordinary circumstances, this is an adaptive frame of mind. But after a traumatic event like a crime victimization, there is a tendency to focus on negatives as if the positives didn't even exist and this serves only to drain energy and sap motivation. Posttraumatic hypervigilance is actually counterproductive to future adaptive behavior and safety because it's not realistic and leaves the victim unable to discriminate between dangerous and safe situations.

As you can imagine, members of critical occupations like law enforcement and emergency services are often confronted with the high-stakes consequences of their split-second decisions and it can eat the hell out them. So, to help your traumatized crime victim patients counteract their all-or-nothing thinking, give them some version of the little speech I present to the public safety tough guys in both formal training courses and individual counseling sessions, and train them to repeat it to themselves as necessary:

> Yes, you are absolutely responsible for what you can control but not for what you can't. Let's put this another way: You are responsible for your efforts, not necessarily the outcome. Now, of course, your efforts influence the outcome, and it's your responsibility to ensure you have taken the reasonable actions to keep yourself safe and to rebound from an adverse event.
>
> But if you can honestly tell yourself (or have someone who's more objective tell you) that you did everything you realistically could to keep yourself and others safe, but some or all aspects of the situation went south due to circumstances beyond your perception or control, then go ahead and feel bad about what happened because trying to be all smiley-faced in

the presence of a profound disappointment is not stress management, it's bullshit.

However, that doesn't mean you have to beat yourself up with unnecessary blame and shame. If it gives you a feeling of greater control, try to figure out what went wrong and, if there's room for improvement, figure out what to do to ensure your safety and others' safety if there ever is a next time. Also remember that even if you didn't take all the precautions you should have, it still doesn't mean you or others deserved to be injured or killed. Use your training and do better next time.

Overgeneralization. In this type of automatic thinking, we take one example of something and apply it to every situation that even remotely resembles it. Or we pick one characteristic of a person—even ourselves—and make that the sole defining feature of that person, excluding or minimizing everything else (trial lawyers and cognitive psychologists will recognize this as the *fundamental attribution error*). Once we've pigeonholed that person or situation, we then interpret everything about them in terms of this first impression. If that sounds a lot like the definition of *prejudice,* it's because prejudice almost always involves some degree of overgeneralization ("Those people are all. . ."). And it's sometimes too easy to prejudice ourselves against ourselves when we feel we're somehow not measuring up to our own standards or to those of others.

As we've seen, self-blame is a common reaction of crime victims, and this often involves overgeneralization, the keywords of which are *always* and *never:*

"I always seem to be at the wrong place at the wrong time. That's why I was attacked."

"I never handle things the right way. I should have gone to the hospital and filed the police report immediately. Now, they say it will be harder to solve my case."

"Why can't I buck up and move on with my life? Nobody else reacts like this. I always fold under pressure."

To counteract overgeneralization, you'll have to help your patient actively seek out realistic exceptions to, or explanations for, the supposed rule and focus on the explanations:

"Well, now that you mention it, I've ridden that subway line for years and always managed to stay out of trouble. I guess a person can't see everything coming all the time."

"I was scared to even leave my room after the assault. The guy had a mask on and told me he knew my address and would come back if I called the police. I was afraid the people at the hospital wouldn't believe me because it happened in my own bedroom."

"Well, yeah, I handled that cancer scare a few years back. In fact, everybody kept saying they couldn't believe how calm and brave I was. So I guess I'm not a total wuss. But being attacked like this threw me more than being sick—this was a *person* trying to harm me, not a disease, and for some reason, in my mind, that made it worse. But I guess if I could get through cancer, I can get through this."

Disqualifying the positive. This cognitive distortion is often a subset of the above one and involves allowing the negative aspects of the situation to eclipse the positive:

"Okay, so I rode the D line without any trouble for 15 years, but I still got jumped this time. What if I'm getting careless?"

You can counteract this in two main ways. One strategy is to help the victim remind himself of what is the exception and what is the rule, so that there is a positive crossover in his thinking, not a negative one.

"Yeah, now that you mention it, one bad day out of 15 years isn't too bad of a record. I guess I'll have to see what happens in the next 15 years before I decide if I'm getting careless."

The second strategy is to have the patient remind himself of what he's doing positively in the here-and-now, that is, utilizing the strategies that help him control his symptoms, drawing strength from his efficacy in doing this, understanding that as he continues to gain mastery, he'll keep getting better. If the patient is really utilizing these therapeutic skills correctly, then this is not wishful thinking but a realistic bumping up of the adaptive odds.

Task-Relevant Instructional Self-Talk (TRIST)

When you first learn a practical skill—from riding a bike to taking an advanced technology course—in the beginning phases, it's common to have your instructor talk you through the steps. For example, when you first learned to operate a car, your driving instructor showed you precisely what to do and you did it. Later, you manipulated the steering wheel, signals, and pedals with explicit verbal guidance from the trainer, then only with a few hints and cues, then maybe with the instructor just observing and making a few comments afterward, and finally doing it all by yourself. That is, the skill became automatic. You learned to drive.

Under conditions of stress, performance automaticity of even well-trained skills often breaks down, and the smooth flow of the activity can be disrupted by distraction, confusion, and high emotion (Doss, 2006, 2007; Hays & Brown, 2004; Miller, 1998h, 2007m; Regehr & Bober, 2004). Athletes, musicians, stage actors, public speakers, soldiers, surgeons, politicians, and police officers all speak of choking under pressure. So imagine the plight of a crime victim trying to negotiate the novel, complex, and confusing world of dealing with the criminal justice system or just getting through her daily routine. Worse, under stress, many people revert to self-criticism and their negative self-statements tend to become increasingly pessimistic and self-deprecatory, ranging from a simple "Oh, no" to a run-on, self-deprecatory harangue: "This is going bad, we'll never make it through this one. What an idiot—I thought I could do this, but I can't. How do I get myself into these hopeless situations?"

A similar problem occurs when learning and practicing the stress management and symptom control techniques discussed in this chapter. In the safe, comfortably cocooned confines of the therapist's office, the patient learns to moderate her hyperaroused states and correct her dysfunctional thinking. But when she attempts to apply these strategies out there in the real world, the results, at least at first, may be less than stellar. Then, the immediate reaction is often: "I'm no good at this, this will never work, I'm doomed."

At these times, it can be very useful to encourage your patient to invoke an internalized representation of you, her therapist, mentally talking her through the exercise or procedure. In fact, many patients report doing this automatically and instinctively during stressful situations.

> To her therapist, Effie admitted, somewhat sheepishly, that, "whenever the going gets tough, I just imagine you're standing next to me, talking to me like you do in your office, telling me what to do to get through the situation. It's like I know it's my own thoughts, but it helps if I think them in your voice or imagine you sitting in your chair over there." When the therapist asked her why she seemed reluctant to tell him this, she said she thought he'd think it might be "cheating" or just immature. So she was pleasantly surprised when the therapist informed her that she had independently discovered and utilized an established technique of stress management.

In fact, Effie's self-discovered coping strategy has been made explicit in a technique devised for public safety and emergency workers called *task-relevant instructional self-talk,* or TRIST (Asken, 1993), which involves using short, clearly articulated phrases that serve as an internal self-instructional guide to applying the subject's skills to the task at hand. I have found the same procedure to be useful with crime trauma victims and other patients in crisis. In TRIST, the patient mentally puts her instructor or therapist on her shoulder—or becomes her own instructor—to guide her through the nuts and bolts of the skill or activity, whether it is a relaxation exercise or a practical life task. That is, in TRIST, the self-talk focuses on the response-enhancing, task-relevant technical instructions on how to carry out the task itself in the real world.

> "Now, I kind of use this as backup," Effie said. "Like when I had to go to court, in order to remember all the points I wanted to make, I imagined my attorney was sitting with me on the stand, telling me what to say and how to say it. I knew it was my own words, but somehow it helped to give him the mental 'credit.' Hey, whatever works, right?"

Using TRIST to cope with real-life challenges. Although the focus of TRIST is mainly cognitive and instructional, there are a number of arousal-regulating and emotion-modulating components, gleaned from some of the techniques discussed above, that set the stage for the proficient application of TRIST to tasks and challenges that need to be mastered in the real world (Asken, 1993).

The first step is to encourage the patient to relax, or at least get him to lower his arousal level sufficiently to focus on the self-instruction he's about to give himself—or, for that matter, to focus on anything else that's relevant to the situation at hand. Indeed, before initiating or changing one's self-talk, it is necessary to take a step back and become aware of what is being said and what needs to be said. Positive and negative thoughts are often mixed. For example, a patient might think to himself, "I've handled this kind of situation fine before, but the present mess looks like it's out of control." In these circumstances, it is necessary to identify both beneficial thoughts and harmful thoughts because you don't want the patient to throw out the good with the bad. Once you've helped him make this differentiation, it is then important to train him how to make a conscious effort to purposefully include those thoughts that seem to help in carrying out the exercise or task and banish those that impede the process.

Next, show the patient how to use positive self-statements and confidence-building affirmations and imagery to bolster himself: "I'm doing fine, this is just a tough call. I'm going to get my bearings and nail this thing." Note that this is not to encourage unrealistic overconfidence or dangerous foolhardiness; if the situation really *is* hopeless, then train the patient to use his wits and common sense to get the hell out of there before risking a full-blown meltdown. In most of these situations, you will be helping the patient to tread the thin line between strategic withdrawal, which bolsters good judgment and self-empowerment, versus premature bailing, which fosters capitulation and avoidance conditioning.

Once the patient has developed confidence in achieving an optimum level of arousal and/or mastering distracting symptoms, next focus on the skill or technique he needs to handle in the specific work or social situation. For the immediate task at hand, have him try to forget about the outcome and consequences and focus instead on the process and execution of the skill. If it helps, have him put you on his shoulder and speak through your voice. In fact, it may help to practice and rehearse some flexible scripts for this purpose. Express the instruction in relatively short, task-relevant phrases and as positive statements. You can have the patient try combining the instructional talk with instructional imagery, picturing himself doing the task correctly, but use this only if it helps not if it distracts him from the task at hand.

Far from being a theoretical exercise, skill in the above-described cognitive control techniques, whether partly intuitive or acquired by painstaking training, can have life-saving consequences during critical emergencies.

Charles was in downtown Manhattan on the morning of September 11, 2001, just beginning work as the manager of a financial firm a few blocks from the World Trade Center when the second tower was hit. In relating his thoughts and actions during the next few hours, it became apparent that he instinctively applied many of the techniques we've just described to handle the emergency and take care of his employees.

"We had already activated our evacuation plan when the first tower got hit and we were watching it all happening on TV, when suddenly there was this big rumble, the building shook, and the power went out. Some of the emergency lights went on and some didn't, so a number of offices were in almost total darkness. There were also no phones and no intercom, and it was up to me and another manager to get almost a hundred people out of the building fast, but the other manager hadn't come into work yet—lucky him. There was also a lot of dust in the air and some people thought it was smoke and that the building was on fire, so they were starting to panic.

"For a few moments, my mind started to go blank. Then, it was funny, but I kind of forced myself to snap out of it by telling myself to 'shut up and do something.' I'd like to say it was some image of my family or a message from heaven or something that motivated me, but I really was just superfocused on doing my job and getting people out of there and I didn't even think about my family till much later when it was all over and I spent 2 days crying like a baby.

"What I did imagine to myself at the time was a mental picture of the building layout that we'd memorized during our emergency drills. I kept telling myself, 'You know this, you've prepared for it, just calm down and put it into action.' My office was near a window and I had some light, so I started grabbing the first people who wandered by and tried to recruit them to find the others. A few were too panicked to help, but some actually seemed reassured that somebody was doing something constructive and offered to help out.

"We located some flashlights and battery lanterns and went room by room and into the stairwells looking for stragglers and people who might be injured. There were some dust masks somewhere, but I didn't think we had time to find them—remember, we didn't know if the whole building was going to come down on top of us—so we just spit into our handkerchiefs and tied them around our faces; one guy used his tie. I seemed to divide my attention between concentrating on the room searches and keeping a 'mental ear' open for anybody shouting from a distant area. Me and my 'volunteers' kept at it until we thought everybody was out of the building.

"There were only a couple of injuries, mainly related to falls and inhaling dust, but nobody was seriously hurt. Later, a number of people came up to me and told me that they admired how calm I'd been during the whole event. 'Calm?' I thought to myself, 'it's a miracle I didn't shit my pants.' What I think they were seeing was my determination, because once I made up my mind to get everyone out, it was like my brain just took charge and went on automatic. Like I said, when it was all over, I spent the next few days blubbering like a schoolgirl, but then after that I seemed to be all right, and a trauma counselor later told me that this was a normal reaction. Believe it or not, the worst part of this was that the whole downtown area was wrecked and we had to spend almost a year getting relocated and back to business."

EXPOSURE THERAPY AND DESENSITIZATION

As we've just discussed, many symptom-oriented treatments for posttraumatic disturbances employ a behavioral or cognitive-behavioral approach.

As we've also seen, many of these posttraumatic symptom–reduction strategies are intended to allow the patient to conduct normal activities in the face of otherwise frightening circumstances. Capitalizing on some of the techniques described above, graded exposure therapies allow crime victims to gradually learn to confront the stimuli they would otherwise avoid because of their posttraumatic stress symptoms (Thompson, 1992). These kinds of therapies are derived from *systematic desensitization,* originally used to treat phobias and now well integrated into behavioral medicine (Miller, 1989a, 1989b, 1994a, 2007m). In the cognitive–behavioral treatment of crime victim PTSD and other traumatic disability syndromes, the aim is to reduce posttraumatic reactions such as flashbacks, intrusive memories, and startle responses through habituation, thereby bringing about the extinction of the conditioned aversive response.

Exposure therapy for desensitization is typically conducted through imagery during a relaxation exercise, as described above, or in real-life—in vivo— situations. Both methods may be used in combination, the imagery exercise paving the way for the in vivo training. In general, such strategies have been found useful in mitigating posttraumatic anxiety, intrusive memories, nightmares, hyperarousal, and hypersensitivity to sounds and other disturbing stimuli (Cooper & Clum, 1989; Keane, Fairbank, Caddell, & Zimmerling, 1989; Thompson, 1992). There is some neurophysiological evidence that exposure therapy enhances the inhibitory effect of the medial prefrontal cortex on dampening the amygdala's alarm signals (McNally, 2007), but this is still under study (see chapter 2).

Bryant, Sackville, Dang, Moulds, and Guthrie (1999) caution that exposure therapies may not be helpful for patients with excessive anxiety, severe depression with suicidal ideation, dissociative reactions, borderline or psychotic traits, substance abuse, or demanding ongoing stressors. My own experience in applying this type of approach has been mixed. Many patients seem to get with the program, learn the relaxation technique, and desensitize themselves effectively to the traumatic situation. However, the most successful cases are typically the ones with the least distressing posttraumatic symptoms. A few of the more severely traumatized patients resist all attempts at desensitization, fearing that letting down their guard during relaxation will render them vulnerable to overwhelming emotional arousal, a problem that has been noted for relaxation therapies in general (Lazarus & Mayne, 1990; Miller, 1994a). In such cases, a supportive–expressive cognitive therapy approach is often successful in helping patients work through the traumatic fear and pain of the injuring event in a more rational manner—trying, in effect, to turn the posttraumatic vigilance and rumination to constructive therapeutic advantage.

Posttraumatic Flashbacks

Waking flashbacks may occur in any sensory modality, and often in multiple senses simultaneously; these symptoms, more than any others, are what make many patients fear they are "going crazy." As noted above, try to normalize the process for your patient as much as possible, helping her to understand that this a natural and expectable part of the recovery process, that the flashbacks will eventually fade, and that there are learnable ways to manage intrusive symptoms (Everstine & Everstine, 1993; Matsakis, 1994; Modlin, 1983; Taylor, 2006). The patient doesn't necessarily have to fight the flashback; it's possible to ride out many episodes without being overwhelmed, once she understands the nature and self-limiting quality of these symptoms—similar to the cognitive–behavioral approach taken with panic attacks and chronic pain flare-ups (Miller, 1993b, 1998h).

Many flashbacks and other posttraumatic symptoms are triggered by stimuli in the environment; others may be elicited by internal stimuli and sometimes these may not be conscious. Anniversary dates, people, places, objects, and certain emotional states can serve as triggers. The first step in helping patients cope with trauma triggers is to help them identify those triggers (Matsakis, 1994). Other times, patients will come to therapy all too painfully aware of what stimuli set off their posttraumatic symptoms; if anything, they are paralyzed into avoidance, withdrawal, and inactivity by their own constant vigilance against exposing themselves to trigger situations.

In either case, once triggers have been identified, the full range of relaxation and behavioral desensitization techniques may be applied. However, as noted above, for many patients, this may be threatening in itself, so for these patients, a more cognitively based approach involves planning ahead for anticipated trigger situations. Matsakis (1994) recommends training the patient to ask herself certain questions when faced with potential trigger situations; these may be individualized for each patient:

- How have I reacted to similar situations in the past?
- Did anything terrible happen?
- What are the chances of something bad happening again?
- If the worst happens, what can I do to help myself?
- Who can I ask for help and how can they help me?

Just the act of going through this kind of mental checklist often helps build a cognitive firewall between the spark of the triggering stimulus and the tinderbox of traumatic memories that can flare into a full-scale emotional conflagration. Additionally, taking time to think it through gives the patient experience in using her own brain to solve problems, thus increasing her sense of control. Similar Socratic questioning techniques may be used by therapists themselves in crisis intervention with suicidal or decompensating patients (Bongar, 2002; Gilliland & James, 1993; Miller, 1998e, 2005d, 2006a). With symptomatic PTSD patients, the therapist may first model these adaptive coping questions and self-statements, and then teach the patient to utilize them in trigger situations.

> "I told my therapist that the problem with asking myself about the chances of it happening again," said Tony of his subway mugging, "is that it very well *could* happen again because I take that train home from work every day and the thugs who ride it aren't going to leave. So we focused on what practical steps I could take to protect myself, like sitting with a bunch of people on the train, not going down onto the platform if I hear a bunch of loud kids, scoping out quick exits if trouble starts, and so on. We developed a 'safety list' of things I could do which made me feel a little better, even though I know I have to be on my toes and riding this line can never be 100% safe. But at least I have some control of some things."

Dreams and Nightmares

Traumatic dreams are seldom rote replications of the traumatic incident itself. Instead, they tend to recapitulate the emotional terror of the event and/or symbolically represent important issues related to the event, such as survival, betrayal, and loss (chapter 7). Matsakis (1994) recommends that the therapist have the patient "rewrite" the nightmares, incorporating empowering themes and outcomes into the revised narratives—a version of cognitive restructuring discussed above, but this time applied to cognitions that occur during sleep.

However, I have found that some patients may view this as trivializing their dream experiences and the trauma itself: "You think I can just rewrite it and it all goes away?" In these cases, incorporating such revisioning into the waking therapeutic imagery exercises is generally more acceptable to patients because it suggests a reinterpretation of alternatives, rather than changing the script of their dreams, which many patients find difficult or impossible to do, especially in the beginning stages of treatment.

Matsakis (1994) also recommends "beating the dreams to death" through repeated exposure and reiteration, thereby stripping them of their intimidating power. This is actually an extension of the technique of repeated ventilation, exploration, and working through of traumatic material in general (chapter 7). Again, my only caveat here is that the reexposure be truly dissipative and stress innoculative, not retraumatizing. This requires that the therapist know when the patient is ready to handle the traumatic dream material and perhaps combining the repetition with other therapeutic techniques, such as relaxation or cognitive restructuring (see above).

> "For this one patient, Geraldine, the dreams didn't start until late in the process," her therapist told me. "We figured maybe she was suppressing the dreams because they would have been too disturbing early in her recovery cycle because, when they did hit, they hit with a bang. She came into one session crying about the nightmares that had been making her scared to go to sleep all week. I had her describe a typical dream to me and then we 'movie-screened' it, that is I had her imagine the dream taking place on a movie screen that she was viewing from a very far distance away. After I had her 'play' it a few times, I encouraged her to get a little closer to the screen, and so on, until she could watch it from the 'first row.' Then, I had her rework the script any way she wanted. Of course, this took place over several sessions, interspersed with other things we were doing and talking about in the sessions. Once she got the hang of these techniques, even the new dreams she was getting didn't bother her as much because she'd learned to put some mental distance between the dreams and her own perceptions and reactions."

Numbing, Dissociation, and Self-Harm

In posttraumatic therapy, intrusive symptomatology constitutes the proverbial squeaky wheel that gets the grease because these symptoms draw the most attention and seem to cause the most distress. For some patients, however, equal or greater disturbance is produced by the zoning-out numbing response of the posttraumatic stress response. These may not be observed unless specifically asked for.

Some patients, especially those who have been multiply traumatized from an early age and/or who may have received diagnoses of borderline personality disorder (chapter 3), characteristically respond to numbing by dissociation and self-mutilating or other self-harming behavior. In such cases, Matsakis (1994) recommends teaching the patient less harmful and more reality-grounding forms of self-stimulation, such as taking a cold shower, drinking a carbonated beverage, using a wrist-snapping rubber band, doing some form of vigorous exercise, or handling a "safe object" such as a teddy bear. Several of my patients have learned to substitute the application of ice or the teeth of a comb to their skin in place of actual physical self-injury with a cigarette or knife blade (Miller, 1998h).

"The first therapist I went to freaked out when I told him I cut myself because he thought I was suicidal after the rape," Cheryl said. "That didn't work out, so I ended up with another psych person, a woman this time, who seemed to get what I was talking about, that poking my skin and drawing blood with my scissors and tweezers and nail clippers and stuff was like letting this stale, choking air out of a balloon so I could breath again and feel real. She was more concerned about me getting infections, so she had me agree to carry around these alcohol pads you get in the drugstore and clean my 'tools' with them and then, if I did any pricking or cutting, to at least put peroxide and a Band-Aid on it later."

"I said okay because she really seemed to be trying to help me, not just follow some set of rules so she wouldn't get in trouble for not reporting me. She said that, since I was over 18 and wasn't actually suicidal, there really wasn't anything to report as long as I wasn't completely reckless and self-destructive about my health. The thing is, because I trusted her more, I was more likely to do what she said and not lie about it."

CONCLUSIONS

As noted earlier, short- and long-term, and behavioral and deep, therapies are fluid concepts that often blend together and, ideally, should be used in ways that reinforce one another. For many crime victims, achieving a state of physiological self-regulation or cognitive–behavioral control of symptoms will be sufficient to return them to an acceptable approximation of normal functioning. Then, often just getting back into real life accelerates the healing process. For other patients, especially those with coexisting psychopathology or preexisting traumatic baggage, more exploratory and integrative strategies may be called for.

CHAPTER 7

Counseling and Psychotherapy of Crime Victims

As effective as they are, therapeutic symptom-reduction strategies have their limitations in dealing with the full cognitive and emotional range of posttraumatic stress reactions and in bringing about a reintegrative healing of the personality after crime victimization. For some victims, the restoration of control and sense of self-efficacy achieved through symptom reduction and practical self-help, as discussed in the last chapter, will allow their natural coping skills to kick in and self-guide them back to their normal lives. But for many victims, some form of constructive confrontation with the traumatic experience and its meaning has to take place in order to achieve a workable degree of mastery and resolution. Again, remember that symptom-oriented therapies and deep therapies are not mutually exclusive; in fact they reinforce each other, which is why some points of the discussion in this chapter and that of the last one may seem to overlap.

GENERAL POSTTRAUMATIC THERAPY GUIDELINES

Once the immediate crisis has passed, the patient is confronted with the process of working through the traumatic victimization and trying to get on with her life. At some point in treatment, the therapist takes the trauma patient back to the event and has her discuss it in progressive degrees of detail. The goal is to counteract maladaptive avoidance tendencies and to diminish the chance that they will congeal into long-standing patterns of behavioral constriction. In the case of the avoidant victim who has been coping with trauma by downplaying its importance, the moment of graphic recapitulation may occur much later in the course of therapy, and its onset may catch the therapist by surprise. This late outpouring of emotion should not necessarily be confused with regression but may in fact represent a sign of progress. Sometimes sufficient therapeutic trust, ego bolstering, and working through of peripheral issues must take place to lay the groundwork for direct exploration of the traumatic event itself (Brom, Kleber, & Defares, 1989; Everstine & Everstine, 1993; McCann & Pearlman, 1990).

In this framework, then, posttraumatic treatment should facilitate the repair of the patient's adaptive defense mechanisms, while at the same time assisting her to reenter family, work, community, and other social roles. With these parallel therapeutic activities, both internal and external psychological integration can proceed. As noted earlier, bringing repressed thoughts to the surface or confronting disturbing or distorted memories should be handled with extreme care and sensitivity to ensure that the experience is one of corrective mastery, not retraumatization.

As I noted in the preface, many of the therapeutic techniques, strategies, and modalities presented in this chapter have derived from my work with traumatized public safety personnel and have been found to be equally efficacious—and, in some cases, even more applicable—to civilian crime victims. Again, however, nothing substitutes for knowing your patient, including his or her personality, social, and cultural profile, in planning and implementing an effective program of treatment.

PHASES OF POSTTRAUMATIC PSYCHOTHERAPY

I've already warned against a rigid adherence to stage or phase models of treatment, but within the bounds of clinical flexibility and common sense advocated by this book, psychotherapy with crime victims may be conceptualized as proceeding across two general phases (Everly, 1994, 1995), which at times may overlap.

The *stabilization phase* allows the crime victim to gradually ratchet down the emotional intensity of the traumatic experience in order to create a secure and safe psychological environment for dealing with the effects of the criminal victimization. Therapeutic strategies and activities at this phase include encouraging the victim to access as many means of practical support as possible (chapter 6) and to obtain as much information and feedback about the event as she is able to assimilate. Time off from work or assignment to lighter duty might ease the transition back to work for the victim, which can be a powerful self-esteem booster. Where appropriate, medication for anxiety, mood stabilization, sleep, or other symptoms may be helpful. Also, the victim should be encouraged to obtain as much positive psychological support as possible from friends and family, while steering clear of people who only serve to bring her down.

In the *working through* stage of therapy, the victim begins to find meaning in what happened to her and to integrate the experience into her belief system and worldview. In constructing such a personal narrative, some elements of the experience and her reactions to it may fit into her existing worldview; in other cases, her core beliefs may have to be expanded or amended to accommodate the traumatic event (see below). Victims may have to mourn the parts of themselves that have been lost as a result of their traumatic experience and develop plans for the future that stake out new territory in terms of their roles as workers, family members, citizens, and so on.

In practice, psychotherapy typically proceeds in the form of a cyclical flywheel, with alternating starts and stops, forward thrusts and backslides, so clinicians need not get too hung up on doing things in the so-called right order. At the same time, however, therapeutic flexibility doesn't mean that anything goes, and in order to be effective, counseling and psychotherapy should always retain some guiding structure and should incorporate a number of essential components (Miller, 1993a, 1998h, 2006m, 2007m), which are described below.

THE THERAPEUTIC RELATIONSHIP

If we agree on little else, most counselors and therapists from diverse theoretical and clinical orientations would concur that the therapeutic relationship is the mainstay of virtually all effective psychological treatment, and we attempt to foster this as early in the therapy process as possible. However, with traumatized crime victims, many of whom have already been peered at, prodded, and clucked over multiple times, trust may be hard to establish at first, especially for those with avoidant, narcissistic, paranoid, or schizoid personalities (chapter 3). Other victims, particularly those with dependent, histrionic, or borderline personalities, may show the opposite pattern, latching on to the therapist like an emotional barnacle, with an overly clingy, childlike approach to the therapeutic relationship.

In the first case, mental health clinicians who work with crime victims should be prepared to put up with questioning by their patients: "Why are you doing this?" "Who's paying you?" "Who's going to get this information?" Some crime victims may be irritated and hostile at first and may expose the therapist to mocking cynicism and criticism about the criminal justice system or mental health profession (Silva, 1991; Wester & Lyubelsky, 2005).

The development of trust during the establishment of the therapeutic alliance depends on the therapist's skill in interpreting the crime victim's statements, thoughts, feelings, reactions, and nonverbal behavior. In the best case, the victim begins to feel at ease with the therapist and finds comfort and a sense of predictability from the therapy process. Some useful guidelines for establishing therapeutic mutual trust (Silva, 1991) include the following:

Accurate empathy. This conveys your understanding of the crime victim's background and experience—but beware of premature false familiarity and phony bonding unless you have been through a similar experience, yourself. Even then, be cautious about therapeutic self-disclosure until you are sure this is something that will enhance the therapeutic alliance, not distance it. The first meeting between yourself and the crime victim should establish a safe and comfortable working atmosphere. This is fostered by your articulating a positive endorsement of the victim's decision to seek help, a clear description of your own clinical responsibilities and limitations with respect to confidentiality and privilege, and an invitation to the patient to state his or her concerns.

Genuineness. Every therapist is a human being with a unique personality, and so you'll likely have your own style of clinical and interpersonal interaction. But in general, strive to be spontaneous, yet tactful, flexible, and creative, and to communicate as directly and non-defensively as possible.

Availability. You should indicate that you'll be accessible and available (within reason) when needed and avoid making promises and commitments you know you can't realistically keep.

Respect. Showing respect should be both gracious and firm, and should acknowledge the crime victim's sense of autonomy, control, responsibility, and self-respect within the therapeutic relationship. Respect is manifested by your overall attitude, language, and behavior, as well as by specific words and actions, such as initially using formal titles, such as Mr. or Ms., until trust and mutual respect allow an easing of formality. Here it is important to avoid the dual traps of patronizing and talking down to the crime victim on the one hand ("There, there, this isn't as bad as you think") and, on the other hand, trying to force bogus camaraderie by assuming the role of a fellow traveler ("Yep, I know just what it's like to be a crime victim: I had my wallet stolen last year")—again, unless you have actually had an equivalent experience and are sure this self-disclosure will help.

Direction. Therapy should, at least initially, be goal-oriented and have a problem-solving focus. To the extent that it is clinically realistic, the therapeutic approach should emphasize active problem-solving approaches before you begin to explore more sensitive and complex psychological issues (Brooks, 1998; Miller, 1998h; Wester & Lyubelsky, 2005). As we've seen in the last chapter, many crime victims do well if they can attain a sense of control by mastering some of the cognitive–behavioral self-regulatory exercises as a boost to dealing with more entrenched traumatic material that may be impeding progress toward recovery.

THERAPEUTIC STRATEGIES

In general, the effectiveness of any therapeutic strategy will be determined by the timeliness, tone, style, and intent of the intervention. Effective psychological interventions with crime victims share in common the following elements (Blau, 1994; Fullerton, McCarroll, Ursano, & Wright, 1992; Miller, 1993a, 1994b, 1998e, 1998h, 2006m; Wester & Lyubelsky, 2005):

Appropriate scope. Utilize only as much therapeutic contact as necessary to address the present problem. In the beginning stages, at least, some crime victims may need continual, long-term support. Others may need to have their therapeutic doses moderated because they risk becoming professional patients or because the very fact of being in therapy acts as a traumatic reminder of the crime. Most patients will start with more contact, then reduce the frequency of sessions over time. Many will show an up-and-down pattern with high initial contact, leveling off over time, then temporary increases in session frequency during times of stress in the course of treatment and recovery. This is especially true when the legal proceedings start, which can often be months or even years after the crime has occurred, opening old wounds just at the time that the victim has begun to heal (chapter 16).

Appropriate focus. Especially at the beginning, the goal is not to solve all the crime victim's problems but rather to assist in restabilization from the traumatic event and provide stress inoculation for future incidents. Clinicians used to carrying out a comprehensive preliminary clinical history, including family background, job record, and so on, may be surprised when, after about 10 minutes, patients interject with, "What does all this have to do with my assault?" Background history is important, to be sure, but often this must be gathered and developed over several sessions, as you hit the ground running with practical clinical interventions to quickly establish a sense of safety and control.

A straightforward, goal-directed, problem-solving therapeutic intervention approach includes the following elements (Blau, 1994):

Create a sanctuary. One thing that the therapeutic environment should always provide is a feeling of safety. The crime victim should feel safe that what she says will be used only for the purposes of her healing and strengthening. Indeed, once the initial wariness passes, many victims report that they find the clinician's office a refuge—perhaps the only refuge—from the legal and family stresses that swirl around them in the wake of the crime, the only place where they can be "real." Of course, the limits of confidentiality must be carefully explained to the patient, since she will probably be involved in legal proceedings and the therapist's records may be subpoenaed or the therapist may be called to testify in court (chapter 16).

Focus on critical areas of concern. As with the general emphasis on quick mobilization of therapeutic gains and the patient's sense of self-control, crime victim psychotherapy should initially be goal-directed and focused on resolving specific adaptation and recovery issues related to the crisis at hand, which is a corollary of the next principle.

Specify desired outcomes. In the beginning, help the patient try to operationalize these objectives, in line with the emphasis on achieving practical goals.

From: "I'd like to feel more at ease with my work and my family."
To: "I want to reduce the number of intrusive thoughts about the attack to a level where I can ride to work without panicking at each red light."
Or: "I'd like to be able to step back for a few seconds to regain my composure before I blow up at my wife and kids again over nothing."

Of course, most distraught patients typically will not come in with a preset list of concrete goals; indeed, traumatized victims are often initially confused about what they hope to accomplish in therapy (e.g., "I just want the pain to go away," "I just want to be able to sleep," "I just want to think clearly"). In the early phases, then, it is primarily your task as the clinician to help the victim sort out, focus, and operationalize his or her goals so that there will be a way of measuring if the therapy process is accomplishing them. Once again, without being rigid, specifying a doable goal and then setting to work on it can serve to focus and empower the out-of-control patient.

Develop a general plan. From the first session, after one or more workable goals have been elaborated, develop an initial game plan that can be modified as you go along. All the details needn't be worked out at this point, and the plan will likely be revised as new information comes in. But you have to start somewhere, so develop a general road map that will allow you to move to the next stage, which follows.

Identify practical initial implementations. Hit the ground running: Begin interventions as soon as possible. This induces confidence quickly, motivates further progress, and allows you to get valuable feedback from initial treatment efforts thus far that will guide further interventions.

Review assets and encourage self-efficacy. Consistent with the overarching aim of posttraumatic psychotherapy as a strengthening, not weakening, process, it is as important to know what personal strengths and resources the patient has as it is to understand his or her vulnerabilities (see chapters 2, 3, 4). Always strive to capitalize on strengths to overcome or work around weaknesses.

THERAPEUTIC TECHNIQUES

Adapted and expanded from psychological work with public safety personnel, the following therapeutic intervention techniques have been found effective in working with traumatized crime victims (Blau, 1994; Miller, 1998c, 1998h, 2000b, 2006m; Miller & Dion, 2000):

Attentive listening. This includes good eye contact, appropriate body language, genuine interest, and interpersonal engagement, without inappropriate comment or interruption. Clinicians will recognize this type of intervention as a form of *active listening* described in chapter 6.

Empathic presence. This therapeutic attitude conveys availability, concern, and awareness of the disruptive emotions being experienced by the traumatized, distressed crime victim. A number of victims have commented that they were put off by their therapist's detached, clinically aloof demeanor and didn't feel as if the therapist really was prepared to engage them. Some of this may have to do with countertransference, vicarious traumatization, and emotional contagion issues on the part of the therapist (McCann & Pearlman, 1990; Pearlman & MacIan, 1995; see also chapter 15). Alternatively, some dependent, borderline, or narcissistic patients (chapter 3) may be unusually demanding of the therapist's time and devotion, necessitating the setting of realistic limits, while still retaining empathic engagement.

Reassurance. In acute stress situations (see also chapters 5, 6), this should take the form of realistically reassuring the crime victim that routine matters will be taken care of, deferred responsibilities will be handled by others, and that the victim has the support of her family, the mental health clinician, and the criminal justice system. It is also helpful to let the victim know, in a non-alarming manner, what she is likely to experience in the days, weeks, and months ahead. Be realistic, but always be reassuring.

Therapists may be surprised that crime victims, even several months down the road, after multiple interviews with law enforcement and judicial personnel, still seem so clueless about the legal system and support services. That's because people only hear things when they're ready. A barrage of information may be too threatening for the crime victim to assimilate from a succession of strangers. The therapeutic relationship may be the first place the patient feels safe enough to fully take in and understand many of the sundry, and at times unpleasant, practicalities of her case. And you may be the only professional she trusts enough to impart this information in a supportive, authoritative way. That's why it's important for therapists who work with crime victims to have some knowledge of how the criminal justice system works, as well as the legal, not just clinical, aspects of their patient's case (chapter 16).

> "What was most helpful to me was that I didn't have to explain everything," Jerome commented. "My therapist seemed to know all about the court system, so I didn't have to rehash it. He told me to ask my lawyer about any specifically legal questions, but it helped to know I was dealing with someone who understood the system."

Supportive counseling. This includes active listening, restatement of content, clarification of feelings, and validation. It also may include such concrete services as community referral and networking with liaison agencies, if necessary (see also chapters 6, 16).

> "In the beginning, I wasn't sure how to get in touch with some of the local victims' services, so I was pleasantly surprised when my therapist reached up and pulled this catalog off his bookshelf that had the names and numbers of about a million different organizations. Not all of them were relevant to me, of course, but I was able to find what I needed and I also could send away for the same catalog if I needed it in the future."

Interpretive counseling. This type of intervention should be used when the crime victim's emotional reaction is significantly greater than the circumstances of the critical incident seem to warrant. In appropriate cases, this therapeutic strategy can stimulate the victim to explore underlying emotional, personality, or psychodynamic issues that may be intensifying a naturally stressful traumatic event (Horowitz, 1986). In a few cases, this may lead to continuing, ongoing psychotherapy for broader life issues. Be careful, however, that you do not reflexively attribute any atypical reaction of the patient to his criminal victimization as stemming from unresolved childhood issues. These may well be important, but be sure you understand what's happening in the here-and-now before delving into past dynamics.

> "It seemed pretty clear from some Freudian slips and other things Jerome was saying that he was overinterpreting the fight at his son's Little League game in terms of some past baggage from his own family-of-origin," his therapist said. "But I decided to take it slow, because Jerome gave me signals early on that he wasn't ready to turn this into a 'ten-year couch deal,' as he called it, and I didn't want to risk alienating him and scaring him away from further treatment. So I kept things focused on the present and waited for him to bring up any other issues from the past."

Humor. Humor has its place in many forms of psychotherapy (Fry & Salameh, 1987), but it may be especially useful in working with some traumatized crime victims (Fullerton et al., 1992; Henry, 2004; Miller, 1994b, 1998e, 1998h, 2006m; Silva, 1991). In general, if the therapist and patient can share a laugh, this may lead to the sharing of more intimate feelings. Humor serves to bring a sense of balance, perspective, and clarity to a world that seems to have been warped and polluted by malevolence and horror. "Show me a man who knows what's funny," Mark Twain said, "and I'll show you a man who knows what's not."

Humor, even sarcastic, gross, or callous humor, if handled appropriately and used constructively, may allow the venting of anger, frustration, resentment, or sadness, and thereby lead to productive, reintegrative therapeutic work. This is true, however, only insofar as the therapist is able to keep a lid on destructive types of self-mockery or inappropriate projective hostility in the form of sleazy, cynical, or mean-spirited sniping, character assassination, or self-deprecation.

Also remember that many traumatized individuals tend to be quite concrete and suspicious at the outset of therapy, and certain well-intentioned kidding and cajoling may be perceived as insulting to the crime victim or dismissive of the seriousness of his plight. In such cases, the constructive therapeutic use of humor may have to await the formation of a therapeutic relationship that allows some cognitive and emotional breathing room, as well as the reclaiming of enough of the patient's confidence and self-esteem so that he can take some perspective on the situation and emotionally unclench. Some extreme events, however, such as the personal violation of rape, sustaining a permanent

physical injury or disability, or the death of a loved one, may never be funny—
ever—and this has to be respected. Still, respect doesn't necessarily mean that
the therapy sessions need to be maudlin affairs. Indeed, some patients may
themselves urge an overly dour therapist to lighten up.

> I sometimes use cartoons from magazines to humorously illustrate a
> practical or clinical therapeutic point. In one group therapy session
> involving physically disabled and brain-injured patients, I passed
> around a cartoon by a famous humorist, known for his insightful
> send-ups of people's hypocritical attitudes toward the physically
> and mentally challenged. Everybody in the group got the joke (and
> the therapeutic point I was trying to make with it), except Ritchie,
> who began railing at me for "making fun of my problem—do you
> think this is a big joke?" Fortunately, the other group members were
> able to bail me out, but my relationship with Ritchie took a long
> time to patch up, and I learned a valuable lesson about "knowing
> your customers" when it comes to alternative or creative styles of
> therapeutic communication.

Utilizing Cognitive Defenses

In psychology, *defense mechanisms* are the mental stratagems the mind uses
to protect itself from unpleasant thoughts, feelings, impulses, and memories.
While the normal use of such defenses enables the average person to avoid
conflict and ambiguity and maintain some consistency to his or her personality
and belief system, most mental health clinicians would agree that an overuse
of defenses to wall off too much unpleasant thought and feeling can lead to a
rigid and dysfunctional approach to coping with life. Accordingly, much of the
work in traditional psychotherapy involves carefully helping patients to relinquish their pathological defenses so that they can learn to deal with internal
conflicts more constructively.

However, in the face of acutely traumatizing experiences, the last thing
the affected person needs is to have his or her defenses stripped away. If you
sustain a broken leg on the battlefield, the medic doesn't stop to clean the
wound, put you under anesthesia, set the bone, wrap you in a cast, and nurse
you back to health. Hell, no: He binds and braces the limb as best and as fast
as he can—with a dirty tree branch and fishing tackle if necessary—and helps
you hobble out of there, double-time.

In the same way, for an acute psychological trauma, the proper utilization
of psychological defenses can serve as an important psychological splint or
emotional field dressing that enables the person to function in the immediate
posttraumatic aftermath and eventually be able to productively resolve and

integrate the traumatic experience when the luxury of therapeutic time can be afforded (Janik, 1991).

In many cases, the clinician will discover that traumatized crime victims need little help in applying defense mechanisms on their own (Durham, McCammon, & Allison, 1985; Henry, 2004; Taylor, Wood, & Lechtman, 1983). Examples of common defenses—all of which can have both constructive or maladaptive effects, depending on how they're used—include the following:

> *Denial.* "I'm just going to put it out of my mind; focus on other things; avoid situations or people who remind me of it."
>
> *Rationalization.* "I had no choice; things happen for a reason; it could have been worse; other people have it worse; most people would react the same way I am."
>
> *Displacement/projection.* "It was my boss's fault for sending me down to the Records Department so late at night; the police took forever to respond to the 911 call; the district attorney is going soft on this case because of politics."
>
> *Refocusing on positive attributes.* "Hey, this was a one-shot deal—I'm usually a cautious, capable person. I'm a smart, strong person: I can get through this."
>
> *Refocusing on positive behaviors.* "Okay, I'm going to follow safety procedures more carefully and talk to administration about getting better security around here. I'm going to advocate for more safety training so nothing like this happens to anyone here again."

Where necessary, at least in the short term, clinicians should know when to actively support and bolster psychological defenses that temporarily enable the traumatized crime victim to continue functioning (Janik, 1991). Just as a physical crutch is an essential part of orthopedic rehabilitation when the leg-injured patient is learning to walk again, a psychological crutch is perfectly adaptive and productive if it enables the psychologically wounded patient to get back on his emotional two feet as soon as possible after a traumatic incident. Only later, when he is making the bumpy transition back to normal life, are potentially maladaptive defenses revisited as possible impediments to progress.

And just as some orthopedic patients may always need one or another kind of assistive walking device, like a special shoe or a cane, some degree of psychological defensiveness may persist in traumatized crime victims so they can otherwise productively pursue their work and life tasks. Indeed, rare among us is the person who is completely defense-free. Only when defenses are used inappropriately and for too long—past the point where we should be walking on our own psychological two feet—do they constitute a crutch in the unhealthy or pejorative sense.

Survival Resource Training

As noted in chapter 2, a recently evolving trend in trauma psychotherapy emphasizes the importance of accessing and bolstering the patient's natural powers of resilience, and the constructive marshalling of strength and resistance to stress and disability (Calhoun & Tedeschi, 1999; Dunning, 1999; Miller, 1990, 1994b, 1998b, 1998h, 2007m; Stuhlmiller & Dunning, 2000; Tedeschi & Calhoun, 1995, 2004; Tedeschi & Kilmer, 2005; Violanti, 2000).

In this vein, Solomon (1988, 1991) has been ahead of the curve in capitalizing on the idea that constructively defensive denial of vulnerability and mortality can be an adaptive response for law enforcement officers, emergency responders, and public safety workers coping with ongoing critical incidents and their immediate aftermath. I have found that this approach can also be productively applied to the psychological treatment of traumatized crime victims.

Remember, accentuating the positive is only an effective therapeutic technique if it is based on reality; otherwise, attempting to force a positive spin on a clearly negative situation will only erode therapeutic trust and credibility or foster self-delusion. However, because human nature is normally risk-averse, in the wake of traumatic incidents that are characterized by fear, danger, injury, or death, victims often dwell on their mistakes and overlook what they did right in terms of surviving the ordeal and coping with the aftermath. Thus, being realistically reminded by the clinician of their own adaptive coping efforts may prove especially empowering because it draws upon strengths that came from the person him- or herself. Termed *survival resource training* (Solomon, 1988, 1991), this intervention allows victims to utilize the fear response to tap into a state of controlled strength, increased awareness, confidence, and clarity of mind.

Before introducing this technique, it is a good idea to ascertain that the patient has sufficient emotional self-control to deal with potentially painful recollections and retellings of the crime experience so that they not constitute a retraumatization. If necessary, this should be preceded by appropriate training in arousal regulation, imagery, and cognitive control techniques, as described in chapter 6.

In the survival resource training technique, the clinician encourages the patient to view the critical incident from a detached, objective point of view, "like you are watching a movie of yourself," and to go through the incident *frame-by-frame*. At the point where he images himself fully engaged in the experience—being attacked, defending himself, running for cover, calling for help, and so on—the victim is instructed to "focus on the part of you enabling you to respond." That is, here we are, you didn't die, so how did you get through it? What did you do—deliberately, reflexively, instinctively, or unconsciously—to help you survive the encounter?

This frame-by-frame replay will usually have to be repeated several times; as the patient's resistance to the retelling subsides, the more he will come to view the recollection as progressively less toxic and more empowering. The retelling will be facilitated by incorporating other therapeutic techniques, such as arousal control and cognitive restructuring (chapter 6). When carried out correctly with the properly prepared patient, the survival resource training procedure typically leads to a mental reframe characterized by controlled strength, heightened awareness, confidence, and mental clarity, as the crime victim mentally zooms in on his capability to respond and survive, instead of focusing on the immobilizing fear, perceptions of weakness, loss of control, or perceptual distortions that may have occurred. Often, this results in the patient's being reminded of how he put his fear on hold and rose to the occasion in order to survive and perhaps even help others (recall the case of Charles in chapter 6). The reframing thus focuses on resiliency instead of vulnerability, strength instead of weakness.

In addition to processing the traumatic incident in the past, realistic feelings of efficacy and competence can also shade over into future incidents, as many crime victims have reported feelings of increased empowerment, confidence, and ability to handle subsequent challenges, such as matters related to the prosecution of the current crime; testifying in court (chapter 16); return to the scene of the crime, such as a workplace (chapter 12); and so on. In addition, a number of victims have felt more confident in other nonemergency but stressful situations, such as employment issues and personal matters, including resolving family conflicts (Miller, 1999d, 2007a; Solomon, 1988). It is especially gratifying to clinician and patient alike when their mutual efforts can turn vicious cycles of demoralization and despair into positive cycles of confidence and optimism. Indeed, this is the hoped-for outcome of most forms of psychotherapy (Miller, 1993a, 1994b, 2006m, 2007m).

> Mitchell had been racked with guilt over his family's horrific home invasion ordeal because he felt he had "dropped the ball" by leaving the alarm off and the door unlocked that day. The three invaders snuck in, then attacked Mitchell and his wife, Gail, in their living room, bound them with duct tape and began to ransack the house. At least one of the intruders had a gun. Mitchell recalls trying to say something to the men, but one of them just punched him in the head and told him to "shut up." They asked Gail where her jewelry

was and where there was any cash, and Mitchell told them what they wanted to know, "just to get them out of there."

When it looked like they had taken what they wanted, the robbers stopped and stood over Mitchell and Gail. One of them wanted to go, but the other two started joking and talking like they were going to rape Gail. Mitchell said something to try and distract the robbers, but one of them started beating him again until he blacked out. When he came to, he could hear Gail screaming in the other room, obviously being assaulted. All three men were in there with her. The chair he was taped to had been partially knocked over and he was half-lying on the floor. By twisting and wriggling his body, he managed to get his hands loose from the duct tape. But the house phone and his cell phone were both in the same room as Gail and the criminals.

Then, Mitchell noticed that the criminals had left the front door partially opened. He could run out, but how could he leave his wife? Then, "it's not like I thought about it, like I came up with the idea; the idea just popped into my head." While the robbers were preoccupied, he ran out the front door, picked up a rock, and threw it through his neighbor's window, setting off their alarm. The criminals in Mitchell's house were obviously startled because they came running out of the house and made their way to a car parked about half a block away. Meanwhile, the surprised and angry neighbor burst out of his house, to see the three men running down the street. Mitchell ran back into his house and discovered that Gail had been sexually assaulted by at least one of the men. Police and paramedics soon arrived and Gail was taken to a local hospital.

The fact that the neighbor was later able to identify two out of the three men running out of Mitchell's house, combined with their clumsily leaving their fingerprints and at least one DNA sample at the scene, led to their arrest and conviction. Mitchell and his wife eventually found themselves in trauma counseling, and, surprisingly, 1 year later, Gail seemed to be doing better than her husband, who was still consumed with the guilty idea that the whole thing was his fault.

To counter this, the therapist employed a range of strategies, including thought stopping, cognitive restructuring, and the frame-by-frame survival resource training technique. He asked Mitchell to recall the event, scene by scene, especially the part where the idea of throwing the rock at the neighbor's house came to him. Reworking the scenario accomplished two things: First, it detoxified the recollection, making it less likely to lead to intrusive flashbacks or nightmares, and second, it allowed Mitchell to focus on the resourcefulness of coming up with a way to save his wife from further injury.

"I guess she could've been killed, with three guys in there," Mitchell reflected. "My therapist's trying to get me to see that saving Gail's life, especially after being tied up and bashed in the head, more than makes up for leaving a door unlocked. That's also kind of what the police said. I get it logically, but I'm not sure I'm, you know, totally convinced inside me. But I'm working on it."

SPECIFIC POSTTRAUMATIC ISSUES IN CRIME VICTIM PSYCHOTHERAPY

Certain issues are particularly common in dealing with traumatized patients in general and crime victims in particular.

Mood Swings

Emotional lability is a frequent posttraumatic symptom (chapter 2), and such mood swings can be confusing and disorienting, especially if they occur or recur late in the treatment process. The patient by this time has gotten a taste of psychological stability and may think the worst of the ordeal is finally over. Then he hits some snag of frustration, stress, or disappointment and is yanked back into a state of anxiety and depression. During this unsettling process, patients will probably require even more therapeutic support than usual because they may feel they are backsliding and "losing it." These episodes should be viewed as an expectable response to these jarring bumps in the road to recovery, and the patient should be reassured that this is not necessarily a sign of regression. A temporarily increased amount of therapeutic contact may be necessary at these times (Everstine & Everstine, 1993; McCann & Pearlman, 1990). Also be aware of the differential diagnostic overlap with bipolar disorder and other mood and personality disorders (chapter 3).

Franco was only a witness and bystander in the workplace shooting that took the life of his coworker and friend a few months ago, and he thought he'd gotten over the worst of it. He'd even gone back to work, but about a week later, "I began crying for no good reason. Like, I'd see a kid in a stroller on the street and all of a sudden, I'd get this wave of sadness and start weeping. If a sad show came on the TV, my girlfriend would come in and I'd be sobbing. Jeez—it was embarrassing. So I asked my therapist about this and she said it was a 'delayed reaction' and not to worry about it for now. So, that's what I'm trying to do."

Anger

At some phase in the therapeutic process, mood swings may portend a phase of emerging anger, as the patient begins to get in touch with the fact that malign or neglectful actions of others have caused his or her trauma. Patients may be angry for any number of reasons (Everstine & Everstine, 1993; Matsakis, 1994), including

- that the trauma occurred at all;
- that it happened to them when it did;
- that they were injured;
- that their loved ones died or were hurt;
- that they have had to suffer secondary wounding and residual physical, psychological, and financial scars;
- that they have been mistreated by the medical and legal systems;
- that they have forever been banished from a sense of rightness and goodness in the world; and
- that they are now forced to engage in a therapeutic process that is effortful, expensive, time-consuming, and emotionally painful and draining.

While this anger must eventually be faced and dealt with productively, pushing the emotion to the surface too quickly may impel the patient

- to act out in a dangerous way;
- to become paralyzed with helpless rage, leading to depression;
- to develop a masochistic transference relationship with the therapist and symbolically recreate the traumatic experience;
- to engage in passive-aggressive behavior in and out of the therapeutic setting; or
- to flee the therapeutic process entirely.

Indeed, much of this anger may occasionally be displaced onto the therapist. Therefore, it is important that the therapist first help the patient to regain the requisite level of ego strength that will enable him or her to eventually express anger appropriately and constructively, in a manner that will not alienate those around her.

Matsakis (1994) has developed an effective program of posttraumatic anger management, the main components of which I have found useful with many traumatized crime victims (Miller, 1998e, 1998h). The program relies on two major aspects of handling anger: venting and validating.

Venting. In the clinical setting, much controversy surrounds whether overtly and forcefully venting anger is a legitimate therapeutic means of letting off steam or whether such emotional displays only serve to reinforce and further entrench the rageful feelings. As in most areas of clinical judgment, the therapist must know his or her patient well enough to determine whether or not angry expressions will be productive and to be able to tell how much is too much. Certainly, there should be nothing in terms of content that is categorically off-limits for discussion. But unproductive spewing for spewing's sake should not be encouraged. Even here, there are exceptions because sometimes the pain of recollection gets too great and the patient really does just have to scream. The key is to allow such venting at an appropriate time and place and to follow it up with constructive therapeutic processing.

There are other, less dramatic, but often equally effective ways for patients to vent (Matsakis, 1994):

- Talking to another person about their anger (obviously, much of this will occur in the therapeutic sessions)
- Speaking the anger into a tape recorder
- Telling God about their anger
- Drawing a picture about their anger
- Writing about their anger
- Keeping an anger diary and discussing the entries during therapy
- Behaving in self-empowering ways that give patients a feeling of greater control

Anger feeds on helplessness, so any way that a patient's sense of mastery can be legitimately increased—getting a better handle on emotions, improving relationships with supportive friends or family members, taking productive action—will go a long way toward reducing the need for defensive, reflexive, angry action.

Validating. Validating the anger is important because, where the trauma occurred at the malicious hands of others, the patient may have very good reason to be angry. But angry feelings need not be expressed as angry acts, because the latter are often ultimately self-defeating, and good judgment in the service of avoiding further self-harm is always an important goal. However, where appropriate, patients can be supported or encouraged to take constructive action, for example, within the judicial system, in support group work, and in political involvement. Indeed, a number of post–September 11th family survivors have turned their grief and anger into constructive action in just this manner (Miller, 2003d, 2003e, 2004a, 2005a, 2005b; see also chapter 14). A more frequent example involves parents who have become active in Mothers Against Drunk Driving (MADD) after the death or injury of their children at the hands of such drivers.

It is important to remember, however, that a socially directed activity must be valid for its own sake, not just be an egocentric vanity project; otherwise, the activity risks turning into an irrational and compulsively driven crusade that ultimately harms both the patient and the people he or she works with. Here is another area where therapeutic and common-sense guidance are crucial. In this vein, therapists must also be careful not to impose their own philosophical or political agendas on patients; rather, they should strive to guide patients to find their own direction and voice (also see below).

EXISTENTIAL ISSUES AND THERAPEUTIC CLOSURE

Taking action in the real world raises another important topic. In virtually every case of significant trauma, the patient struggles with shattered assumptions and fantasies about fairness, justice, security, and the meaning of life, and it is part of the essential task of psychotherapy to help the traumatized crime victim come to terms with these existential issues. Some patients obsess over what they did or should have done to avoid or escape more serious harm or to help other people, and with these individuals, the therapeutic task becomes one of reorienting these patients to a more realistic state of self-acceptance. Many patients need to pass the anniversary date of the traumatic event, especially if their trauma was severe, before they can begin to bring the trauma response to closure. The process of simultaneously externalizing and integrating the crime trauma allows the last stages of recovery to take place. As the patient approaches closure, the therapist can help him or her form a newly realistic and adaptive self-image, which becomes the foundation for a healthy future (Calhoun & Tedeschi, 1999; Everstine & Everstine, 1993; Rudofossi, 2007; Tedeschi & Calhoun, 2004; Tedeschi & Kilmer, 2005).

Making Meaning From Trauma

Everly (1994, 1995) emphasizes the need to help traumatized patients reintegrate their sense of self as well as their shattered worldview in order to regain a feeling of existential safety. This necessitates carefully paying attention to what the patient tells the therapist in order for the clinician to discern what specific aspects of the patient's self-schema and worldview have been most affected. Then, posttraumatic reintegration can be approached from one or more of three main perspectives.

Trauma integrated into the patient's existing worldview. The message here is that these things happen, people do hurt other people, but there are certain precautions one can take to minimize the risk of this happening in the future, so that the patient can feel safe again.

> "I guess people just can't take it for granted that they'll be safe in their own home," Mitchell later reflected on his home-invasion experience. "We can't afford to move right now, with the housing market being what it is. But we put in a new alarm system and we now have a dog. We're going to be careful, but other than reasonable precautions, we're not going to live in constant fear."

Trauma understood as a parallel aspect of the existing worldview, that is, an exception to the rule. According to this interpretation, society sets up rules and structures to keep most of us safe most of the time, so this tragedy, while certainly awful, is a one-shot deal that will most likely never happen to the same person again. Of course, this must be realistically based: In some communities, risk of repeated exposure to crime is a grim reality that must be respected.

> Franco tried to be philosophical about the workplace shooting he witnessed: "It sucked what happened to Manny, but hey, how often does something like this happen? This was just one crazy guy and usually the customers are pretty happy with us. So I guess it's kind of like a plane crash: Everybody thinks about it a little when they travel, but they don't get too worked up about it because it's rare and life has to go on, right?"

Trauma illustrates the need to create a new and modified worldview. That is, the trauma can be used to demonstrate the invalidity of the patient's existing perspective and the need to construct an alternative one in which the trauma more readily fits. For example, your assault shows that the world is not all filled with good people, that justice doesn't always work out, that sometimes the innocent suffer and the guilty go free. But you can fashion a new way of looking at things that allows both realism and cautious optimism; you can learn to be realistic, even skeptical, about human nature and motives, but without allowing yourself to turn into a soul-shriveled cynic.

"Hey, so I guess 'we're not in Kansas anymore,' right?" Franco went on with a laugh. "There's some bad, crazy people in this freakin' world. I was never such a trusting soul to begin with, but I can't let this sour me on the human race. Shit happens but life goes on, I guess."

Everly (1995) believes that each of these approaches is successively less ego-syntonic and therefore successively more difficult to apply in therapeutic practice. However, I have found that much depends on the nature of the traumatic event and the type of patient. Predominantly externalizing patients seem to adhere to the once-in-a-lifetime, "lightning doesn't strike twice"–type of explanation, putting their trust in fate or God or sheer statistical improbability. The "what can I personally do to keep this from happening again"–type of reframe appeals more to patients who already possessed a degree of self-efficacy before the trauma and are therefore willing and able to try to solve problems by their own efforts once the therapist shows them the way.

Finally, therapists must be mindful of patients who suffer from *enhanced integration* of the traumatic theme into their self-concept and life narrative (Berntsen & Rubin, 2007). For these patients, many of whom may be characterized by dependent, histrionic, borderline, or narcissistic personalities (chapter 3), the crime victimization becomes the exclusive focal point of their entire existence and their lives become a ceaseless search for validation of their martyrdom. For such patients, the therapeutic emphasis must be on decathecting from the traumatic victimization and finding non–crime related activities that encourage these individuals to resume a so-called civilian life. In such circumstances, these patients will often subtly or overtly shift gears to another alleged source of their woundedness and betrayal, such as family traumas, illness, or disability. Alternatively, they may quit treatment with you and start over with another, more sympathetic clinician, until that sours as well, and so on.

Healing With *HEARTS*

Hanscom (2001) describes a system of posttraumatic therapy that emerged from her work with survivors of torture and that may be applied more broadly to victims of violence of many types, including crime victims. In this model, an essential condition of healing is the reestablishment of the experience of trust, safety, and the ability to have an impact upon the world. This relearning relies less on particular therapeutic techniques and procedures than on the compassionate human interaction and therapeutic alliance between the survivor and a counselor who is willing and able to listen effectively.

Hanscom calls her approach the *HEARTS model,* which is an acronym for the following:

H = *Listening to the HISTORY* includes providing a gentle, encouraging environment for communication, using attentive body language to "listen with the whole person," attending to the patient's voice tone and ebb and flow of speech, observing the speaker's movements, reactions, and facial expressions, remaining quietly patient while the person finds his or her voice, and listening uncritically and compassionately.

E = *Focusing on EMOTIONS and reactions* involves using reflective listening, asking gentle questions, and naming and identifying the emotions expressed in the narrative. This will seem familiar from our discussion of active listening in chapter 6.

A = *ASKING about symptoms* incorporates the therapist's own personal and therapeutic style to investigate current physical and psychological symptoms, including possible self-harm and suicidality. Often, patients will be reluctant to reveal seemingly odd or embarrassing symptoms unless you gently probe for them.

R = *Explaining the REASON for symptoms* includes showing how the symptoms fit together, describing how the body reacts to stress and trauma, explaining the interaction between the body and mind, and emphasizing that these are normal symptoms that normal people have to a very abnormal event (see chapter 2). Anything you can do to realistically normalize and destigmatize the patient's experience will move her in the direction of healing.

T = *TEACHING relaxation and coping skills* involves instructing the patient in relaxation skills, such as abdominal breathing, meditation, prayer, imagery, visualization, and others, and discussing coping strategies, such as recognizing how he or she has coped in the past, reinforcing old and healthy strategies, and teaching new coping skills. Essentially, this incorporates elements of symptom control described in chapter 6 and techniques similar to survival resource training as discussed above.

S = *Helping with SELF-CHANGE* involves discussing the person's world view—the original view, any changes, adaptations, or similarities—and recognizing the positive changes in the self, similar to Everly's (1994, 1995) tripartite existential conceptualization discussed above.

Existential Trauma Therapy: Beware of False Angels

In general, existential treatment strategies that focus on a quest for meaning, rather than just alleviation of symptoms, may productively channel the worldview conflicts generated by the trauma event, such as helping the patient to formulate an acceptable "survivor mission" (Shalev et al., 1993). Indeed, in the best cases, the rift and subsequent reintegration of the personality leads to an expanded self-concept and even a new level of psychological and spiritual growth (Bonanno, 2005; Calhoun & Tedeschi, 1999; Davis et al., 1998; Neimeyer, 2000; Tedeschi & Calhoun, 1995, 2004; Tedeschi & Kilmer, 2005). Some trauma survivors are thus able to make positive personal or career changes out of a renewed sense of purpose and value in their lives. Of course, not all crime victims will be able to achieve this successful reintegration of the ordeal, and many struggle with at least some vestige of emotional damage for a long time, perhaps for life (Everstine & Everstine, 1993; Matsakis, 1994; McCann & Pearlman, 1990).

Therefore, my main caution about these transformational therapeutic conceptualizations is that they be presented as an opportunity, not an obligation. The extraction of meaning from adversity is something that must ultimately come from the patient him- or herself, not be foisted upon the patient by the therapist. Such existential conversions by the sword are usually motivated by a need to reinforce the therapist's own meaning system, or they may be part of what I call a therapeutic *Clarence-the-Angel fantasy* (Miller, 1998h), wherein the enlightened therapist swoops down and, by virtue of the clinician's brilliantly insightful ministrations, rescues the patient from his or her darkest hour and gives him or her a proverbial new lease on life.

Realistically, we can hardly expect all or even most of our traumatized patients to miraculously transcend their tragedy and thereby acquire a fresh, revitalized, George Bailey–like outlook on life—how many *therapists* would respond this well? But human beings do crave meaning (Yalom, 1980), and if a philosophical or religious orientation can nourish the patient in his or her journey back to the land of the living, then our therapeutic role must sometimes stretch to include some measure of guidance in affairs of the spirit.

CONCLUSIONS

Psychotherapy with traumatized crime victims must span the range from concrete, supportive, and directive approaches to the most abstract and even—in the broadest sense—spiritual modalities. But as challenging as it is to help patients who have been directly victimized by crime, it may be harder still to effectively mitigate the impact of a loved one's murder on surviving family members.

CHAPTER 8

Family Survivors of Homicide

Symptoms, Syndromes, and Practical Interventions

In the last three chapters, we've discussed counseling and psychotherapeutic approaches for individuals who have been directly victimized by violent crime and have survived to become our patients. But many victims of violence don't survive, and the task of coping with trauma falls upon the loved ones they leave behind, who may then turn to us—or be sent to us—for help.

EFFECT OF A LOVED ONE'S MURDER
ON FAMILY MEMBERS

Murder is the ultimate violation that one individual can inflict on another, a brutal, deliberate assault forced upon an unwilling victim. The murder of a family member rakes survivors over the jagged existential terrain of fairness, justice, faith, and the very meaning of life. The pain of homicide bereavement is described by most survivors as intense, persistent, and inescapable, and the cruel and purposeful nature of murder compounds the rage, grief, and despair of survivors. Unlike the unfortunate, but relatively controlled and decorous demise of a relative with a progressive illness, bereavement by sudden and unanticipated violence robs the family of the innoculatory balm of anticipation. Added to this is the stark confrontation of the survivors with their own mortality and vulnerability as the illusion of safety and order in the world is shattered (Amick-McMullan, Kilpatrick, & Resnick, 1991; Armour, 2003; Bard & Sangry, 1986; Getzel & Masters, 1984; Janoff-Bulman, 1992; Miller, 1998e, 1998h; Neimeyer, 2001; Park & Folkman, 1997; Rynearson, 1984,

1988, 2001; Rynearson & McCreery, 1993; Sprang & McNeil, 1995; Sprang, McNeil, & Wright, 1989).

For many survivors, the first news of the homicide strikes a mortal blow to the self, evoking their own sense of personal loss. Family members are typically preoccupied with the nature of the injuries inflicted on the victim, the brutality of the killing, the types of weapons used, and the victim's suffering. Families may clamor for information about the identity of the murderers and any possible relationship to the victim the perpetrators may have had. The greater the perceived intentionality and malevolence of the killing, the higher the distress seen in the survivors (Carson & MacLeod, 1997; MacLeod, 1999; Ressler, Burgess, & Douglas, 1988; Sewell, 1993, 1994).

Of all crimes, murder usually has the highest *clearance rate,* that is, the proportion of crimes that are actually solved; yet approximately one-third of murders remain unsolved (Federal Bureau of Investigation, 1994), creating an endless purgatory of unknowing for many bereaved families (Masters, Friedman, & Getzel, 1988).

Disenfranchised Victims, Disenfranchised Grief

Families of murder victims who were involved in drugs, prostitution, domestic violence, or other criminal activity, or who may be members of ethnically, economically, or socially marginalized groups, may suffer *disenfranchised grief* (Doka, 2002; Jones & Beck, 2007; Spungen, 1998). Such disenfranchised mourners may receive little or no ritual support from the community (Neimeyer & Jordan, 2002). The snubbing and sometimes snide reactions and attitudes of other people to the survivors and their identification with the victim may result in *secondary victimization* (Hatton, 2003; Rando, 1993; Rynearson, 1988, 1994). Consequently, the ability of the family to find or make some meaning of their loved one's death can be disrupted by the victim's—and, often by extension, the family's—stigmatized social status (Armour, 2003).

The agenda of the criminal justice system often ignores or discounts the family members, while the media's interpretation of the crime and the community's response to it attempt to alter, reconstruct, and alternatively diminish and inflate the meaning of the tragedy for the family. Ironically, after all the unwanted attention has petered out, families are often left alone to face the grief, rage, and sense of violation that accompanies the stark fact of their loved one's murder (Armour, 2003).

Anger, Agitation, Anxiety—and Activism

Some survivors may be seized with an impulse to "do something." A deep and justifiable anger toward the killer alternately smolders and flares as investigations and legal actions meander along. Even where the murderer is identified, caught, and convicted, the anger may persist for years. A common coping mechanism for dealing with rageful feelings and impulses consists of ruminating on fantasies of revenge. Actual vengeful attacks by family members on perpetrators are extremely rare, probably due in large part, first, to the sheer impracticability of getting at the killer, who, especially in high-profile cases, is invariably sequestered and protected; and, second, to the basic moral values and common decency of most families, who are typically not looking to correct one atrocity with another. Many families may direct their energies toward efforts to aid in the apprehension and prosecution of the killers, which can be seen as either a help or hinderance by investigators (Joyce, 2006; Ressler et al., 1988; Rynearson, 1988; Rynearson & McCreery, 1993; Shorto, 2002; Sprang & McNeil, 1995).

> "The attitudes of the different detectives varied," said Selena. "A few were happy that we took such an interest, at least at first, I guess, because they thought it would give them more clues. But a few seemed to resent us calling or coming down to the station, with an attitude like, 'Don't you people have anything better to do than come around here and tell us how to work our cases?' Well, no, we *don't* have anything better to do. Our mom was killed and we want her killer caught. Most of the cops just got used to us and kind of tolerated us, I guess."

Even more common than anger, a pervasive fear of everything begins to loom in the survivors' consciousnesses, starting with their first awareness of their loved one's death, and often persisting for years. Survivors' heightened sense of their own vulnerability may spur them to change daily routines, install house and car alarms, carry weapons, refuse to go to out after dark, or shun certain locales. There may be phobic avoidance of anything related to the crime trauma, including people, places, certain foods, music, and so on. Survivors may experience psychophysiological hyperstartle responses to such ordinarily nonthreatening stimuli as crime shows on TV, kids shouting in the street, arguing among family members, the sound of overhead airplane engines, or news stories about crime or about any, even unrelated, accident or tragedy.

The survivors' usual range of territorial and affiliative activity becomes constricted as the home is turned into a protective fortress, strangers are avoided, and unfamiliar surroundings are circumvented. All family members may be outfitted with pagers and cell phones and may have to submit daily schedules of activity, as there develops a compulsive need for family members to be close at hand or reachable at a moment's notice. Older children and adolescents, in particular, may resent this babying restriction of their autonomy and independence (Rynearson, 1988; Rynearson & McCreery, 1993; Sprang & McNeil, 1995).

Survivors may overidentify with the slain victim, sleeping in the dead relative's bed, wearing his or her clothing, or even assuming vocal and behavioral characteristics of the slain person. Many survivors feel like pariahs, cast out of a pretrauma Edenic state of normal existential comfort that the rest of us civilians take for granted to assuage our sense of vulnerability, but which is no longer a coping option for survivors of violent homicide: "We know better— the world is a cruel and ugly place." Survivors may have frequent nightmares of the imagined horrifying death of the victim, or wish-fulfillment dreams of protecting or rescuing the victim. Their grief may be compounded by guilt if they feel they should have forseen the attack or done more to keep their loved one safe—this may be especially true in cases of home invasion or other close-to-home crimes, or in crimes involving children (Ressler et al, 1988; Rynearson, 1988; Rynearson & McCreery, 1993; Schlosser, 1997; Sprang & McNeil, 1995).

Family Coping Strategies

Following a traumatic bereavement by homicide, families may employ a range of coping strategies to help themselves make it through the aftermath of the death (Sheehan, 1991; Violanti, 1999). Some try to mentally distance themselves from the experience, at least for brief periods of time, by immersing themselves in work or family responsibilities. Even the myriad details surrounding the arrangements for funerals and financial matters in the wake of the death can be helpful if they permit a temporarily defensive intellectualization that protects against being emotionally overwhelmed.

To that end, many families who describe feeling drained and beaten by their own emotional storms make a conscious effort to exert self-control whenever they can, keeping their feelings to themselves, especially in front of outsiders. Paradoxically, this may prompt well-meaning others to urge them not to "hold back," to "let it all out," when that's exactly what the family members may have been doing for the past days or weeks, and now they crave some composure so they can feel normal even for a brief time.

Many families seek social support and are able to accept sympathy, understanding, and advice from friends and family members. On the other hand, some withdraw from people and isolate themselves. Others become irritable and snappish, and eventually alienate potential sources of support. Children may complain that their surviving parent is "taking it all out on us." Many survivors are so cracked and scarred emotionally that they fear any kind of human contact will cause them to "split wide open." Others have trouble dealing with their free-floating rage and resentment at how "other people just get to go along with their damn lives because their loved one wasn't killed."

Everybody's health suffers. Common psychophysiological disorders include appetite and sleep disturbances, gastrointestinal problems, cardiovascular disorders, decreased resistance to infectious disease, and increased anxiety and depression. A significant number of family members die within the first few years of any kind of violent criminal homicide (Armour, 2003; McFarlane, Atchison, Rafalowicz, & Papay, 1994; Prigerson et al., 1997; Schlosser, 1997; Sprang & McNeil, 1995). In one study (Kenney, 2003), homicidally bereaved men were found most typically to suffer from heart problems and early deaths, while women were seen as more prone to mental health problems. Men's problems were thought to be rooted in the repression of emotion inherent in traditional male gender roles, while women's related to their more traditional emphasis on emotionality.

> "It's strange how different members of our family handled it in different ways," Selena went on. "Dad just basically clammed up, went to work early, came home late, asked if there was any news about the case, had dinner, and went to sleep. On weekends, he kept himself busy with work around the house or went out for long periods of time, but we don't know where. My little brother took it the hardest, started getting stomach aches and migraines, and almost dropped out of high school. I guess I was more like my father. I was set to graduate college that year, so I focused on that because I knew mom would've wanted me to pursue my education.

> "It's creepy; there was a general feeling in the family like a bomb went off, but the house didn't fall, it was just all cracked and crumbled, like even a light touch or somebody sneezing or raising their voice could make it come crashing down, but we're all walking around pretending not to notice because we don't know where to go or what to do about it."

Victim Family Reaction Patterns

Just as there are different patient dynamics that need to be assessed and accommodated in treatment (chapters 3, 4), such diversity of reaction patterns applies to families as well. Vesper and Cohen (1999) describe five types of family reactions in the face of trauma and, especially, its legal aftermath, which are presented here, along with my own comments and suggestions.

The contemptuous family. These families cope with adversity by getting upset, berating and blaming each other, and denying the existence of problems. For these families, secrecy and deception are the rule. Therapists may have to start by getting the family members to communicate and cooperate with each other over small matters, such as daily routines and ground rules for children, before moving on to the big issues related to their loved one's murder.

The brittle family. Members are reluctant to depend on one another for support and understanding. They prefer to rely on others outside the family for communication, assurance, and caring. Helping these families make any kind of a connection, even an outside one, can be productive because it can often serve as a bridge to forging links among family members themselves.

The hierarchical family. This family functions with a sense of internal unity and purpose but with little flexibility in roles and responsibilities. Specific family members, usually the elders and senior children, make decisions. While having a strong head of the household to make the command decisions can inject an element of order and stability into an otherwise chaotic situation, the risk is that family cohesion may crumble if this rigid hierarchy begins to unravel. Some flexibility in family decision making should be encouraged.

The enduring family. This family relies on faith—typically, religious faith—to deal with tragedy. They expect such challenges will occur from time to time and will result in the consequences that divine providence deems appropriate. As long as this remains a healthy coping mechanism, therapists should reinforce this form of meaning making.

The functional family. When faced with trauma, this family supports and bolsters more severely affected family members while working harmoniously to afford support and caring to one another. There is a sense of internal control over life's events and adversities that adds meaning to life and a commitment to each other. The therapist's task is simply to encourage such family members to keep on providing positive support.

Grief, Grief Work, and Complicated Bereavement

Grief work is the term often used for the psychological process that moves the family member from being preoccupied with thoughts of the murdered victim, through painful recollections of the loss experience, to the final step of settling the trauma as an integrative experience (Parkes, 1975; Parkes & Brown, 1972). Those who appear to adapt best to stressful experiences in general typically have a range of available coping strategies and resources, which permits greater flexibility in dealing with the particular demands of the traumatic event (Aldwin, 1994; Bowman, 1997, 1999; Miller, 1998h; Silver & Wortman, 1980).

Persons who cannot find any kind of meaning in their trauma are more likely to suffer from *complicated bereavement* (Armour, 2003; Horowitz et al., 1997; Neimeyer, Prigerson, & Davies, 2002). The conventional grief literature states that most survivors of nonviolently bereaved family members—traffic accidents, natural or manmade disasters, terminal illnesses—eventually make a reasonable recovery and move on. Nonviolent death bereavement is typically described as a process of initial denial and disbelief, followed by acute separation distress, and then by adjustment and recovery (Raphael, 1983; Worden, 1991).

However, Murphy (1999) found that 30% of parents of children who died violent deaths experienced no diminishment of their trauma responses over time. They continued to suffer persistent thoughts of reenactment, remorse, retaliation, and overprotection of other family members. Moreover, those parents who could not find meaning in their loss suffered increased levels of mental distress, marital dissatisfaction, and impaired physical health than those who were able to carve out something positive from the experience.

More recently, Murphy, Johnson, and Lohan (2002) found that the majority of parents of children who died violently by accident, suicide, or homicide described persisting and long-lasting psychological distress that did not abate with time. Indeed, 5 years after the violent bereavements, almost two-thirds of these parents suffered from some diagnosable mental disorder, with about a quarter of parents suffering from PTSD, women more so than men. Many parents felt that they were given insufficient time to mourn by their places of employment and many took personal leave or sick leave to give themselves more time to grieve.

Neimeyer et al. (2002) view the symptoms of complicated bereavement as constituting an inability to reconstruct reality in a personally meaningful way. These authors posit that unless efforts are made to integrate the meaning of the loss, symptoms will not be significantly reduced by psychotherapy or psychotropic medication. Even family church attendance and prayer by homicidally bereaved parents did not improve outcomes over time if these activities did not contribute to a meaningful integration of the traumatic loss of their child. Although participation in a support group seemed to offer some benefit, mutual support did not aid in the reduction of mental distress and PTSD over time.

Hatton (2003) points out that interventions recommended for homicide survivors are generally consistent with American and British bereavement theory based on studies of traumatic loss (McCann & Pearlman, 1990; Rando, 1993). The grief work hypothesis—the idea that suppressed emotion engenders psychopathology and that healthy mourning must include cathartic emotional expression—underpins much of this post-Freudian, psychodynamically influenced literature. Stroebe (1992–1993) critiqued the universality of the Western grief work hypothesis by noting that several cultures avoid accepting death, for example, through explicit ancestor worship, or actively work to suppress grief, without apparent ill effect. In fact, in Western culture, current grief theory may describe patterns of mourning more typical of women than men.

Clinicians thus need to be especially aware that different patterns of coping with loss and bereavement do not necessarily imply pathology, but they also have to be sensitive to those cases in which they do. Indeed, active clinical encouragement of emotion-suppression may be therapeutically essential at certain stages of the victimization or grief process, as described in chapter 6.

CHILD-SPECIFIC POSTTRAUMATIC SYMPTOMS AND REACTIONS

The impact of homicidal bereavement on families most often means that children of varying ages will be involved, and special consideration applies to them, from both a clinical and family perspective.

Children's Understanding of Death

Yalom (1980) points out that adults often discount or underestimate children's understanding of, and concern with, death issues, largely because of the adults' own uncomfortable feelings about the subject. Most adults today probably have a far easier time discussing sex with their children than death. Adults—family members or clinicians—should not ignore or dismiss a child's questions about and reactions to a loved one's traumatic death by homicide; however, they should realize that the child's understanding of what a parent, counselor, or other adult tells him or her will be influenced by his or her stage of cognitive development and maturity level (Adler, 1997; Poltorak & Glazer, 2006; Ronen, 2002).

Infants and toddlers (1–3) generally have no concept of death as such. What they may feel acutely is simply the stark absence of the parent or other adult. They may also be very sensitive to the general sense of grief and turmoil swirling around them in the aftermath of the murder, but they possess insufficient verbal or conceptual cognitive ability to understand what is going on or express how they feel. Already-frayed parents may then find themselves putting up with regressive behavior, tantrums, and other forms of acting out.

The most effective strategy for parents is simply to maintain their own poise and demeanor. These young children will take their emotional cue from the adults around them. As much as possible, work with your patients to help them provide as stable an environment as possible for their children during this crisis time. This advice actually applies to children of all ages but is especially important for the younger ones.

Young children (4–7) often do not understand that death is universal, that everyone dies, and therefore they may be incredulous as to why their loved one had to be taken from them. Young children relate death to their own experience and often conceptualize and describe it as "going away" or "going to sleep," the implication being that the loved one may come back. In other cases, young children may protect themselves by distraction and denial (in combination with the belief that the dead one will return) and may show what seems to the adults to be an unnatural calm and unconcern, a business-as-usual attitude that may be mistaken for lack of respect or denial of reality. In some cases, this may be an adaptive repression of the fear associated with the death of the loved one.

Adult caregivers should provide the bereaved child with a reality-based explanation for the loss and yet simultaneously respect the child's adaptive defenses. It is appropriate to use culturally accepted concepts like going to heaven if this has been part of the family's belief system. In homicide cases, some children will want to know why the "bad man" killed the adult family member and whether they and surviving family members are safe. Encourage your adult patient to err on the side of reassurance: Whatever the parent or other caretaker can do to make their child feel safe ("The bad man can't get us") will go a long way to minimizing their distress in the long term.

Older children (8–12) will be heavily involved in their own lives with school, peers, sports, and so on. They may use these resources to buffer themselves against the grief and confusion swirling around them. Adults may be annoyed that they disappear during family mourning times. Younger children in this age range may objectify and/or personify death as the bogey man or some equivalent incarnation they recall from a horror movie. They may also conceptualize death as punishment. In that the developmental social-cognitive task of middle childhood is to formulate a healthy personal identity, traumatic homicidal bereavement may lead to problems of self-control and interpersonal functioning. Also, kids can be very supportive to one another or they can be exceedingly cruel, so peers may either help or aggravate the bereaved child's efforts to cope with the loss.

Advise your patients to keep their children productively occupied but to be available to answer age-appropriate questions when asked. Maintain family routines as much as humanly possible and insist that regular rules of curfews, homework, and discipline continue to be followed. If the children ask about what happened, explain it to them in language they can understand but that won't further frighten and traumatize them.

Most *adolescents* (13–18) understand the universality of death but may be fixated on their own sense of immortality through expanding social roles or risky behavior. Developmental tasks of separation and individuation from the family may be disrupted by the traumatic death of a parent or sibling. The chronology of adolescence spans a wide range of maturity levels, and each child deals with death in his or her own way.

Again, encourage your adult patients to try to maintain family rules and routines. Some adolescents may complain that their parents or other adults are being tough, but most will appreciate the adults' effort to maintain family cohesion, even if they don't admit it. Have your patient engage the adolescent by giving him or her concrete tasks to perform that contribute to the family coping efforts, like answering phones or picking up supplies from the store.

Child-Specific PTSD Symptoms

Certain PTSD symptoms seen in children following crime bereavement trauma may differ from those of the adult syndrome (James, 1989; Johnson, 1989; Miller, 1999d, 1999e; Quinn, 1995) and may include the following (see also chapter 2).

Repetitive play. Children may reenact the traumatic crime over and over again in play with dolls, toy soldiers, toy guns, and so on. This appears to be a behaviorally based equivalent of the more cognitively based intrusive thoughts and imagery of adults. Homicidally bereaved adolescents may obsessively replay music, videos, or videogames that reflect themes of violence or retribution.

Self-blame. Children, more so than adults, may fixate on what they might have done to bring the violence upon their slain family member. Children are used to being chastised and blamed by adults in authority, and younger children may fantasize that the loved one's murder was punishment for some imagined wrongdoing on the child's part, or that they should have somehow done more to help their families who were victimized. Other children may torment themselves over the fact that "I should have been better behaved," or "I should have listened more" to the slain adult.

Foreshortened future. Children may express the belief that they will never grow up, and that there is little point in preparing for the future by continuing to go to school, to follow adult advice, or to make new friends because, "what if someone kills me too?" They may also be terrified that the remaining parent will die suddenly.

Regression. Children may stop developing, or regress, cognitively, psychosocially, and emotionally. Developmental milestones that have been passed years ago may reappear. Older kids may wet the bed, play baby games, reacquire tastes for previously abandoned foods, or prefer to play with younger children. Cognitive regression may occur in the form of loss of acquired academic skills, more primitive handwriting, reversion to baby talk, or even complete mutism. Alternatively, some grade school–aged kids may try to "grow up too fast" by engaging in rule-breaking or frankly delinquent behavior.

Atypical cognitive disturbance. In addition to concentration and memory impairment that may affect schoolwork, memory lapses may occur for blocks of time surrounding the news of the murder and the family's reaction to it. In older children and adolescents, some of this may be abetted by new or increased drug use.

Somatization. Children, more so than adults, tend to communicate with their bodies and may therefore be likely to express their distress somatically. The physical symptoms may be a bid for attention, especially in younger kids who fear that the family has forgotten about them due to their preoccupation with mourning and funeral arrangements. Other kids may develop symptoms that suggest to them that they're dying, representing their overall fear of death, instigated by the homicidal bereavement. The two motives may be intertwined.

INTERVENTION WITH FAMILY SURVIVORS
OF HOMICIDE

Because the murder of a loved one affects so many aspects of the survivors' lives so sweepingly and penetratingly, intervention begins from the moment the crime comes to the attention of law enforcement and/or mental health professionals. Consequently, clinicians must be prepared to offer help and support at every stage of the homicidal bereavement process. This chapter will describe how to help families through the initial stages of the death notification and identification of their slain loved one. The next chapter will discuss a variety of therapeutic strategies for guiding families through the crisis of homicidal bereavement.

DEATH NOTIFICATION AND BODY IDENTIFICATION

In some cases, the family member may have actually witnessed the loved one's death. In those cases, first responders should employ the principles of on-scene crisis intervention described in chapter 5. However, often the murder takes place outside the family's awareness and it becomes someone's job to tell them and to help them identify the remains of their loved one.

Why Death Notification?

A frequently neglected topic in the criminal justice and mental health treatment process is the nature of proper notification of family members that a loved one has been killed or that the body of a missing relative has been located and identified. This is another area where mental health clinicians can assist law enforcement's efforts to provide exquisite sensitivity and support in breaking this worst of all possible news to families.

Not just police officers or mental health clinicians but all health care providers need to display a certain degree of sensitivity and decorum in assisting their patients' families in coping with death—untimely or not. At least one study has shown that patients maintain certain expectations of their physicians after a loved one has died, even from natural causes (Dangler, O'Donnell, Gingrich, & Bope, 1996). Most bereaved family members expect a telephone call shortly after the death. Many would like their doctor to specifically inquire about how they're doing in coping with the family member's passing. Most subjects in this study reported that they don't actually expect the physician to attend the family member's funeral; however, a number of patients have told me directly that they appreciated cards of condolence from the physician and the practice staff. In fact, some physicians do this routinely.

In general, any concern shown for the family members after their loved one's anticipated death by illness is greatly appreciated, and the healing effect of this kind of contact should not be underestimated by clinicians. How much more so, then, can sensitive interaction with the family of a deceased person who died suddenly and violently at the hands of a malicious perpetrator impact on the family's ability to cope with the wrenching and seemingly interminable ordeal ahead.

Making a Death Notification

Over the last several years, several thoughtful and practical death notification protocols have been developed, some directly for the families of murder victims, others for different kinds of bereavement, such as motor vehicle fatalities, military deaths, or acts of terrorism (Boss, 1999, 2002; Collins, 1989; Dias, Chabner, Lynch, & Penson, 2003; Eberwein, 2006; Miller, 2006m, 2007i; Nardi & Keefe-Cooperman, 2006; Parrish, Holdren, Skiendzielewski, & Lumpkin, 1987; Ptacek & Eberhardt, 1996; Spungen, 1998; Stewart, 1999; Von Bloch, 1996; Wells, 1993), which I have integrated into the following set of recommendations.

Preparation. Several authorities stress the importance of adequately preparing for the death notification visit. Broadly, preparation includes specialized training for this kind of detail, which is often neglected in both law enforcement and mental health curricula. Preparation also more narrowly applies to the specific call, including clarification of seemingly obvious matters such as the correct name and address of the family, as well as basic facts of who the survivors are: spouse, parents, children, and so on. Although you never want notifications to appear over rehearsed or to seem like an act, a basic run-through of what is to be said and anticipating any reactions and the appropriate responses to them are valuable.

Initial contact. Whenever possible, go in person. Unless there is absolutely no other choice, death notification should never be made over the phone. Go in pairs or in a small group, and decide who will be the lead person whose job it will be to actually say the words and give the bad news. The other team members provide backup support, monitor the survivors for adverse reactions, and provide temporary supervision of young children during the notification, if needed. If no one is home when you get there, wait a reasonable amount of time. If you are queried by a neighbor, ask about the family's whereabouts, but don't reveal the purpose of your visit to anyone but the immediate family. If the family still doesn't show up, leave a card with a note and a number to call. When the call comes, return to the family's home to make the notification. Needless to say, make sure you have the correct family and residence.

Sometimes, an initial contact by phone is unavoidable, as when the surviving family member lives alone and/or in an isolated location. In such cases, Stewart (1999) provides a set of recommendations for death notifications of auto crash victims that can be applied to notifying survivors of murder victims. This involves making two calls, the first informing the family member that his or her loved one has been involved in a crime and encouraging him or her to summon another person who can provide support. In most cases, the survivor will insist on immediately being fully informed of the grim details. In this case, the notifier should use judgment and discretion in providing enough information to satisfy the family member's curiosity but making sure to reserve further details until the support person arrives.

The second call confirms the arrival and presence of the support person and then progresses to the full death notification itself, along with follow-up contact information for the survivor to get more information later. Again, phone notification should be used only as a last resort: When at all possible, death notifications should be made in person.

More applicable to the medical or mental health setting, as opposed to the law enforcement context, is the after-death telephone call (Loboprabhu, Molinari, Pate, & Lomax, 2007) by the health care provider, which is in line with the findings on family preferences and expectations of their doctors (Dangler et al., 1996) cited above. During these calls, begin by identifying yourself and expressing your sympathy at learning of the loved one's death. Then, ask open-ended questions about the circumstances surrounding the death. Listen without interruption and ask brief clarifying questions as needed. At the end, provide validation of feelings, general support, and any practical advice on coping that seems appropriate. I have also found this format to be useful in the first live counseling session with the family following the death of a loved one who has been my patient, or in the initial session for a new patient or family referred for bereavement counseling.

Presenting the information. When you do arrive, ask for permission to enter. Suggest that family members sit down face-to-face with you. Ask if there are any other family members in the house who need to hear this information. Conversely, ascertain if some family members (e.g., young children, frail elderly) may be better off not being present during the notification. Some authorities suggest gently probing about what the survivors know so far: "What have you been told?" "Have you heard anything on the news?" Then prepare the family that bad news is coming, get to the point quickly, and state the information simply and directly. If the facts are clear, don't leave room for doubt or false hope. You needn't be brutally blunt or insensitive, but try to use straight language and avoid euphemisms. Use the deceased's name or his or her relationship to the family member being informed:

> "We're sorry to have to bring you this terrible news, Mrs. Jones. Your daughter, Helen, was killed in a store robbery by a suspect that the police are actively trying to apprehend. Helen and her personal effects are at Municipal Hospital."

Allow time for the news to sink in. It may be necessary to repeat the message several times in increasingly clear and explicit terms. Tolerate silence and be prepared for the calm to be broken by sudden explosions of grief and rage. Intense reactions should be physically restrained only if there is some danger to self or others. In the face of outright denial, be as gentle as possible, but make it clear that the death has in fact occurred.

Answer all questions tactfully and truthfully, but don't reveal more information than is necessary at that time. Repeat answers to questions as many times as necessary. Try to be as calm, supportive, comforting, and empathic as possible. Let the tone and cadence of your voice register the appropriate amount of respect and dignity, but don't become overly maudlin or lose control yourself.

Loboprabhu et al. (2007) recommend a problem-solving form of notification, summarized by the acronym *TALK*:

Think before you speak: Decide if what you're going to say will be helpful in the immediate crisis situation.

Avoid unnecessary burden to the family by addressing only those issues that need to be dealt with at the present time. Violations of this principle commonly made by law enforcement personnel usually involve using the death notification to conduct investigative interviews about the crime. Unless there is extreme urgency in catching the killer, it is usually better to wait until the survivor has had a chance for the news to sink in so that he or she can provide coherent information. Mistakes typically made by responding mental health professionals usually involve trying to conduct psychotherapy during the notification. Clinicians should use the minimal amount of intervention necessary to calm the situation and set the stage for possible follow-up counseling later. The notification is the time for crisis intervention, not therapy.

Listen (and, I would add, *Look*) for problems that might not be immediately apparent, such as suppressed grief or rage in a too-quiet family member, a distraught but silent family member in another part of the house, or signs of danger to the notifier, such as a disturbed or disoriented family member who misinterprets the presence of police and feels sufficiently threatened to attack or flee. I would also add that some family members may be evasive or hostile because they have something to hide from the law; therefore, officers making death notifications should make it crystal clear that this is the only purpose for their visit.

Know what to say now versus later. This is an extension of the above principles of economy and efficiency of crisis intervention strategies. Size up the situation and decide what are front-burner versus back-burner issues to be tackled now versus later.

Practical assistance. Offer to make phone calls to family, friends, neighbors, employers, clergy, doctors, and so on. Ask family members if they want you to get someone to stay with them. Respect the family's privacy, but don't leave a family member alone unless you're sure they're safe. High emotionality can impair memory, so give pertinent information and instructions in writing. Provide family members with the names and telephone numbers of a victim advocate, prosecutor, medical examiner, social service agency, and/or hospital; try to consolidate all the information onto one sheet. Many law enforcement and victim advocacy agencies have printed cards for this purpose.

Explain to family members what will happen next, for example, body identification, police investigation, and criminal justice procedures. If this is a high-profile case, brief them on how to handle the media. Give family members as much information as they ask for, without overwhelming them. Repeat the information as many times as necessary.

Determine if the family members require some means of traveling to the medical examiner's office, hospital, or police station. Offer to drive them or arrange for a ride if they have no transportation. Be sure to provide a ride back home, and try to assist them with babysitting arrangements and other needs. If the notifying team is made up of police personnel and a victim advocate, the advocate may remain with the family members after the police leave.

Death Notification Do's and Don'ts

Note that there are some death notification tactics that surviving family members themselves have identified as decidedly *not helpful* (Eberwein, 2006):

- *Giving unsolicited and unnecessary advice.* "You ought to take some time off from work till things calm down."
- *Encouraging too-quick recovery.* "I know this is tough, but time heals all wounds."
- *Minimization or false cheerfulness.* "Every life has its tragedies, but people are amazingly resilient."
- *Attempts by the notifier to falsely bond or identify with the homicide survivor's feelings.* "I know what you're going through, my grandmother died of cancer last year."

Notification strategies that survivors *do find helpful* include the following:

- *Genuine expressions of concern:* "I just want you to be all right for now, so whatever you need me to do, just tell me."
- *Having the opportunity to vent feelings:* "Whatever you want to tell me is fine and if you don't want to talk, that's okay, too."

- *Just having the presence of another person:* "Someone is going to stay with you as long as you want."

As always, use your judgment, experience, and empathic instincts to find the right words to say that will provide family members with some degree of comfort during this ordeal.

Body Identification

If physical remains have been located, the next step for families is often the identification of their deceased loved one. The finality of identifying the deceased's body can have a paradoxically dual effect. On the one hand, there is the confrontation with the victim's remains and the final shattering of any hope that he or she may still be alive. On the other hand, the actual sight of the deceased often provides a strange sort of reassuring confirmation that the victim's death agonies may have fallen short of the survivor's imagined horrors, and even if not, that the physical presence of the body at least means that the victim's suffering is finally over (Rynearson, 1988, 1994, 1996; Rynearson & McCreery, 1993). Outcome studies of mourners of a death from natural causes report shorter periods of denial and higher total recall of the deceased in those who were able to view the body prior to burial (Sprang & McNeil, 1995).

Referencing the 9/11 World Trade Center attack, Boss (2002) hypothesizes that seeing the remains of a loved one provides a certain cognitive certainty of death, allowing the relaxation of defenses and permitting the survivors to unyoke their self-image from that of the heretofore missing person. In this respect, survivors may actually yearn for some form of physical remains because, paradoxically, having the body enables them to let go of it. Otherwise, so-called *ambiguous loss* can result in rigidity of defenses and constriction of life. There appears to be a primitive, visceral need to be in the presence of physical remains—even a particle of tissue or a swab of DNA—before one is able to separate psychologically from the lost person.

A number of authors (Collins, 1989; Eberwein, 2006; Nardi & Keefe-Cooperman, 2006; Spungen, 1998; Stewart, 1999; Von Bloch, 1996; Wells, 1993) have provided useful guidelines for helping survivors through the process of body identification.

> *Family choice.* Unless there is a legal requirement, let survivors make the choice as to whether they want to view their loved one's remains. Some family members may be anxious or intimidated about making or declining such a request or articulating their wishes, so ask them. In cases

where it is forensically essential to involve the family in the identification process, for example, when the victim has been missing for a long time, be sure to provide appropriate support.

Physical contact. Family members may want to touch the deceased. For some, this may be a way of beginning to accept the reality of the death, a way of finally saying goodbye. This should not be rushed. Spouses and children may want to keep the deceased's hand in their grasp for a while. Parents may want to hold their slain child and not let go. Be prepared to give them a reasonable amount of time. In some cases, where evidence is still being collected, law enforcement may not want the body moved or touched. If this restriction is unavoidable, inform the family and arrange for another viewing, if they choose, when all the evidence collection has been completed. Bear in mind, however, that this may be postautopsy and the body may be in a radically altered condition.

In fact, if the victim's body is significantly mutilated, dismembered, burned, decomposed, or disintegrated, identification may have to be made through dental records, personal effects, and so on. Explain to the family members why this is necessary and give them the choice of whether or not to view or touch the remains. If they choose to do so, try to arrange to have the viewing area as clean as possible. Major wounds should be dressed or covered and the viewing area should be reasonably free of blood spills and other debris. Understand, however, that law enforcement may insist on keeping the body as it was found if evidence is yet to be collected, so inform the family of that. Again, provide the appropriate support.

No remains. Where no body has been recovered, state this plainly. If there is hope that remains may yet be found, state this too, but try to be as realistic as possible about the odds. There is, in fact, some precedent for this. Ships sunk at sea, planes immolated in crashes, or buildings pulverized in bombings rarely produce substantial remains. In such cases, notify the family of whatever identification procedures may be occurring, such as DNA-matching, and direct them to the proper authorities. Also, if artifacts from the victim are found at the scene, such as a pair of glasses, a piece of jewelry, or a child's toy, these might be in police custody for use as evidence in later prosecution. Let the family know this and explain to them the procedures for reclaiming these heirlooms, should they wish to do so.

When no definitive remains are found, symbolic remains may serve as a surrogate. For example, following 9/11, an urn of ashes from Ground Zero was offered by the City of New York to each family of a missing person.

Boss (2002) quotes the brother of a man missing in the World Trade Center debris as stating that "I choose to believe that part of my brother's body is in these ashes." Through this symbolic device, he was able to relinquish the ambiguous hope for his brother's return and move on to accepting his death. Yet this was not enough for the wife of that same missing man—she needed to wait for definitive proof of death and seemed to be prepared to hold on as long as it took.

Boss (2002) observes that a well-developed capacity for dialectical thinking and higher ambiguity tolerance in general tend to characterize people who can resolve the issues of ambiguous loss. These individuals are able to hold two opposing ideas in their minds at the same time, such as "My son is gone, but he is also still here and always will be in some ways." Or, "I'm moving forward with my life, but I won't stop looking for him." In this way, when there is no clear answer, the only way to stave off total despair is to hold on to both the possibilities of absence and presence.

Death Notification and Body Identification With Child Victims

Although loss of any family member is wrenching, special sensitivity is needed when the victim is a young child. Ahrens, Hart, and Maruyama (1997) surveyed parents of children who died or who were dead on arrival at a hospital emergency department. When the death notification was carried out in a sensitive, respectful, and empathic manner, this had a powerful immediate and long-term positive effect on the family's ability to cope with the child's death. Most parents found it reassuring and comforting to hold their dead child. Almost all the parents wanted some physical memento of the child, such as a lock of hair or a mold of the hand. Notifiers should do whatever they can to afford parents and other caretakers as much support and comfort as the situation allows.

Notifier Stress

Notifying family members that a loved one has died can be stressful, even for professionals who deal daily in life and death, such as medical and law enforcement personnel (Nardi & Keefe-Cooperman, 2006; Stewart, 1999). For example, a sizable proportion of physicians report feeling uncomfortable informing patients and their relatives that a medical condition might be terminal (Ptacek & Eberhardt, 1996).

Hard-boiled cops aren't necessarily immune from notifier stress, either. For police officers, and perhaps for some medical professionals as well, the fact of a victim's death may signify that the professional has "failed" to protect their charge, and this may induce feelings of guilt in facing the survivors (Swisher, Nieman, Nilsen, & Spivey, 1993). Police officers, and also some doctors, tend to adopt a "110 percent" mind-set, where "failure is not an option," so when failure occasionally drops in unbidden, they have a hard time dealing with it (Miller, 1995b, 2006m; Wester & Lyubelsky, 2005).

Even military Survivor Assistance Officers (SAOs) and Casualty Assistance Officers (CAOs) report heightened emotional turmoil and somatic symptoms when making death notifications to family members of soldiers killed in battle (Bartone, Ursano, Wright, & Ingrahan, 1989; Ender & Hermsen, 1996). The higher the level of distress shown by the survivors, the greater the stress experienced by the SAOs/CAOs, although this appears to be moderated by personal characteristics of the notifiers, such as dispositional hardiness and the quality of collegial and social support, as well as sociocultural similarities and differences between the notifiers and survivors in ethnic, economic, social, and traditional family backgrounds. The latter also affects both the handling of the death notification call and the notifiers' psychological responses to it. These findings argue for better cross-cultural training, as well as the importance of maintaining professional support networks for these professionals.

CONCLUSIONS

Because of the multiplicity of persons and personalities involved, family bereavement by homicide is one of the most challenging facets of crime victim intervention a clinician will face. While some families may move on, given a firm but gentle push in the right direction, for others, the practical helping strategies discussed in this chapter may need to be followed and supplemented by more intensive and extensive counseling and psychotherapy.

CHAPTER 9

Family Survivors of Homicide

Psychotherapeutic Strategies

When a family has been traumatized by a loved one's murder, the whole family is the patient. In many cases, the clinician will initially be impressed, if not overwhelmed, by the sheer intensity of the bereaved family members' distress, which may be as great or greater than that of direct victims of nonlethal criminal violence. Other times, some family members may be numb and silent while others walk around in a near-hysterical or rageful state. While some family therapy strategies are similar to those used with individual patients, others differ and these are important for the clinician to know.

FAMILY THERAPY FOR BEREAVEMENT BY HOMICIDE: GENERAL CONSIDERATIONS

As with psychotherapy of the direct victim (chapters 6, 7), psychotherapy of family survivors of homicidal bereavement has several dimensions. In some ways, the principles of psychological intervention applied to family survivors of homicide reflect generally validated principles of grief counseling and bereavement therapy (Lindy, Grace, & Green, 1981; Rynearson, 1996; Sprang & McNeil, 1995; Spungen, 1998).

One consideration has to do with what exactly is *individual* and *family* therapy, because, in many cases of family bereavement by homicide, individual and family sessions will shade into one another, as family members show up for treatment sessions alone, in pairs, or in different group configurations. Thus, the question, who is the patient? in any given session may be somewhat fluid and flexible.

Also, the effects of successive traumas may be cumulative (Alarcon, 1999; Weiner, 1992), and therapy for homicidal bereavement may have to deal with unresolved traumatic material from the past, which will almost certainly be reevoked by the more recent trauma of the murder. Also, other aspects of life cannot automatically be put on hold when the death occurs, so therapy must address coexisting issues such as school and job problems, marital conflict, substance abuse, or other preexisting family stresses. This may require some additional flexibility of prioritization by the therapist in terms of what are considered "front-burner" versus "back-burner" issues (Spungen, 1998).

> "One minute we'll be talking about how their son is having panic attacks in school that prevent him from staying in class," explained the family therapist, "then the conversation will shift to his little brother's ADHD and how he inherited that from his father, who's had some trouble with the law. So, the discussion will slide around to various topics, and what I do is let the narrative flow at its own pace and in its own direction and look for threads of commonality or common themes to tie together the traumatic material and the everyday concerns. Sometimes there are those threads and sometimes there's not and you have to be careful not to push it. Sometimes, it's obvious that the patient is shifting to these more mundane topics to defuse some of the intense emotionality of talking about the murder. So you let the narrative go where it needs to, but I kind of 'ride shotgun' and keep an eye out for themes that can tie the topics together. But sometimes you just have to let the patient talk."

The basic element of all effective psychotherapy, especially trauma therapy, is to provide safety and support. Throughout the course of treatment, the supportive nature of the clinical intervention and the therapeutic relationship are essential elements in the traumatic resolution for families. The nature of the therapeutic relationship may serve to buffer the effects of the trauma, increase self-esteem, and alter the family's role functioning, thereby helping to mitigate the traumatic impact of the event (Sprang & McNeil, 1995).

In cases of homicidal bereavement, this includes emotional, educative, and material support. In addition to regularly scheduled sessions, psychotherapists should be available by phone or beeper for family members who just need to reach out for a few words during periods of crisis, but they must also be prepared to set limits and encourage patients' independence and autonomy. Mental health clinicians should educate family members as to the nature of the grief process, and they should identify and normalize the sometimes baffling and frightening symptoms and reactions that family members may experience. Realistic reassurance should be provided that families can live through this, but clinicians should stay away from comments that suggest that the experience will be "resolved" or that families will "get over" the loss any time soon. At this early stage of the traumatic bereavement, there is no way families will believe this, and they may resent what they perceive as the therapist trivializing their pain by suggesting it is something that can be "gotten over with" like a bad cold.

FAMILY THERAPY FOR BEREAVEMENT BY HOMICIDE: EFFECTIVE STRATEGIES

Again, for a number of therapists and counselors, many of the following psychotherapeutic strategies and techniques may seem familiar from their own work with diverse populations. That's because they largely represent specialized adaptations of the principles of good mental health treatment to the special needs of homicidally bereaved families. Some of these strategies will be similar to those discussed with regard to direct crime victims, while others will be relatively unique applications to homicidally bereaved family members.

Spungen (1998) cites Getzel and Masters's (1984) delineation of the basic tasks of family therapy after bereavement by homicide:

- Helping the family understand and put into perspective the rage and guilt they feel about their loved one's murder
- Helping survivors examine their grief reactions and other people's availability to them so that they regain their confidence in the social order
- Helping the family accept the death of their loved one as something tragic and irrevocable yet bearable and livable
- Assisting members of the immediate and extended kinship system in establishing a new family structure that permits individual members to grow in a more healthy and fulfilling manner

Physical Self-Control

Trying to help families achieve some measure of order and control in the midst of the emotional maelstrom of homicidal bereavement may seem like an impossibly daunting task, but sometimes the best place to start is with the physical. Most survivors will be on high physiological alert, experiencing anxiety, panic, dizziness, headaches, stomach distress, sleep disturbances, ruminating thoughts, impaired memory and concentration, or other signs and symptoms. Training family members in relaxation, biofeedback, or meditation exercises that reduce arousal (chapter 6) can show them that they can at least control *something*—their own bodies. This may give them the confidence to try to gain increasing control over other chaotic aspects of their now upside-down lives.

Emotional Control and Expression

Some survivors cope by maintaining a steely reserve, an unnatural calmness of mood, speech, and behavior, which may sometimes reflect an innate stoicism of character but may also be a typical posttraumatic sign of emotional numbing. In the early stages, this should be accepted, since this rigid emotional splint may literally be the only thing that is holding the person together. As time goes on, you can gently guide the explorative process to gradually unbind the emotionally constricted survivor, but this should always be done in the context of respecting the individual's ability to handle the emotions, and always with the ultimate goal of increasing, not diminishing, the person's sense of control.

Other survivors may want to vent and, indeed, the therapist's office may be the only place where they feel safe enough to do so. With such individuals, be careful to remember the difference between *venting* and *spewing*. The former is a cathartic, albeit sometimes painful, expression of suppressed emotions that leads to a feeling of relief and possibly greater insight and control. The latter is an unproductive emotional regurgitation that often heightens distress, clouds understanding, and leaves the person feeling even more out of control. Therapists have the responsibility to monitor and guide the expressive process so that it heals, not hurts.

Guilt and Anger

Two especially important issues that are frequently intertwined are guilt and anger. As noted in chapter 8, in an attempt to make some existential sense out of their loved one's death, family members may blame themselves for the victim's fate. As unfair to oneself as some of these self-reproachful rationales may seem to others ("If we didn't have a fight the night before, he wouldn't have left for work so early in the morning, and so he wouldn't have been held up and shot at that gas station"), families may cling to these pseudoexplanations to provide at least some kind, any kind, of meaning to the unspeakable event. Being angry at oneself is at least one way to seize a form of psychological control of the situation, and some of this internalized anger may be projected outward onto the police department, the criminal justice system, the medical establishment, mental health clinicians, or society in general.

Or vice-versa. Sometimes there is a legitimate basis for the family's anger that is partly expressed outwardly and partly internalized. Maybe the recidivist criminal really was let out of jail too early. Maybe the city really should have authorized funds for increased police patrol of dangerous neighborhoods instead of spending the money on a damn stadium. Maybe the media really are acting like slime, calling the house every 5 minutes and ambushing the grieving family outside their home or business. Maybe those blissfully stupid and uncaring ordinary people really do have absolutely no clue and don't give a crap about the pain and suffering endured by the homicidally bereaved family because it hasn't happened to them—yet.

Therapeutically, anger must be handled carefully, allowed to come out at a controlled pace in the venting-not-spewing format noted above. The feeling of anger must be acknowledged, even if the therapist doesn't necessarily agree intellectually with its intensity or its targets. Guilt feelings also should be acknowledged, and it is usually a futile exercise to try to talk someone out of the self-reproachful mentality that is temporarily allowing his or her psyche to stay glued together. Having the individual explore the reasons for his or her feelings can often delicately guide him or her into a more realistic view of causation and responsibility. Equally important is helping the family—when they are ready—to channel guilt and anger feelings into productive activities that may actually make a difference in how the system works and may serve to memorialize the slain loved one.

Family Role Realignment

One important therapeutic task is to help the family members reconfigure their respective roles in the absence of the missing murder victim. Aside from all the other stresses associated with the traumatic bereavement, different family members will have to pick up new and different responsibilities, from paying the bills, to preparing meals, to helping with homework, to participating in social functions. The stresses associated with these role shifts should be expressed and acknowledged, and the therapist should support and assist family members in making these transitions.

Here, timing is everything. Even though the activities of different family members may shift dramatically from the moment of the loved one's death, a permanent internalization of the shift in family roles must await the time when the family members have achieved some kind of stable acceptance of the missing member's absence. This can't be rushed, and you may have to do a little psychological juggling act with some families: helping them maintain a sense of order and stability within existing family routines and rituals, while gently guiding them to subtly rearrange the family role configuration so that the slain member's memory becomes a healed-over scar, not an oozing gash.

Memorialization and Reintegration

Related to role realignment of individual family members are grief and closure exercises that enable the family to master and integrate the traumatic bereavement, partly through memorialization activities that allow planning for the future while honoring the past (Sprang & McNeil, 1995; Spungen, 1998). For example, pictures and other mementos of the murdered loved one can serve as comforting images. In reviewing family picture albums together, the therapist and survivors can try to summon nurturant, positive imagery that may counterbalance the grotesque recollections of the homicide. Similar memorializing activities include writing about the deceased or creating a scrapbook. Many family members will do this spontaneously.

Again, none of this should become an unending, unhealthy, consuming preoccupation, although, in the early stages, some leeway should be afforded to allow the memorializers to get it out of their systems. Family members should collaborate in these personalized memorial rituals and projects as a way of forging a renewed sense of meaning and commitment within the family structure. But some family members may still be too traumatized by any invocation of the slain loved one to participate productively in such an exercise. As with all of the techniques and exercises in this chapter, where some family members are ready and some are not, the ones who can do it should be encouraged to use whatever coping strategies they are up to, while other family members should be allowed the flexibility to proceed at their own pace.

> "One of the things we found most helpful and comforting in working with our counselor," said Jewel, "was that she never made any of us feel like a failure if we couldn't accomplish some therapeutic homework assignment or task. She'd ask us if we'd like to try it again and if so, she'd explain and show us what to do, but if not, she'd say, 'How about trying something else,' or just let us talk about what we wanted and approach the topic another way. Eventually, we usually got around to dealing with the important stuff. This was different than the last counselor we went to, a psychologist who kept giving us printed homework sheets and other rigid stuff, like we were taking a course in school. I'm sure he meant well, but it was, like, just too much material to throw at us with all the other stuff we had to do, and we just got turned off."

Psychotherapeutic Strategies

Family members of murder victims may come to therapy as a family unit or as individual patients. As noted above, often there will be mixing and matching of attendees, as some members show up for all or most sessions and others appear more sporadically.

At some point, especially once a trusting therapeutic relationship has formed, the bereaved family member will want to talk about the deceased and about his or her reaction to the death and its aftermath. This needs to be carefully paced and titrated. In cases of individual and family therapy for parents of murdered children, Rynearson (1988, 1994, 1996) cautions against pushing the cathartic narrative too quickly, especially in the early stages of treatment. A common defense against overwhelming emotional turmoil is for many bereaved family members to adopt what appears to be either an unnatural flippancy or a hyperrational facts-only attitude, which others may mistake for unconcern or callousness. If, immediately following the homicide, some family members cope better by using the twin emotional crutches of avoidance and denial, this should be provisionally respected by the therapist. Remember, even in orthopedics, the useful and legitimate function of a crutch is to support a limb until sufficient healing occurs to begin more active rehabilitation (Miller, 1998h).

When the therapeutic narrative does begin to flow, psychotherapy for homicidal bereavement combines many of the features of individual PTSD therapy and family therapy modalities. Therapists should inquire about individual family members' private perceptions of death. Nihilism and despair are common early responses, and helping patients and families to recover or develop sustaining spiritual or philosophical beliefs or actions can buffer them against the destabilizing and disintegratory effects of the murder.

Once the psychological coping mechanisms of self-calming and distancing from the homicide event have been strengthened, therapy can begin to confront the traumatic imagery more directly. Less verbally expressive family members may be asked to draw their perception of the scene of death in order to provide a nonverbal expression of reenactment that can be directly viewed by and shared with the therapist. Family members can then be encouraged to place themselves within the drawn enactment to allow the process of abstract distancing to take the place of mute avoidance. In these exercises, family members often portray themselves as defending, holding, or rescuing the deceased. Therapeutic measures may also involve exploring the family members' concepts of life and death, as well as encouraging both private meditative and socially committed activities, such as support groups or political or religious anticrime activities (Rynearson, 1996).

Recall, however, the Clarence caveat mentioned in chapter 7 concerning the encouragement of existentially elevating experiences from psychologically debasing trauma. Although some families have described their ability to eventually create a posttraumatic growth experience out of the homicidal bereavement of their loved one, psychotherapists should be careful not to turn this into an expectation, which can risk further demoralizing an already reeling family by giving them one more thing to feel bad about. However, when family members indicate an ability and willingness to take this existential step, therapists must be willing and able to guide them responsibly along this path (Miller, 1998h).

Gender-Based Therapy

Also recall the discussions in chapters 2 and 3 highlighting that individual reactions to trauma, including crime victimization and homicidal bereavement, will be powerfully influenced by the patient's personality and family background and demographic factors such as sex, race, and social class. Recently, a number of clinicians and researchers have endeavored to take some of these factors into account in helping crime victims and their families.

Kenney (2003) has studied how men and women react differently to the murder of a family member and how gender-traditional coping styles help or hinder their traumatic resolution and recovery. Kenney's findings reinforce a dynamic I have seen repeatedly in clinical practice with families of traumatically deceased victims, usually children, some who have died by homicide, but also in cases of fatal traffic accidents or death from terminal illness.

Kenney's (2003) findings show that men who adhere to a traditional masculine gender role express the most difficulty in coping with their loved one's death. These men feel trapped between guilt and grief over not protecting the deceased and their surviving family members on the one hand, and a need to be strong and resolute on the other. A vicious cycle typically ensues between guilt from a perceived failed-protector status intensifying grief and depression, while their need to remain strong necessitates consciously suppressing or unconsciously repressing these feelings. The result is typically a waxing and waning cycle of eruptions of anger—the quintessential masculine emotion—which only serves to highlight their sense of waning self-control, leading to further depression and self-deprecation, which sets up the whole cycle again.

When turned outward, this guilt-driven anger is manifested in furious rage directed at the offender and others; when directed inward, it may congeal into suicidal depression. In either case, men experiencing this guilt-repression–anger-depression dynamic appear to have great difficulty coping and remain stuck in this mode for extended periods of time. Moreover, not only does this holding pattern act as an obvious block to their resolution of grief, it frequently results in physical health problems.

Conversely, men who display more flexible gender roles tend to cope better by being more expressive of their feelings and adhering less rigidly to the traditional masculine stereotype of the strong protector. This seems to allow them to escape the guilt-driven grief, repression, and anger cycle found in the more poorly coping men. Moreover, men who display more flexible gender roles appear to be more receptive to learning alternative ways of conceptualizing their role with regard to the loved one's death and to acquiring skills to control their anger and/or channel it into productive action. In this way, they feel less consumed by their supposed failure to protect their families and are better able eventually to move on to actively work their way through the grief process.

My own experience in working with law enforcement and public safety personnel, industrial workers, military personnel, business executives, physicians, airline personnel, and others in traditionally masculine professions—and with traditionally masculine perspectives and attitudes—has been that sometimes this so-called traditional male coping pattern can be deleterious to health and recovery, but that other times it can actually help by serving the kind of psychic splinting function important in the technique of utilizing cognitive defenses, described in chapter 6 (Janik, 1991). For many of these men, their sense of self-control in the face of personal tragedy is the only antidote they have to being overwhelmed with feelings of helplessness and despair (Brooks, 1998; Miller, 1995b, 2006m, 2007m; Wester & Lyubelsky, 2005). This tough-it-out stratagem can be productively used to keep these men in a focused, functional mode so that their enhanced feelings of efficacy in helping their families in the here and now can, for the time being, counteract the guilt and grief of allegedly having let them down in the past.

Another important implication of this approach is that the other family members typically take their emotional cue from the primary male member and, if dad is falling apart, then there's nothing else for the rest of the family to hang onto, which can lead to serious psychological disintegration of the family unit. By bolstering the husband and father figure, the clinician assures that other family members have someone to draw strength from, thereby enhancing their own coping efforts and further reinforcing dad's confidence that he has something unique and powerful to contribute to his family's welfare: "I'm being strong for them." Only when this attitude degenerates into self- or other-directed destructive anger does the therapist have to step in and function as a moderating force. Later—and it may be months or even years later—the therapist can help this tough guy step out of his mental suit of armor, once a basic inner core of resilience and self-efficacy has been built up. Thus, for some men, there need not necessarily be a contradiction between tough coping styles at critical stages in the grief recoil process and more flexible coping styles later on in recovery.

In Kenney's (2003) study, women who cope poorly were found to be enmeshed in a different kind of grief cycle than men. These women continually ruminate on the events surrounding the murder, their feelings of loss and grief, their victim status, and their fears for the future, which only serves to intensify their distress over time and block the resolution of their grief. Conversely, women who do not allow themselves to wallow in the helpless victim role fare better emotionally and are less likely to remain frozen in their despair.

While never encouraging wallowing for its own sake, I would urge caution in trying to jump-start the self-efficacy process too soon in many of these traumatized women. Sometimes a period of "there-there" nurturing is what many women—and some men—require to give their mental batteries time to recharge sufficiently to power up their autonomous coping efforts. At these times, the therapist may have to function as a surrogate parent or spouse-figure (while not being obvious about it) as he or she bolsters the real parent's or spouse's inner resources to eventually assume this role.

Kenney (2003) generally recommends that the therapy process for these traumatically bereaved men and women work on encouraging more flexible gender roles of coping and balancing a focus on oneself with involvement with other individuals, productive goals, and activities. As long as this is done at a proper pace and respects the clinical and demographic characteristics of each individual patient, it is overall sound advice and good clinical practice with these families.

"I hate to admit it," Max said, "but at first, I thought the worst part of my son being killed was putting up with his mom's crying. It's not that I'm, like, insensitive or anything, but here I was, trying to make all the arrangements, taking care of business, talking to the cops and the funeral home and trying to work out time off from my job, and all Francine can do is sit there and bawl, like she's the only one this is happening to. After the funeral, I started staying late at work, and on the weekends I'd find something to keep me busy, so me and Francine hardly said 10 words in 4 weeks. Our older son, Matthew, was already married and out of the house. Then, one day, my wife decides we have to go to counseling or she's getting a divorce. 'You're heartless,' she tells me. Truth is, I do love the woman, so I said okay, but I was nervous about what this mental help stuff was all about.

"First thing I told that shrink was 'I'm not the kind of guy who talks about things a lot.' I figured he'd give me some speech about getting in touch with your feelings, but he surprised me because he just said, 'Talk about whatever you want—it's your nickel.' He didn't push me and he didn't give me any psychobabble and, after a few sessions, I actually started warming up to the guy and started talking about things, not just Patrick's death, but a whole bunch of things I never really discussed with anyone.

"But one thing he said made a particular impression—I'm paraphrasing: 'This isn't like TV, Max, where everything goes according to a script. Everyone deals with things in their own way. Just do two things: figure out a way to use your style of coping in a healthy way, and, two, try to be a little understanding if someone else's style isn't the same as yours.' Funny thing is, once that sunk in, I actually felt less impatient with Francine. She started giving me my space and I started being a little more open with her, and we started to get along a little better, which I'm sure is what Patrick would have wanted."

Existential-Empowerment Family Therapy

In chapter 7, we discussed the role of existential therapy with direct crime victims. For many family members of murder victims, this approach can also be important in allowing them to craft a vessel of meaning to ferry them through the raging currents of their loss.

While many authors describe existential approaches to therapy as piecemeal or peripheral components of the overall therapeutic course, Armour (2003) has developed a program explicitly designed for helping families of homicide victims gain meaning through specific behaviors that have symbolic significance. In varying forms, and with the appropriate patients, I have found this approach to be a valuable addition to the therapeutic armamentarium for traumatically bereaved families of many types, including those affected by homicide, accidental death, or terminal illness. The specific application to families of murder victims is described here.

Armour (2003) characterizes what she calls the *"characteristics of meaning making grounded in action"* as consisting of *"the intense pursuit of what matters,"* which is defined as a form of coping comprised of intentional acts that have symbolic meaning. The idea is to channel efforts to find meaning in the trauma into active problem solving or striving to attain valued goals. Perhaps to reduce unwanted pressure, the meaningfulness related to the post-homicide experience rests primarily on the process of the pursuit rather than the specific outcome; that is, the gain is in the doing, not necessarily the finishing, which is like the behavioral equivalent of cognitive mindfulness training—or constructing a Japanese garden. Over time, active engagement in these meaning-making activities is intended to help the homicide survivors reconstruct a more empowering self-identity—to "relearn the self" as well as "relearn the world" (Attig, 1996). Creating positive narratives about their actions in response to the post-homicide experience facilitates this re-authoring of the self.

Various methods of Amour's (2003) meaning making grounded in action include the following, along with my own observations and suggestions. Note that this approach may seem too abstract and philosophical for many patients, but where the family can be engaged, it often serves as a refreshingly creative and expansive counterbalance to the typical cognitive therapy emphasis on goals and benchmarks.

Asserting the truth. Homicide survivors may create meaning by constructing narratives that express the truth as they see it concerning the facts and events of the murder. They have become exquisitely sensitive to the ignorance, incompetence, and hypocrisy of others, and they assert their right not to be swayed or deterred by the distortions of reality and hidden agendas promulgated by the media, the criminal justice system, and even well-meaning clinicians. They are able to recount numerous examples of small and large injustices dealt them, which justifies their suspiciousness, anger, and resentment and allows them to claim their worth as undeserving victims of crime. As a result, they have come to assert a tough-minded adherence to their own perception of the truth and may listen politely to others' renditions, but make it clear that they believe what they believe and are prepared to make decisions on that basis.

> "Here's something else I hate to admit," said Max, "but I came close to clocking the pastor of our church. Like I told you, right after Patrick's murder, I was a ball of rage and didn't want to hear anything from anybody, and here we are, sitting in the house after the funeral, and Pastor Johnson comes by and starts up with, like, a little sermon on how this is 'God's will' and 'we have to learn to accept it.' And I'm sitting there, just staring at him, thinking, 'You get *your* kid killed and then come tell me how to accept God's will.' I thought I was going to have a stroke. Other people must have seen my face because some people stopped talking and started walking over. But I held it together and just told the pastor that we were tired and this wasn't a good time."

Following one's own path. Homicide survivors may come to adopt positions based on their own moral precepts and the meanings they assign to particular situations. They draw strength from their hard-won beliefs, and this gives them the confidence and autonomy to make decisions on their own behalf. They forge a renewed identity out of their experiences that may not conform to the role that others would place them in, but they don't care because they are guided by their inner beacon. Some of this comes from the realization that their ordeal as homicidally bereaved family members creates some separation between them and ordinary civilians, and they are able to stand apart from the crowd with a feeling of wholeness and self-satisfaction at having lived through and survived a near-impossible ordeal.

"For a while after Patrick was killed," Francine said, "I was a real bitch around everybody, which of course they didn't like because they had some idea that I was supposed to be 'noble' about my loss. 'You've been watching too many damn *Lifetime Channel* TV movies,' I thought. My counselor said I had a right to my feelings, but he suggested I go easy on these other, clueless, people because, after all, what they know about this kind of thing all comes from television and movies."

Fighting for what's right. Many homicide survivors feel ill-treated by the actions of others. They are frequently thrust into interactions with the public, the media, and the criminal justice system that rob them of important rights and deprive them of the ordinary ability to control one's own life that other people take for granted. They may respond by assertively holding the responsible parties accountable and claiming what is rightfully theirs. Their actions are impelled by a moral indignation about the importance of what they've been through and their right to be heard in their own voices. In part, their struggle is a form of existential self-preservation, to help them reestablish a moral and principled world. Again, while it is important to help empower patients who want to be empowered, this should never be something that is foisted upon patients by the clinician; if a family wishes to cope by fading into the background, that's their choice.

Armour (2003) cites one example in which a homicidally bereaved father breaks through the dispassionate courtroom climate to raucously applaud the jury's conviction of the murderer, to revel in the victory over the forces of evil. In doing so, he reestablishes that his family, rather than the state, is the aggrieved party, and congratulates the judge, jury, and prosecution on a job well done. His applause also pointedly provokes an uncomfortable reaction from the murderer, which is the only direct way the father can grasp a small measure of well-deserved comeuppance, to validate the fact that the father and his family are a force to be reckoned with, not mute, impotent "victims." In another example, a homicidally bereaved mother prominently attends every hearing held for the eight boys who killed her son. She symbolically watches over and stands up for her son by "sitting in" for him and thereby making the murderers, as well as the criminal justice system, accountable to her.

Fighting to fix what's wrong. As we've discussed at several points in this book, a number of homicide survivors turn their grief and pain into productive action and work to correct the injustices in the society around them. These survivors feel a fierce commitment to honor the memory of their loved one and make sure he or she did not die in vain. They do this by taking actions that provide purpose and create meaning out of an otherwise senseless act. At times, their zeal may turn this project into a relentless crusade, as they forcefully demand action, admonish others for their shortcomings, and seek to assertively enlighten people who they perceive as willfully ignorant. Some of the motivation for this comes from the ego-splinting function of social action, discussed earlier. Forcefully creating change in the world enables the families to achieve a measure of cognitive and practical control and reestablish a sense of order. Righting wrongs makes the family feel potent and worthwhile and validates the homicide as an event with meaning. The only caution is that this not become an unhealthily all-consuming struggle.

> "A local TV station wanted to do a documentary on 'Families Coping With Murder,' or something like that," Francine said, "and they asked us if we wanted to be in it. By that time, with Patrick gone and the trial over, we were exhausted from fighting the good fight and just wanted to be left alone, so we said no. But we did take up an offer by a POMC [Parents of Murdered Children] representative to speak to their local group. Max and I felt this would be a more personal kind of contribution. And we met some very nice people."

Helping others. In line with the above, many homicide survivors feel compelled to impart their hard-earned wisdom to others who are going through the same horrible experience. This is yet again another way of validating the meaning-making purpose of their loss and giving voice to their loved one's murder. As with other actions, by converting their bad fate into good works in contributing to the coping and welfare of others, they attempt to transcend their own trauma and make the world a worthwhile place to continue living.

> "Probably the best thing about the POMC meetings is that we were able to give advice to other families who were just starting the process of going through what we went through," Max said. "Less than a year ago, I was a depressed, angry basket case, and here I am, a fountain of wisdom for these new people [laughs]. There was this one guy who really wasn't doing well, who had that same clenched-up look I used to walk around with, and I just walked over, introduced myself, and let him talk it out—kind of what our family counselor let me do in the beginning, and he just couldn't believe that someone could live through something like this and survive. He was already divorced and didn't have any other children, and

I remember almost feeling guilty that I was 'luckier'—if you can use that word—than this poor guy, and I kind of adopted him and made him my project. I'm not a religious man, but I started thinking maybe there's a purpose to all this, or at least I can make a purpose out of it."

Living the purposeful life. As just noted, some homicide survivors resolve to live their lives more intentionally and purposefully. Typically, their experience has wrenchingly altered their old beliefs and priorities. Some families cling to already existing meaning systems in religion, culture, family traditions, and so on, while others find themselves in existential terra incognita, having to construct a worldview and direction in life from the ground up. But, typically, once some purpose is identified and endorsed, it is followed with a fierce devotion as it contributes to further validating the horrific experience the family has been through and gives them a reason to move on. It is important to note that while religious support is often sought and/or encouraged by others, research has shown that, in some cases, religious coping can be associated with greater distress among homicide survivors (Hatton, 2003; Thompson & Vardman, 1997).

"I think that experience with the pastor burnt me out on the church aspect of it," Max went on. "Up to then, I always accepted what other people told me about the world, God, and so on, but after Patrick was killed, there was no way I could just go back to believing the way I used to believe. Francine seems to be better with it than I am, and she's gone back to church, but I still can't bring myself to go. I remember my counselor talking about 'creating your own meaning' or something like that and, at the time, I remember thinking, 'What the hell is this guy talking about?' But after the famous 'pastor incident' [laughs], I started to see what he meant. I gotta believe in something, but I just don't know what that is, yet."

Finally, the sad truth is that some members of a given family may be more willing or able than others to leave the grimmest parts of the past behind and move on; other family members just can't let go, no matter what. In such cases, family separations may be necessary for some members to escape the stifling emotional turmoil of unhealthy family enmeshment and misery in order to make a fresh start and find their own way back into the world of the living (Barnes, 1998; Miller, 1998h, 1999d).

In this regard, clinicians need to remind themselves of the limited therapeutic goals in most cases of homicidal bereavement. Don't expect families to totally work through the trauma of a murdered loved one, and don't tell them they'll "get over it"—they won't. The bereaved family will always maintain an attachment to the slain loved one, especially a child, and it would be a mistaken therapeutic objective to insist on complete decathexis. Instead, it is hoped that the bereaved family will learn to maintain involvement with others, while always retaining an internalized relationship with the slain child's, parent's, or sibling's image (Miller, 1998h, 1999d; Rynearson, 1984, 1988, 1994, 1996, 2001; Rynearson & McCreery, 1993).

The therapist's task then is, first, to keep the family members from destroying themselves and one another, and second, to restore some semblance of meaning and purpose in their lives that will allow them to remain productive, functioning members of their community. Often, the crucial first step is to get the family members to believe in one simple fact: "You can live through this." In the best of cases, family members may grow from such a horrendous experience as the brutal murder of a loved one, but—recalling the Clarence caveat from chapter 7—such cases are the blessed exceptions, not the rule, and most families do well just to survive (Miller, 1998h, 1999d).

WHAT DO HOMICIDE BEREAVEMENT COUNSELORS FIND EFFECTIVE?

What I've presented thus far is a menu of treatment options, culled from the literature and my own clinical experience, that have proven useful in helping families cope with homicidal bereavement.

But don't take my word for it.

Hatton (2003) surveyed the opinions of 116 homicide bereavement counselors and therapists regarding the types of interventions they endorsed and recommended for family survivors. The survey group included psychologists, social workers, grief counselors, clergy, self-help group members, court-based victim advocates associated with clinics, and employees of victim/witness assistance programs listed in the National Organization of Victim Assistance (NOVA) directory.

Perhaps not surprisingly, a number of counselors entered this specialized field based on their own experiences of homicidal bereavement, and this study suggests that the counselor's own bereavement status may influence his or her clinical approach. Counselors who were themselves survivors were much more willing to spend time on the emotional pain experienced by the family members than were nonsurvivors, who were more likely to intellectualize the loss and discuss coping strategies rather than focus on processing the raw emotion of bereavement. Counselors who are survivors may be more willing to accept the intense emotions that accompany homicide bereavement precisely because they have been through it themselves. Relatedly, survivor-patients may express their feelings more openly and straightforwardly to a survivor-counselor, knowing they are talking to a fellow traveler. Survivor-clinicians also reported making themselves more available, timewise, to the bereaved than did non survivors. This suggests that counselors may modify some of the traditional limits associated with clinical practice when they identify strongly with patients due to their common experiences.

More generally, however, the counselors in this survey were ambivalent about advising homicidally bereaved family members to seek assistance and support exclusively from other survivors. Self-help groups were strongly endorsed, with survivors rating them significantly more highly than did non survivors. Counselor-survivors also appeared more sensitive than nonsurvivors to the possibility that intervention could itself be traumatizing. While they eschewed suppressive and distracting techniques in favor of more emotionally cathartic forms of therapy, they cautioned against the use of extreme emotional venting or flooding therapies, which they apparently understood from their own experience to be potentially retraumatizing.

In the discussions earlier, I identified guilt or self-blame as a prominently reported finding in surviving family members of murder victims. However, fewer than one-fifth of the counselors in Hatton's (2003) survey cited these feelings as a major difficulty for survivors. The study author speculates that the victims' rights advocacy movement of the past several decades, as well as the general social climate, may have served to reduce crime victims' and survivors' propensity toward self-blame.

Again, in contrast to my discussion in chapters 3 and 4 of the importance of considering individual personality factors in the evaluation and treatment of crime victims and surviving family members, the counselors surveyed in Hatton's (2003) study ranked survivors' character problems among the least important factors in the development of complicated bereavement and, consequently, to the success or failure of treatment, in comparison with other variables. And in contrast to some grief and trauma specialists who recommend a thorough pretreatment assessment of trauma survivors to screen for specific problems or syndromes (Hymer, 1984; McCann & Pearlman, 1990; Rynearson, 1994), the counselors in Hatton's study appeared to apply a crisis intervention model to pretreatment assessment, which downplayed formal diagnosis in favor of the immediate application of effective interventions. They strongly favored giving concrete, practical assistance to homicide survivors, further evidence of a preference for offering nonpathologizing help. Nevertheless, the counselors noted that survivors who seek help typically required a relatively lengthy period (6 to 18 months) of regular support, more in line with a long-term treatment model.

I believe these apparent contradictions can be resolved by noting that interventions with trauma victims of any kind need to be focused and practical from the get-go (Miller, 1998h). Individuals in dire stress require effective help *right now* and that help needs to continue as long as it's needed. But that does not preclude learning more and more about your patient over successive sessions and building up a diagnostic and psychosocial profile that enables you to fine-tune the therapy as time goes on, which can only serve to enhance its effectiveness. It has been my experience in supervising other clinicians that all effective therapists, even those who explicitly claim to pooh-pooh diagnostic labels, nevertheless instinctively use some form of implicit classificatory system to tailor their treatment to the specific needs of their patient. No effective therapist I've ever worked with has employed a blanket, one-size-fits-all therapeutic approach to his or her patients; rather, he or she typically employs an intuitive understanding of human dynamics and human differences to guide his or her interventions.

POSTTRAUMATIC THERAPY OF HOMICIDALLY BEREAVED INNER-CITY YOUTH

Recall from chapter 1 that, in some neighborhoods, rates of crime victimization and homicidal bereavement are disproportionately high. Temple (1997) has described a treatment approach that he has found successful in working with inner-city youth whose siblings have been victims of homicide. He notes that, in addition to the usual traumatic bereavement issues, siblings of murder victims often struggle with urges and social pressures toward retaliation, thereby putting themselves and others at increased risk for counter-retaliation and violent death. Older siblings may be plagued with guilt for not looking out for the younger brother or sister, and this may further fuel the impulse toward self-justifying revenge.

The treatment goals of Temple's (1997) program, called *contextual therapy,* include the following:

- Rapid restoration of family functioning following the homicide
- Prevention of retaliatory violence by family members of the deceased
- Encouraging the family members to develop future plans based on honoring the memory of the murdered family member

These goals are achieved by quickly and effectively connecting the involved families to as wide a range of practical and supportive services as possible and by encouraging them to support one another. In addition, psychotherapy with siblings focuses on deriving some meaning or lesson from the deceased's life and death, and on honoring the deceased's memory by both symbolic artifacts (e.g., a scrapbook or photo album) and behaviors (e.g., establishing a productive direction in life, becoming active in antiviolence programs).

In addition, the contextual therapy program concretizes the therapeutic gains by awarding therapeutic "Certificates of Healing" to siblings who have shown courage and dedication in confronting their feelings and developing ways to positively honor the memories of their murdered family member.

SELF-HELP, SUPPORT GROUPS, AND VICTIM ADVOCACY

As we've seen throughout this chapter, sometimes the best help is helping the patient to help him- or herself. As with trauma patients generally, the best immediate intervention with homicide survivors is usually the most practical and self-empowering. Much aid to crime victims and survivors is not what would ordinarily be considered therapeutic from a strictly clinical point of view; rather, it involves directing patients to appropriate self-help groups and support organizations (Brown, 1993). If patients can't find a good local group, have them contact the various local, state, and national victims' rights organizations that pertain to their specific needs. If they are unsure of which group to choose, they can contact one of the two national umbrella victims' rights groups: the National Organization for Victim Assistance (NOVA) and the National Center for Victims of Crime. Often the therapist may have to assist the patient in accessing this help—you may even have to (with permission) make the call yourself on the patient's behalf.

Workers in the victim services field offer certain general advice for survivors of a murdered family member (Brown, 1993). Ordinarily, it takes about 18 to 24 months just to stabilize after the death of a family member, and the worst part may be a delayed reaction that occurs several months after the murder, when the psychic Novocain has worn off. Paradoxically, this is just the time when others may be expecting the patient to be "getting over it."

When people ask your traumatically bereaved patient how she's doing, encourage her to answer honestly, albeit diplomatically, and not to always just say "fine." Within certain limits, such as casual greetings, patients needn't be afraid to let others—especially close friends and family members—know how they really feel. The line between forthright self-disclosure and immoderate spewing is often a delicate and shifting one, however, and therapists may have to assist patients in role-playing appropriate responses to questions by others. Also, patients need to know when they can self-protectively decline to elaborate on their emotional states in response to questions that may have less benign motivations behind them, that is, from trauma junkies or people who are otherwise getting off on the patient's ordeal.

FRIEND: I haven't seen you in over a year, Francine. I heard about Patrick; I'm so sorry. How are you doing—really?

SURVIVOR: Some days are better than others, but we're all helping each other out.

FRIEND: You know, you can always talk to me if you want to.

SURVIVOR: I appreciate that, Vivian, but this has been a rough year and I think we're all talked out for now. But thanks for your concern and I'll keep it in mind for the future.

However, where the survivor is up to it, talking with a true friend or with others who have been there and survived can often be as helpful as formal psychotherapy. Survivors should be advised to let their emotions emerge at their own pace. They should be reassured that it's okay to feel a little sorry for themselves, as long as this doesn't interfere with adaptive coping efforts. They should try not to let themselves be thrown by other people telling them "how well you're handling it" (Brown, 1993) when they really feel like they're about to shatter into a million pieces. And family members should always know that you, their trusted counselor, will be there to guide them competently, responsibly, and healthfully.

CONCLUSIONS

Whether working with individuals or families, the essential psychological principles of crime victim intervention will enable the therapist to handle a wide variety of patients and problems. However, some clinicians may be faced with caseloads that include a high number of specific types of victimization scenarios, and in these cases, more specific, detailed, and at the same time, broader knowledge and skills will be needed.

PART III

Special Victims

Applications of Crime Victim Counseling and Therapy to Populations at Risk

CHAPTER 10

Rape and Sexual Assault

*In the criminal justice system, sexually based offenses are considered espe-
cially heinous . . .*

Thus intones the introductory voice-over of TV's *Law and Order: Special Victims Unit*. But why are these crimes more heinous than others and why are
their victims special?

SEXUAL ASSAULT: A SPECIAL KIND OF TRAUMA?

Sexual assault may be special for several reasons. First, although it can theo-
retically happen to either sex, women are disproportionately represented
among its victims. So one-half of the human population is naturally going to
be more concerned with the danger of this kind of crime happening in their
daily lives than the other half.

Second, unlike almost any other kind of violence, sexual assault corrupts
what in other contexts can be the most intimate and tender of human encounters. The same act—the exact same act—can be a gift of love or a weapon of
plunder, depending on the circumstances and the relationship between the
parties. No other physical encounter between human beings carries such a
contrapuntal potential for good or evil.

Finally, it's sex. And human beings are just naturally intrigued and titil-
lated by this singular human function that plays such a powerful role in all
human societies, whether flaunted, suppressed, or some uneasy combination
of the two.

PSYCHOLOGICAL EFFECTS OF SEXUAL ASSAULT

By some estimates, sexual assault affects one-fourth of women and up to 7% of men and is associated with significantly increased risk of anxiety, depression, substance abuse, and PTSD (Elliott, Mok, & Briere, 2004; Resick, 1993). Individual differences (see chapters 3 and 4) account for the severity of PTSD symptoms after sexual assault. In particular, the PTSD symptoms of women who perceive negative events as uncontrollable are likely to be more severe than those of the women who perceive that they have some ability to predict and control what happens to them (Kushner et al., 1993).

In addition to the general effects of crime victim trauma discussed in chapters 2, 3, and 4, Macy (2007) cites Riger, Raja, and Camacho's (2002) characterization of the relationship between sexual violence and health as the *radiating impact of violent victimization*. In this conceptualization, violence influences women's physical and mental health, as well as echoes out to affect careers, friendships, families, and whole communities. Despite this impact, a surprisingly small number of sexual assault victims seek mental health services for problems related to their assault (George, Winfield, & Blazer, 1992; Golding, Siegel, Sorenson, Burnam, & Stein, 1989; Ullman, 2007).

Neuropsychological Effects

Sexual assault may have effects on the brain. Jenkins, Langlais, Delis, and Cohen (2000) examined neuropsychological functioning among rape survivors. They found that, carefully controlling for comorbid psychological disorders and substance abuse, performance of rape survivors with PTSD was significantly worse than that of other groups on measures of sustained and divided attention. Although the attentional dysfunction reported in this study was mild, the affected women reported that it significantly impaired their handling of day-to-day tasks.

The authors posit that PTSD victims sleep poorly, are easily startled by extraneous stimuli, and spend considerable energy trying to avoid intrusive thoughts. Each of these factors could impair performance on tests of sustained attention. Alternatively, dissociation is a common feature in PTSD victims, and this would also be expected to significantly interfere with one's ability to concentrate and sustain attention.

A third possibility is that impaired attention in PTSD may also be the result of brain dysfunction. As discussed in chapter 2, possible substrata include alterations in noradrenergic function (Bremmer et al., 1995) and damage to limbic structures produced by stress-induced elevations in glucocorticoid levels (Sapolsky, Krey, & McEwen, 1984). It is also possible that some rape victims may have sustained a traumatic brain injury during a violent sexual assault (Miller, 1993e), although presumably this factor was controlled for in this study.

PSYCHOLOGICAL TREATMENT OF SEXUAL ASSAULT VICTIMS

Although there are literally hundreds of different intervention programs for treating sexual assault victims, for this chapter I've selected a few that best consolidate and illustrate the main concepts and approaches I use in my clinical practice. One prototypical program derives from the work of Muran and DiGiuseppe (2000). Other elements will already be generally familiar from previous chapters on general therapeutic strategies for crime victims; here, we apply these concepts and strategies to the specific concerns of treating sexual assault victims.

Establishing and Maintaining the Therapeutic Alliance

As we've seen, the therapeutic alliance is the backbone of any successful treatment effort and may be especially vital in cases of sexual assault where it becomes necessary to discuss matters of great personal intimacy. Even more so than with other trauma victims, the beginning stages of therapy may be the most dicey with rape victims and may carry the greatest risk of premature termination because of the sheer discomfort of talking about these subjects. This is even more critical if the victim is female and therapist male. Rape victims' trust of others and even their own selves has been shaken by their experience, and the therapist should convey a sense of validation and acceptance by words, voice tone, body language, and general attitude. Certain female victims will prefer a same-sex therapist because they just do not feel comfortable talking about these things with a male. Other victims may actually prefer a male therapist because it eliminates the perceived competition factor that often occurs between women and also allows the formation of a trusting, nonexploitive relationship with a male clinician as an antidote to the victim's poisonous experience with the rapist.

Setting Therapeutic Goals

As with crime victims generally, the sexual assault victim's experience should be validated and her reactions normalized. Reaching agreement of the goals of therapy may not be easy with the rape victim, especially in the early stages when she may believe that only continued and complete avoidance of the topic is an acceptable outcome: "I just want to forget it." As noted in chapter 6, in the early stages, this reactive avoidance should be respected, and the therapeutic process should concentrate on achieving an atmosphere of safety, which can later provide the context for coaxing out further constructive recollection and reintegration.

Telling the Story: Resistances and Resolutions

Once agreement on the goals is reached, the therapist and patient can work toward devising the activities that will make those goals achievable. In one way or another, this almost always involves talking about the traumatic sexual assault, which, for many patients, generates tremendous anxiety, as if putting it into words makes it real again. Muran and DiGiuseppe (2000) have found that *discomfort anxiety* and *shame* are two possible anxiety reactions that may inhibit the process of therapy at this point. That is, merely recounting the events of the rape often brings the sensory images and feelings flooding back, which can be retraumatizing if not handled correctly. Also, many victims have come to assume that they must have done something wrong to bring the assault upon themselves.

Many sexual assault victims have been discouraged by friends and family from recalling and relating their traumatizing experience. In some cases, this represents the efforts by otherwise well-meaning people to spare the victim the presumed pain of reliving the experience. In other cases, it represents the listeners' own discomfort at hearing about an assault on safety that implies that the listener could be vulnerable, too; that is, the identification factor prompts a shush response: "Come on, don't torment yourself, try to put it out of your mind." In many cases, the listener's response is a combination of these motives.

In other instances, the opposite occurs: Not-so-well-meaning listeners want to get off on the lurid details of the rape and may encourage the victim to spill every gruesome detail, in the guise of supporting the victim by helping her to get it all out, as in, "I'm your friend, you can tell me anything." At some point, the victim picks up on this salaciously voyeuristic attitude and is now stuck as to what to do. She may not want to alienate the listener by expressing her hurt and outrage directly, so she tries to find a gracious way of discontinuing the narrative. If she does confront the issue directly, the other person is likely to act shocked—*shocked!*—that the victim would impute such base motives when "I was only trying to help." Either way, the relationship will be strained, and the victim will be all the more reluctant to tell her story again to anyone.

Sometimes there may be a less creepy motive for a listener wanting to hear the whole story from the victim. Remember the identification factor. Many listeners, especially if they are women of the same age and demographic group as the victim, want to go over every detail to assure themselves that nothing like this could ever happen to *them*. Perhaps the victim walked down the wrong street or got into the wrong cab. Maybe she shouldn't have had that last drink and then would have seen through the façade of the guy in the club who seemed so nice when they were just talking at the bar. What if she didn't fight back hard enough or run when she had the chance? Although this self-protective motive is probably more benign than that of the sleazy voyeur, the victim still senses that the reason the listener is paying so much attention is for the listener's sake, not hers.

Finally, husbands or boyfriends of the victim may give her the third degree to assure themselves that she didn't "ask for it" or even that she didn't willingly place herself at the wrong place at the wrong time: "Well, there were plenty of places you could have gone with your friends for girls night out. Why'd you pick Dirty Jack's? You know that place is a hangout for lowlifes." This is sometimes followed by the statement, or with the implication hanging in the air, "So, you were looking for a little side action and it got out of hand?" Indeed, a number of sexual assault victims have reported that the hardest time they've gotten is precisely from these suspicious partners who should be their closest supports. No wonder that, by the time the victim gets to your counseling office, she may have tremendous difficulty relating the story that has so far been used against her.

A number of recommendations have been offered for overcoming resistance to telling the story (DiGiuseppe, 1991; Muran & DiGiuseppe, 2000). All rely on the basic features of universalization, validation, and destigmatization of the victim's reaction; that is, the therapist tells the victim that most survivors of sexual assault have these difficulties telling the story, that there is a good reason for this response based on the psychophysiology of the trauma response (chapter 2), and that the victim is not crazy, weak, or weird for having this reaction.

In a more therapist-active approach, the clinician deals with patient resistance by adopting a kind of Socratic dialogue-like approach, which DiGiuseppe (1991) calls the *hypothesis drive assessment*. Here, the therapist makes general statements about how traumatized sexual assault victims feel about their experiences, including, by implication, the patient:

"You know, many women who have gone through a sexual assault find it too upsetting to talk about. I wonder if that's something you've experienced."

The therapist waits for the patient to respond, and if she agrees, the therapist continues:

"Some women feel ashamed about what happened. They think that other people will somehow look down on them or even partially blame them for the assault. Sometimes, they've even heard this, directly or indirectly, from other people. In other cases, the rape is just too hard to talk about. Living through it was hard enough without having to rehash it. Almost all these women have had to tell their story at least once, if not many times, to a law enforcement officer or a doctor, and some of these people may not have been the most sensitive. So telling it again already has a bad association. Do any of these reactions sound like you? Which ones? Anything I left out?"

The primary benefit of this multiple-choice format is that it allows the victim to impart to the therapist a certain amount of information with a minimal response requirement. It also illustrates to her that others have gone through this and that she is not alone. Some clinicians are concerned about leading the patient, but as long as you allow her to choose her own alternative, it is still her story. Besides, she is encouraged to add as much of her own voice as she is comfortable doing.

As the patient is relating her experiences, the therapist should assess for posttraumatic symptoms (flashbacks, nightmares, hyperarousal, numbing) and the degree to which she has difficulty or avoids recalling and retelling parts of the traumatic event. After the patient has recounted the trauma experience and has begun to feel comfortable in the therapeutic setting, the therapist can begin to gather information about immediate presenting problems; daily functioning; clinical and psychosocial history, including any previous traumatic experiences; general premorbid adjustment; interpersonal relationships; and available social support. Data collection also includes assessing suicidal risk, as up to one in five women who are raped attempt suicide (Kilpatrick, Saunders, Veronen, Best, & Von, 1987).

For some patients who have particular difficulty recounting the traumatic sexual assault, it may be more effective to put the cart before the horse and focus initially on more innocuous background aspects of history taking, allowing the patient to get into a flow and rhythm of providing information and then gently moving over into an inquiry about the rape itself.

PSYCHOTHERAPEUTIC STRATEGIES
FOR REGAINING CONTROL

One of the reasons patients often cite for not being able to talk about the sexual assault is that "it just makes me too nervous—I just start sweating and shaking and then I just want to crawl into a hole and go to sleep." Psychological discomfort triggers psychophysiological hyperarousal, which further upsets the patient, creating yet another vicious cycle. Other patients' nervous systems may go on red alert as a conditioned response to any person, place, or thing that reminds them of the rape, severely limiting their life activities. For these patients, it will be crucial to help them get a handle on both their body's and mind's reaction—and overreaction—to trauma triggers.

Many of the cognitive–behavioral techniques for managing physiological symptoms described in chapter 6 can be adapted easily to the treatment of rape and sexual assault victims. Muran and DiGiuseppe (2000) have outlined a particular set of strategies that they have used successfully with this group and that I present here, along with my own comments and suggestions.

Stress Inoculation Training

Stress inoculation training (SIT) was originally developed in the early 1970s as a cognitive–behavioral modality to provide stressed and traumatized patients with a sense of control and help them overcome fear and anxiety by teaching them practical coping strategies they can apply in stressful situations (Meichenbaum, 1985). It has been adapted and expanded for the needs of sexual assault victims by Kilpatrick, Veronen, and Resnick (1982), Calhoun and Atkeson (1991), and Muran and DiGiuseppe (2000).

SIT is presented in two phases. The first phase is educational, in which the behavioral and psychophysiological rationale of the program in the effective treatment of rape-related symptoms and stress reactions is presented to the patient. Disturbing responses to sexual assault are explained as occurring in three dimensions: physical (symptoms), behavioral (impaired activities), and cognitive (distortions in thinking). The interrelationship among these dimensions is discussed, using specific examples from the patient's experience.

The second phase of SIT is the actual training in a variety of coping skills, which include the following:

> *Controlled breathing.* Deep diaphragmatic breathing is taught and practiced at a rate of approximately 4 seconds each for inhaling and exhaling, but therapists should be flexible and take their cue from the patient. The initial instruction is to place one hand on the chest and the other hand on the abdomen, then expand the stomach like a balloon, with as little movement as possible from the hand on the chest. The procedure should be demonstrated and practiced to attain a smooth and fluid breathing style. As noted in chapter 6, this may be facilitated between sessions by a commercially prepared or custom-designed tape or CD.

Muscle relaxation. Muran and DiGiuseppe (2000) prefer Bernstein and Borkovec's (1973) adaptation of Jacobson's (1938) original progressive relaxation technique, taught through simultaneous instruction and demonstration, but any valid version of this technique (chapter 6) is useful. Typically, a muscle group is tensed for 5 to 10 seconds, attending to the sensation of the tension. Then the muscle is relaxed, and attention is focused on differentiating between the sensation of tensing and that of relaxing. The procedure is practiced in the therapy sessions and may be taped for daily home practice.

Covert modeling. Here, the patient is instructed to imagine an anxiety-producing situation, in this case, the sexual assault, and imagine herself confronting it successfully, using the coping strategies she has learned to manage her fear and anxiety reactions. Readers will recognize this as a form of the imagery exercises, such as VMBR, described in chapter 6.

Role playing. The therapist models a desired coping skill, adaptive behavior, or communication style; then the roles are switched and the patient practices the skill. For example, the patient may need to communicate her sexual discomfort or fears with her partner. Also, *assertiveness training* lends itself very well to this approach.

Cognitive restructuring. Recall from chapter 6 that the rationale of cognitive restructuring is to counteract irrational catastrophizing beliefs and replace them with more rational, realistic, and adaptive beliefs and attitudes. However, Muran and DiGiuseppe (2000) point out that, when dealing with the aftermath of the most extreme types of trauma, what constitutes an irrationally catastrophizing mindset, as opposed to one that is adaptively vigilant (remember Peter Rabbit from chapter 2), often boils down to a clinical judgment, and in some cases, a value judgment. Telling a traumatized rape victim that her ruminative thought of, "This was a terrible thing that happened to me—what if I get raped again?" is irrational will likely be perceived as insensitive and invalidating and will strain therapeutic credibility, as the patient thinks (or, more rarely, tells the therapist directly): "Easy for you to say, sitting there in your nice, safe, comfortable chair. You're not the one who was choking on your own pantyhose while some monster was poking your genitals with a knife." Better to validate the horror of the experience itself and focus the cognitive restructuring strategies on more appropriate dysfunctional beliefs, such as self-blame or the belief that the patient has become "damaged goods."

Even here, caution is advised. Recall from chapter 7 that seemingly maladaptive self-blame may be the patient's only antidote to the far more disturbing belief that fate is random, her actions are meaningless, the world is unpredictably dangerous, and she is helpless and powerless to prevent something like this from happening again. If something I did caused or contributed to the rape last time, this reasoning goes, then if I do something *different* next time, maybe I won't ever get raped again. This is, paradoxically, self-protection by self-blaming, and therapists must be careful that, if they strive to strip this tattered emotional field dressing from the festering emotional wound, they'd better have a clean, fresh, soothing psychic poultice to take its place.

Still, blame—*causality,* really—need not be entirely eliminated but can be productively redirected by taking thoughts that attribute the traumatic event to fixed, immutable qualities of character ("I'm a stupid slut for going to that bar") and restructuring them in terms of potentially changeable behaviors ("I should never have gotten in a car with someone I just met in a bar"). This strategy retains credibility by refusing to sugar-coat what the patient did that may have set her up for the assault, but at the same time this strategy realistically offers a behavioral and existential escape clause by empowering her to do something different, should the situation ever arise again (Janoff-Bulman, 1979; Meyer & Taylor, 1986). It also makes therapeutic change more palatable because it doesn't insist that the patient alter her entire lifestyle. For example, she may have no intention of discontinuing her visits to singles' bars because that may be her only practicable venue for socializing, but at least she can learn how to protect herself from the same kind of bad experience happening again, without totally turning her life inside out and becoming a recluse.

> *Thought stopping.* As noted in chapter 6, the purpose of thought stopping is to end obsessively looping maladaptive self-statements. The patient is instructed to catch herself thinking about a feared subject or disturbing rumination and report it to the therapist. In session, the therapist interrupts this thought by yelling "Stop!" and clapping simultaneously (or smacking the desk, snapping fingers—use your ingenuity). Then, the patient is instructed to practice this, first aloud and then subvocally, aided by a sharp, covert self-stimulus, like a skin pinch, rubber band snap, fingernail jab, or noninjurious tongue bite (again, be creative). Some examples of typical maladaptive self-statements following a sexual assault cited by Muran and DiGiuseppe (2000) as targets for thought stopping are as follows, along with my own comments and caveats:

> > *"I'm damaged goods now. No one will want me."* Ascertain if this has a basis in reality. For example, although it may not be true that "no one" will want her, this won't be very reassuring if the rape victim is reeling from the rejection by the boyfriend or husband who has been the primary partner in her life.

"I deserved this because it was my fault." As noted above, try to reconceptualize *fault* as *causation* that can be altered.

"I'm scarred for life; I'll never be the same again." As discussed in chapters 2 and 7, a severe trauma will most probably change the victim in some way, and trying to deny this may be unrealistic and countertherapeutic. But there is a difference between a small, barely perceptible scar—physical or psychological—that is noticeable once in a while, and a huge gash that assaults the victim's senses every time she looks at—or thinks about—herself. Set realistic goals and work toward them.

"This has to be a secret. Nobody can ever know that I was raped." Typically, this means that the victim wants to keep this a secret from certain people—usually romantic partners, relatives, or friends—because she fears rupture of these relationships or just doesn't want to be endlessly interrogated. Whenever possible, this should be respected. In fact, some overly voluble victims may need special guidance in how to pick appropriate people to share their experience with and who to keep out of the loop because it's none of their beeswax.

"If I was aroused during the assault, I must be a slut or a sicko." In many cases, simple education about the facts of sexual physiology may disabuse the victim of this belief. But sometimes, a sexual encounter that began pleasantly enough turns sour in the course of the act itself. Or the patient may have had a few nice dates with the same man in the past and had gotten used to being pleasantly aroused. This time, however, it was a forced situation, but the old feelings came back automatically as a form of Pavlovian conditioning. Explain this to the victim in terminology she can relate to.

"I shouldn't cry this much. I should be getting over this by now. Most normal people wouldn't react this way." As this book has hopefully made clear, most people will show a wide range of reactions to trauma, in both intensity and type, based on the nature of the event and the patient's baseline personality. Unless clearly dangerous or pathological, patients' reactions should be tolerated and validated, and practical strategies should be offered for dealing with extreme reactions.

"I'll never trust anyone again." In well-meaning attempts to give the patient hope, many clinicians try to pooh-pooh this notion as quickly as possible: "Of course, you'll trust again; just give it a little time." But sometimes taking such an interpersonally nihilistic stance serves a self-protective function for the patient, especially early in the recovery process. By eschewing all future trusting relationships, she at least

tells herself that she'll never put herself in a position to be duped and betrayed again. Later in the treatment process, when some degree of confidence in herself has been restored, this issue can be revisited. Also, problems with trust may have predated the sexual assault for some patients and have been exacerbated, but not caused, by the recent assault.

Bear in mind that the purpose of thought stopping is not to permanently eliminate or change the dysfunctional thoughts: That may occur later through cognitive restructuring, by utilizing other cognitive–behavioral techniques, or in the course of more extensive psychotherapy. The primary purpose of thought stopping is just to help the patient get herself unstuck from unproductive rumination. In fact, the thought doesn't even have to be dysfunctional, per se; it can be an otherwise rational, adaptive thought ("Here's what I need to do to be safe"). But, like an ostensibly valuable download that takes up so much disk space that it freezes your computer screen, an otherwise positive cognition may prove ruminatively maladaptive by monopolizing the patient's brain space, freezing out other productive thoughts, feelings, or activities.

Guided self-dialogue. This technique, similar to the self-talk technique described in chapter 6, involves assessing maladaptive cognitions, such as the examples listed above, and substituting them with more adaptive ones. In addition, the technique can also be used to help the patient guide herself through an actual behavior in the real world (see TRIST in chapter 6). In Muran and DiGiuseppe's (2000) system, adaptive self-statements are taught in the face of a distressing situation in the following four phases:

1. *Preparation.* Identify the problem and appraise the negative outcome: "I can't go back onto the college campus because that's where I was attacked."
2. *Confrontation.* Break down the goal into manageable steps: "I'll go there during the day when there are lots of people around. I'll make sure to look before I get out of my car or enter a classroom. I'll take it one class at a time. I'll have an exit plan in case I start to feel unsafe."
3. *Management.* Conceptualize anxiety as manageable and temporary: "I'll use the skills my therapist taught me to keep my fears and anxieties under control so I can concentrate on the course material. I'll also have a graceful exit plan in case I need to bail, but I'll try to accomplish a little more each day."
4. *Reinforcement.* Make positive self-statements after taking action: "Okay, here you go, Chrissy. I'm getting out of my car. There's the

Science Building. I'm making sure my car door's locked. Okay, it's a little walk to the entrance. Everybody's walking around, there's lots of people. I'm going into the building—keep going, Chrissy, you're doing great. Okay, now the elevator to the second floor and find my Chem class . . ."

Exposure Therapy and Desensitization

Many clinicians have advocated various forms of imaginal and in vivo (real-life) exposure therapies for treating posttraumatic symptoms of many types, from military trauma, to transportation accidents, to crime victimization (Falsetti & Resnick, 1995). As discussed in chapter 6, the primary rationale of exposure therapy is to confront the feared stimuli in imagination so that fear and anxiety decrease. This is similar to watching a scary movie over and over: At first it may be quite frightening, but by the tenth or twentieth viewing it is, if anything, innocuously boring. Analogously, a repetitively replayed frightening memory becomes less intimidating as it is recounted numerous times in an objectively safe environment. As I noted previously, the main caution is that these therapies be truly *de*sensitizing, not retraumatizing; there's a difference between watching a horror film and living through it. This exposure therapy methodology has been extensively researched and explicitly applied to the treatment of sexual assault victims by Foa, Rothbaum, Riggs, and Murdock (1991).

In this treatment model, in vivo exposure to fear cues is used to extinguish the fear associated with stimuli that have been paired with the traumatic event. For example, for a woman who was raped in a parking garage, in vivo exposure might entail sitting in a parking garage with her therapist. She would monitor her anxiety, which should gradually decrease as she is able to learn that it was not the parking garage itself that was dangerous, but much more specifically and restrictedly, her assailant that posed the threat.

Obviously, the use of therapist-guided in vivo exposure will be limited by the practicalities of clinical practice (you can't sit in a car, take a plane trip, dance at a club, or go to work with every patient). What I have found more practical is to cotrain a family member or other significant other to serve as a kind of "desensitization coach." The greater overall availability of this person, plus his or her familiar and trusted status, usually makes him or her more suitable to guide the in vivo practice. Potential downsides include the possibility of personal issues clouding the exercises, so therapists should try to assess and train these helpers as well as possible. In virtually every case, the in vivo practice should be preceded by desensitization through imaginal exposure, enlisting whatever cognitive–behavioral strategies from this chapter and chapter 6 that will aid the process.

Because of its potential for retraumatization, exposure therapy should not be undertaken lightly. Despite its purported success in a number of treatment settings, possible adverse complications have included precipitation of panic disorder, exacerbation of depression, relapse of alcohol abuse, and hypersensitization and retraumatization (Pitman et al., 1991). Even more hazardous is the use of flooding in the absence of supportive cognitive–behavioral modalities because it does not address faulty cognitions, teach physiological self-regulation, or enhance the development of coping skills.

Programmatic Desensitization for Sexual Assault Trauma

Foa, Hearst-Ikeda, and Perry (1995) developed what they call a *clinical intervention brief prevention program* for treating complicated PTSD reactions in victims of sexual assault. The program is not characterized as therapy per se, but is described to assault victims as a psychoeducational course that aims at facilitating their recovery by teaching stress-management skills that they may use as needed.

This program consists of techniques that Foa et al. (1991) have found effective for alleviating chronic PTSD in assault victims and that, by now, should be familiar to readers of this book:

- Education about common reactions to assault
- Breathing and relaxation training
- Reliving the assault by imaginal exposure
- Confronting once-feared, but now-safe situations (in vivo exposure)
- Cognitive restructuring

The program takes place over four meetings:

Meeting 1 is devoted to information-gathering, education, and orientation to the program. The therapist evaluates the victim's posttraumatic symptoms, presents an overview of the program, and describes the agenda of the meeting. The normal reactions to assault are discussed to educate the victim about posttraumatic reactions and to normalize them. During this discussion, the therapist notes any trauma-related cognitive distortions or irrational beliefs in the patient's view of the world or about herself. Next, the therapist and the victim construct a list of situations and people that are objectively safe but that she has been avoiding since the assault.

Meeting 2 begins with a discussion of the past week's problems. In the first part of this meeting, the information collected in the introductory meeting about avoided situations and people is rank-ordered according to the degree of anxiety each scene evokes. Next, a rationale for imaginal exposure to memories of the assault, that is, reliving the trauma, is presented in terms of putting so-called unfinished business into proper perspective by repeatedly "beating the memory to death" until it loses its power to frighten and hurt. The patient is helped to construct a hierarchical list of feared situations. Instruction is then provided in deep breathing and muscle relaxation, and the relaxation procedure is audiotaped, so the patient can listen to the tape and practice relaxation at home. Next, the victim is instructed to close her eyes and relive the assault "as if it were happening now," and this narrative is also audiotaped. Every 10 minutes, a reading is taken of the patient's fear level regarding the relived assault memory. During the reliving exercise, the therapist makes note of cognitive distortions that the victim expresses about the dangerousness of the world and her perceived helplessness. After the reliving exercise, there is a discussion of these distorted, exaggerated, or irrational beliefs. Readers may note the similarity of this approach to Solomon's (1988, 1991) frame-by-frame reprocessing, discussed in chapter 7.

At the end of the session, the therapist suggests that the patient use the audiotape to relive the traumatic experience several times during the ensuing week and to confront a few of the situations each day from the list that has been created at the beginning of the session.

Meeting 3 begins with a review and discussion of the previous week's homework. Next follow 45 minutes of imaginal exposure to memories of the assault. The remainder of the session is devoted to cognitive restructuring, starting with a rationale for the technique and a description of common cognitive distortions, such as global unpredictability and uncontrollability, negative self-views, fears and expectations for the future, and beliefs about the world and its inhabitants.

The therapist helps the patient identify distorted cognitive assumptions about the dangerousness of the world and her own coping abilities. Homework assignments focus on daily, audiotape-assisted repetition of imaginal exposure and on continuing to confront feared situations. The patient is instructed to use a diary to record her negative thoughts, distressing feelings, and cognitive distortions three times daily. Finally, she is reminded to continue the relaxation and breathing skills when she notices herself becoming anxious.

Meeting 4 begins with the homework review. The participants practice imaginal exposure to assault memories, which is followed by cognitive therapy that includes a discussion of the thoughts and feelings that were recorded in the daily diary. The therapist reviews the skills the patient has learned during the program, the progress she has made, and the schedule of follow-up sessions.

Foa et al. (1995) studied the efficacy of this brief intervention program with 10 female victims of recent sexual and nonsexual assault. Two months post assault, victims who had undergone the cognitive–behavioral prevention program had significantly less severe PTSD symptoms than victims in the assessment control condition. Five and a half months post assault, victims in the brief prevention group were significantly less depressed than victims in the control group and had significantly less severe reexperiencing symptoms. The prevention program was also effective in reducing depression.

Foa and colleagues (Foa et al., 1995; Foa & Kozak, 1986; Foa & Riggs, 1993) hypothesize that their behavioral intervention program enables victims to repeatedly relive the traumatic memories, thus activating the trauma structure and its emotional component. By the end of the session, the emotional response to the traumatic memories decreases for most victims, thus signaling habituation and desensitization within a session. Repeated reliving produces a long-term decrease in emotional responding, that is, habituation between sessions. What they don't make explicit, but what is probably a crucial component of the program's success, is that this exposure and reliving occurs in the context of group collegial support, within an atmosphere of safety and trust. These very human emotional-bonding factors may be overlooked in programs that purport to be strictly cognitive–behavioral in nature.

The victim's mistaken view of herself as totally incompetent and helpless is also addressed in this intervention program in two ways. First, the victim realizes that she can confront the traumatic memories and tolerate the resulting emotional activation. This realization helps modify her perception of herself as a weak, inadequate person. Second, she acquires specific effective techniques for coping with anxiety, such as relaxation and cognitive restructuring. The experience of being able to successfully control her anxiety provides evidence that contradicts the victim's self-perception of being inadequate, thus enhancing her perception of self-competence.

An extension of this approach was studied by Echeburua, de Corral, Zubizarreta, and Sarasua (1997). Their study compared self-exposure and cognitive restructuring with progressive relaxation training in the treatment of adult rape victims and adult victims of childhood sexual abuse. In contrast to Foa et al. (1991), Echeburua et al.'s (1997) exposure procedure is applied to intrusive thoughts more than to traumatic memories. The cognitive structuring technique focuses on

- normalizing the stress reaction to the sexual assault,
- modifying guilt and other negative thoughts about the rape, and
- putting the experience in a positive perspective by emphasizing adaptive coping skills and hope for the future.

Results showed that the self-exposure and cognitive restructuring modalities were far superior to progressive relaxation in reducing traumatic stress symptoms in these sexual assault survivors immediately and at 12-month follow-up. In fact, the authors report a startling 100% success rate at 12 months for their cognitive behavioral treatment program.

As with most posttraumatic therapeutic modalities discussed in this book, the key elements of the above programs appear to be the instillation of hope, control, and empowerment by the progressive mastery of practical coping skills and the reconceptualizing of the self as an active, competent agent in directing one's own life—effectively reversing the Peter Rabbit effect described in chapter 2. Drawing from the above examples, therapists can custom-design their own protocols for the particular patients they treat. These modalities can be presented in either individual or group formats.

I have found that some patients are more receptive to a didactic or coaching model that enables them to put some cognitive distance between their emotional reactions and their thoughts and memories of the traumatic event. Other patients need a warmer, more nurturant, therapeutic environment in order to feel comfortable exposing themselves to disturbing thoughts and recollections. This should be actively abetted by encouraging the victim to seek positive social support (Golding et al., 1989; Popiel & Susskind, 1985; Ullman, 2007). For some patients, making gains in the ability to achieve a sense of self-control and competence can pave the way toward the more expansive and integrative therapies discussed in chapter 7. For others, just being able to function day by day in the real world is enough. In each case, know your patient, establish realistic goals, and devise your treatment strategy accordingly.

SEXUAL REVICTIMIZATION

An emerging body of evidence shows that women who experience sexual violence once in their lives are at increased risk for subsequent sexual victimization, that is, *revictimization* (Eby, Campbell, Sullivan, & Davidson, 1995; McFarlane et al., 2005; Resick, 1993). Repeated experiences of violent victimization can have a cumulative impact on women's well-being and their subsequent risk of revictimization, setting up a vicious cycle (Arata, 2002; Casey & Nurius, 2005; Miller, Markman, & Handley, 2007). Sexual revictimization can exacerbate physical and mental health difficulties, including anxiety, depression, PTSD, dissociative disorders, and suicidal risk (Breitenbecher, 2001; Classen, Palesh, & Aggarwal, 2005; Desai, Arias, Thompson, & Basile, 2002; Maker, Kemmelmeier, & Peterson, 2001; Messman & Long, 1996). Yet, in the sexual assault treatment literature, sexual revictimization has not been explicitly and comprehensively addressed until Macy's (2007) recent review of the topic.

Treating Sexual Revictimization

As we've seen in chapter 7, coping strategies are often classified into two areas: (a) *adaptive coping* that emphasizes recovery from a traumatic event, and (b) *proactive coping* that entails preparations to avoid and defend against future threats (Roth & Cohen, 1986). Most often, these two types of coping are seen as distinct entities, without overlap. However, some researchers argue that these two types of coping actually reflect two sides of the same coin.

Macy (2007) presents a program for dealing with sexual revictimization that incorporates both prevention and intervention, adaptive coping and proactive coping, which I describe here along with my own comments and suggestions.

To begin with, counselors and therapists often downplay or avoid addressing their patient's high-risk lifestyle factors for fear of appearing to blame the victim. However, prevention efforts that fail to target these risk factors are neglecting a key element in the woman's safety. For example, sexual revictimization is often associated with alcohol and substance abuse, and these factors must be dealt with in any comprehensive treatment program. Also, certain personality traits and disorders, such as dependent, histrionic, and borderline (chapter 3), appear to set some women up for revictimization and, with these women, more extensive and longer term therapy for issues of personal boundaries, emotional self-regulation, pathological dependency, and impaired self-image (Linehan, 1993; Sperry, 1995, 1999) may be necessary to mitigate the risk of revictimization. These kinds of interventions can incorporate the confidence-building and self-empowering strategies discussed earlier in this chapter and elsewhere in this book.

Macy (2007) recommends encouraging proactive coping efforts that build upon the victim's sense of mastery and meaning that is developed in the initial self-protective and adaptive phases of therapy. This would include practical knowledge and skills to help her avoid future assault threats through, for example, the development of mindfulness, threat perception, and self-reflection skills, as well as how to resist temptations to fall back into maladaptive patterns that set her up for further victimization.

I have found that these types of cases usually require long-term therapy that waxes and wanes in frequency and intensity. That is, patients come in initially for several weeks or months until their lives achieve some degree of stability. Then, long stretches of absence follow, as the patient attempts to get on with the business of living in the real world. These are punctuated by periodic repeat visits, sometimes just for a therapeutic tune-up, but more commonly because of some new or reoccurring crisis in the woman's life.

Also, as noted in several places in this book, therapists who work with crime victims may have to get used to the fact that what we consider dysfunctional or maladaptive behavior from the perspective of our parochial middle-class lifestyles may actually be vital to the physical and psychosocial survival of many of our patients. For example, a young, impoverished single mother's only way of keeping herself and her kids going may be to supplement her low-paying job by dealing pot and cruising the bars and hangouts at night in hopes of meeting a man who's not a total pig and who might offer at least some temporary protection and companionship. Telling such a woman not to drink alcohol, to keep away from drugs, and to stay out of potentially dangerous social situations may elicit no more than a blank stare or wry "what-planet-are-you-on?" smirk. As long as no reportable activity is occurring (such as child abuse or neglect, or imminent harm to self or others), it is our challenge to keep our patients safe while keeping it real.

> "It took me a few sessions to even tell my therapist about the drugs," said Cherette, "because I thought he'd either bust me or at least tell me he couldn't see me anymore. But I figured I had to trust somebody and, besides, seeing him was a condition of my continued employment, okay? So I had to meet with this guy every week. So one day I just figured, what the hell, whatever happens, happens, and I just told him. He looked at me for a second, then asked me some questions about my kids and some other things, and then he told me that, as long as I didn't do nothing around my kids and continued working and basically stayed out of trouble, we'd deal with the rape and my own behavior in picking the wrong men over and over again, because this is what kept putting me in danger. He did tell me that drugs and alcohol were going to set me up to get assaulted again and that I should consider that because, after all, I did have Nelson [her son] to consider and what if something happened to me? So I told him I'd think about it and maybe stay away from Dirty Jack's and try some other, less rough places to meet people."

MARITAL RAPE

Mental health clinicians seem to prize stable relationships, yet *stable* doesn't always mean safe and healthy, because even a long-term, stable relationship does not guarantee freedom from sexual exploitation or abuse. As recently as 1970, in all 50 states, a husband could legally have sex with his wife against her will and not be charged with rape. By 1994, all states had criminalized marital rape, although the exact terms and definitions differ from state to state. According to some estimates, rates of marital rape continue to be relatively high, ranging from 10% to 14% of all married women. However, such statistics should be interpreted with caution since many victims of what would legally constitute marital rape may not always identify themselves as victims. Although the phenomenon of marital rape has been known for some time, it has not been discussed as a clinical treatment issue until Martin's (2007) recent review.

Marital Rape: Descriptive and Clinical Features

Martin (2007) describes *threatened or forced sex* as occurring when the woman is physically coerced into having sex against her will. She cites Finkelhor and Yllo's (1985) study of 326 women living in the Boston area. The study classified forced sex in marriage into four categories:

Battering rape was the most common form of marital rape in the sample. In these cases, marital rape was not necessarily sexually motivated per se but was an extension of general violence in the relationship (see chapter 11).

Force-only rape was the second most common form of marital rape. These marriages were characterized by continuous disagreements over sexual preferences and activities but otherwise contained a minimal degree of violence. Perpetrators of this form of marital rape only employed enough physical force to achieve their desired sexual act.

Obsessive rape, the least common form of marital rape in this sample, was characterized by unusual sexual activities such as bondage and the use of pornography.

Non-physical sexual coercion occurs when a husband uses his resources or power in the relationship to force his wife to comply with his sexual demands. This type of interpersonal coercion actually takes place far more often than physical threats or use of force. Here, the woman consents or acquiesces to unwanted sex largely out of her fear of the repercussions—emotional, financial, or otherwise—of resisting.

Risk Factors for Marital Rape

Although a variety of characteristics of both men and women have been hypothesized as risk factors for marital rape, very few have been rigorously studied and the field is rife with conflicting findings. For example, many of the risk factors for male violence in general apply to propensity to commit marital rape, such as personal and family history of violence, unemployment, hypermasculine orientation, alcohol and drug use, and the presence of sexually coercive fantasies. Risk factors for being victims of marital rape include being younger, having experienced rape previously outside marriage, and being currently divorced or separated from one's husband (Delosi & Margolin, 2004; Martin, 2007).

What the literature seems to be more consistent about is that individual characteristics of the marital partners are less reliable predictors of marital rape than the overall quality of the marriage as a whole (Martin, 2007)—although it might be hard to separate the quality of any relationship from the characteristics of the members of that relationship. Marital characteristics associated with an increased risk for marital rape include nonsexual marital aggression, low marital quality, status disparities between the partners, as well as continuous disagreements over finances, alcohol or drug use, and sex. These factors seem to have an additive effect so that the more of these factors exist in the marriage, the more likely the risk for marital rape.

Resistance to Marital Rape

Not all marital rape victims choose to resist, many finding it more expedient to go along with the unwanted sex, perhaps convincing themselves that nonconsensual sex within a marriage is not really rape, or that it constitutes "wifely duty," or that "he's a good guy in other ways," which may even be true. Other women may fear alienating the affection or good will of their partners or simply fear losing their financial support. Still others acquiesce because they are simply too physically weak to resist and don't want to be injured. When it occurs, resistance is more likely to be verbal than physical, such as distracting the perpetrator or trying to talk him out of it. Even physical resistance can involve nonforceful measures such as avoiding the perpetrator, running away when he makes an advance, or covering and shielding oneself from the advance. More forceful forms of resistance include hitting, kicking, or pushing the perpetrator away (Martin, 2007).

Effects of Marital Rape

Research has shown that victims of marital rape suffer from a variety of psychological disorders, most commonly depression and PTSD symptomatology. Victims are at higher risk for suicide. Marital rape victims also report a high rate of physical health effects, such as physical injuries, gynecological problems, and chronic illnesses (Martin, 2007). Although less common, marital rape victims occasionally kill or seriously injure their partners (see also chapter 11).

Self-Help Efforts of Marital Rape Victims

Sometimes the most effective measures for stopping marital rape are the ones victims undertake themselves. Marshall (1996) interviewed 172 women who had experienced high rates of psychological, physical, and sexual abuse by their partners. Many of these women sought help from their church, their physicians, mental health clinicians, and social service agencies. Bergen (1996) interviewed 40 victims of marital rape and found that the majority sought help from the police or rape crisis centers, although fully 80% of these women were dissatisfied with the police response (see also chapters 5, 11).

McFarlane et al. (2005) investigated intimate partner sexual violence in a sample of 148 women who had experienced domestic violence (chapter 11) and were seeking an order of protection from the court. Contacting the police, applying for protection orders, and confiding in friends or family were related to a reduced risk of reexperiencing intimate partner sexual assault. The most effective measure was seeking a court order of protection. Victims of intimate partner violence in this study also seemed to grow more emboldened with each self-help effort, increasing their help-seeking behaviors after every assault, which implies that the women in this sample were largely satisfied with the responses they got from the legal system.

Psychological Interventions for Marital Rape

In addition to general crime victim posttraumatic treatment modalities cited in chapters 6 and 7, and more specific therapeutic measures for victims of sexual violence described above, a few specialized treatment modalities for marital rape victims have been outlined by Martin (2007).

> *Stress inoculation therapy.* A variety of behavioral medicine modalities, such as heart rate biofeedback, systematic desensitization, stress inoculation, and cognitive–behavioral therapies, have been adapted for the treatment of marital rape by Hanneke and Shields (1985). Resnick, Kilpatrick, Walsh, and Veronen (1991) found stress inoculation therapy (SIT) to be effective in reducing overall psychological distress, intrusions, avoidance, and fears associated with marital rape. SIT facilitates physiological, cognitive, and behavioral coping for fear and is carried out in two phases. Phase one focuses on education and the identification of fears, while phase two teaches patients adaptive strategies for dealing with anxiety. Patients are also taught coping techniques that are targeted for the physiological, cognitive, and behavioral responses. These kinds of techniques will be familiar to readers of this book.
>
> *Cognitive processing therapy.* Cognitive processing therapy (CPT) was originally developed to treat PTSD in rape victims (Resick & Schnicke, 1992) and has been applied to the treatment of victims of marital rape

(Westwell, 1998). CPT consists of 12 phases of treatment and three major components (education, exposure, and cognitive therapy). The goal of CPT is to identify and challenge maladaptive beliefs that victims hold, and addresses relevant issues of safety, trust, power, esteem, and intimacy.

As always, successful psychotherapy with crime victims involves breaking up vicious cycles of helplessness and despair and turning them into positive cycles of confidence and hope, using the vehicle of the therapeutic relationship to propel the assimilation of practical coping skills and self-empowering attitudes and strategies.

CONCLUSIONS

Men who rape typically regard women as mere objects for their gratification. And men who rape their wives may regard "their" women as personal property to be used as they please. This chattel mentality may extend to their perceived right to keep their property in line by any means necessary. In such cases, this may result not just in sexual violence but in violence more generally within the relationship.

CHAPTER 11

Domestic Violence

O. J. Simpson owes me lunch. I'll explain. On January 24, 1995, the trial opened in which O. J. Simpson was accused of murdering his wife, Nicole Brown Simpson, and her friend, Ronald Goldman. As most Americans know, this case became a bellwether for the issue of domestic violence, and one of the local mental health associations in Florida convened a full-day conference, to be held October 3rd of that year, to address the wide range of social, political, and legal issues related to the topic of domestic violence. To this end, the conference committee enlisted a panel of speakers, including attorneys, judges, social service workers, victim advocates, and a psychologist: guess who. My presentation was scheduled to take place right after lunch, at 1:00 p.m., and was to address the psychological factors, in both victims and perpetrators, that contribute to domestic violence. So far, so good.

Fast-forward to October 3, 1995. I decided to arrive early, so I could have lunch with a few of the other speakers and conferees who were colleagues and friends of mine. I arrived at the conference center at about 11:30 a.m., only to discover that all the good parking spots were taken up by local news media vehicles, and I was forced to deposit my car on a grassy knoll some distance away. "Cool," I thought to myself, "It's about time the media took mental health issues seriously." Still, I was a little suspicious of all this attention for a local conference.

I walked inside, stopped off at the registration table to get my speaker's ID badge and ribbon, and walked into the main conference area to search for my lunch companions, just around noon. Almost immediately, a camera was shoved in my face, and a news commentator, who apparently had spied my speaker's badge and rushed over for a sound bite from this local expert, asked me, "What do you think the verdict will be? What impact do you think it will have on women's rights?" Give me credit for one thing: I was able to cough up a reasonably articulate one- or two-liner that seemed to satisfy the newsie before he rushed off to ambush the next presenter. But my erstwhile lunch companions were nowhere to be found. And the general tone of the whole place was something like subdued pandemonium.

Then, one of the conference organizers spotted me and pulled me aside: "Dr. Miller," she said, "there may be a little change in the program; I hope you don't mind." "Uh-oh," I'm thinking, "now what?" She went on to tell me that, earlier that morning, it had been announced that the O. J. verdict would be rendered at precisely—you guessed it—1:00 p.m. today, and would I mind if they played the verdict on TV and then my presentation could comment on the verdict—as long as, of course, I didn't go too much over my time limit.

Okay, I'm thinking, I'm a sport, and, besides, what better way to get a lunch-addled conference crowd to find their seats on time and actually pay attention to what I'm saying. The conference organizer then showed me the podium where I'd be speaking, which was flanked on either side by two huge wide-angle TV screens, poised to dwarf the puny human figure that would soon be squeaking out his commentary. I was told that we'd wait until the verdict was announced on TV, allow some time for the audience to react, and then I'd go on to present my program. And, oh yes, they had some questions for me and other matters to attend to before the news broadcast, so no time for lunch (okay, a quick bagel and coffee, but that doesn't count).

To my last day, I'll remember the exact time the O. J. verdict was announced—1:12 p.m.—because I was zeroed in on my watch, calculating how much presentation time I'd have to shave off with each passing minute. When the not-guilty verdict finally came forth, the reaction of the conference audience—most of whom were mental health, social service, and criminal justice professionals involved daily in dealing with domestic violence cases, and most of whom were women—replicated the reaction of viewers around the country: Some factions gasped in disbelief; others sat stonily and registered no response at all; a few tried to conceal expressions of satisfied vindication. This was the act I had to follow.

I clambered up onto the podium between the now blankly looming TV screens, which seemed to be mutely glaring down on me, as if to chide: "And after this, what could *you* possibly have to say?"—a sentiment which also seemed to be reflected in the intently skeptical stares of my growingly antsy audience. I began my presentation with a standard review of the risk factors for domestic violence in both perpetrator and the victim, and about a quarter of the way through my speech, the hands started shooting up. If I didn't previously believe in the power of displacement and projection, I certainly did so then, because many audience members proceeded to assail me mercilessly for even the mere suggestion that there was anything in a woman's personality or behavior that would justify her being abused by her mate.

Which, of course, was not what I said and I tried to explain as much, but the audience was having none of it. I fielded more questions, made some basic points of my presentation, philosophically accepted my conscripted whipping-boy role as "evil-male-psychologist-stooge-of-the-masculine-industrial-complex-who's-blaming-the-victim again" by absorbing some of the pain and outrage swirling around the room, and basically I felt lucky to get out of there alive and let the next presenter take over—a female judge. I stuck around for about an hour to answer a few stray questions and do one more brief media sound-bite, then hightailed it back to my office for my afternoon appointments. I never did get lunch.

Because it intersects so many areas—psychology, sociology, anthropology, criminal justice, politics, even religion—the topic of domestic violence continues to be a volatile and contentious issue. Furthermore, like the discussion of marital rape in chapter 10, what makes these crimes so vexing is that, on the one hand, they take place in the home, which is the one place most people expect to feel safe, and they are perpetrated by a spouse or other close relation, which toxically commingles intimacy and violence. On the other hand, the very familiarity of the persons involved and the home environs in which these acts take place make the pattern so much harder to break and the danger harder to see coming, until something irrevocably harmful occurs.

DOMESTIC VIOLENCE: CLINICAL AND DEMOGRAPHIC FEATURES

A considerable body of research and clinical experience (Aldarondo & Straus, 1994; Appel & Holden, 1998; Arias & Pape, 1999; Browne & Williams, 1989; Burke, 2007; Campbell, 1992, 1995, 2002; Cascardi, O'Leary, & Schlee, 1999; Cavanaugh & Dobash, 2007; Clements & Ogle, 2007; Coker et al., 2002; Crofford, 2007; Farr, 2002; Follingstad, Wright, Lloyd, & Sebastian, 1991; Gleason, 1993; Golding, 1994, 1999; Kellerman, 1992; Kennair & Mellor, 2007; Lesserman & Drossman, 2007; Logan, Walker, Cole,

& Leukefeld, 2002; Mbilinyi, Edleson, Hagemeister, & Beeman, 2007; Mercy & Saltzman, 1989; Schafer, Caetano, & Clark, 1998; Shackleford, Buss, & Peters, 2000; Sheridan & Nash, 2007; Simmons & Lehman, 2007; Stark & Flitcraft, 1996; Tjaden & Thoennes, 2000; Tolman & Raphael, 2000; Vitanza, Vogel, & Marshall, 1995) has established some basic facts about domestic violence:

- Domestic violence is the leading cause of serious injury to women in the United States.
- Domestic violence adversely affects approximately 1.7 million women at any given moment.
- Every 9 seconds, a woman in the United States is beaten by her husband or boyfriend.
- Over 20% of couples in the United States have experienced one or more episodes of partner violence over the previous year.
- In their lifetime, over 20% of women experience physical violence, over 7% are raped by their intimate partner (chapter 10), and almost 5% are stalked.
- Although some women exclusively batter men, this is the exception; more commonly, it is the male partner who is the batterer or both partners become embroiled and injure each other.
- Partner violence affects gay and lesbian couples at about the same rate as heterosexual couples, i.e. approximately 1 in 4 relationships.
- Many gay and lesbian couples are reluctant to report abuse for fear of further stigmatization or because such reports are not taken as seriously as those of heterosexual couples by law enforcement and the judicial system.
- While cases of child abuse by adults are usually considered separate from domestic violence between adults, some cases of parent abuse by children occur that are difficult to classify.
- The most common mechanism of injury in domestic violence is blunt force trauma to the head, face, or body; the next most common source of injury is strangulation.
- Children are often injured while trying to protect their mothers from being beaten. Conversely, women may be beaten in the course of trying to prevent their children from being attacked. Even pets may be attacked and injured.
- At least 2,000 women are killed each year by a domestic partner; in fact, women are more likely to be killed by a domestic partner than by a stranger or anyone else.
- The risk of lethal violence is increased in cases where the batterer makes frequent threats to kill the victim, uses a weapon against her, chokes her, or commits sexual violence against her.

- The aftermath of domestic violence can affect the victim's physical and mental health long after the battering relationship ends, and includes major depression, psychosexual problems, anxiety, panic disorder, PTSD, substance abuse, headaches, fibromyalgia and other chronic pain, chronic fatigue syndrome, temporomandibular joint disorders, irritable bowel syndrome, and suicide attempts. These effects are more severe, the greater the intensity and frequency of the violence.

Definitions of Domestic Violence

Some researchers (Johnson, 1995; Leone, Johnson, Cohan, & Lloyd, 2004) have dichotomized domestic violence into two main types: *Intimate terrorism* is characterized by one partner's efforts to exert general control over the other partner, using a variety of coercive strategies, including physical violence. There may be a cold and calculated quality to this violence, betraying its primarily manipulative nature. *Situational couple violence* is less directly coercive but arises mainly in specific situations where conflict escalates into physical aggression, in other words, when the perpetrator loses it. Alternatively, this classification may represent less of a dichotomy and more of a spectrum that ranges from instances of situational couple violence to more enduring patterns of intimate terrorism (Hughes, Stuart, Gordon, & Moore, 2007).

FACTORS CONTRIBUTING TO DOMESTIC VIOLENCE

There are a number of factors that contribute to domestic violence; typically these factors will have an additive or cumulative effect, each one multiplying and exacerbating the effects of the others.

Personality and Psychopathology

Many individuals endure strained marital relationships without resorting to violence. In general, the demographic profile for men who are prone to violence at home is similar to that for violence in general:

- Men with *antisocial personality disorder* tend to view their marriage as just another relationship to exploit, so may quickly resort to violence when they don't get their way.
- Men with *narcissistic and paranoid personality disorders* tend to have thin and easily bruised egos and may misinterpret innocuous statements and actions by their mates as signs of disrespect and betrayal that deserve retaliation.

- *Borderline and dependent personality disordered* men are likely to be pathologically enmeshed with their mates, yet they try to conceal their dependency behind a façade of independence and hypermachoism.
- Women who are domestic violence perpetrators are also most likely to have a borderline personality configuration, which puts them at greater risk of perpetrating acts of violence toward their relationship partners, which may spur vicious cycles of retaliation, leading to greater violence and resulting in dual arrests (Allen & Farmer, 1996; Dutton, 1995; Weaver & Clum, 1993).

Socioeconomic and Cultural Influences

Low socioeconomic status is a risk factor for domestic violence for several reasons. First, individuals with a higher rate of psychopathology, substance abuse, impulsivity, and risk factors for crime and violence in general tend to cluster within this demographic group. Second, economic strain, not to mention increased exposure to crime and poorer access to health care, puts additional psychosocial stress on these families, further reducing frustration tolerance and increasing violence-proneness. Finally, women in these strata tend to have far fewer employment and family options than middle-class women and may therefore opt to stay in heavily flawed relationships because, "better a dirty pair of pants to wash than no pants at all." Often it may boil down to a paycheck and sheer survival. But nobody likes to feel like they're trapped, so the victim may well rationalize that the man and the overall situation are not really that bad and that "he really loves me."

Alcohol and Drug Abuse

No drug makes someone commit domestic violence or any other kind of crime, but most substances reduce already fragile inhibitions and may lower the threshold to impulsive action of any kind, including violence. Substance abuse is also a broader risk factor because it interferes with other life tasks, such as employment, further increasing economic strain. Drug use almost always involves participation, at some level, in the criminal subculture of one's community, and, in some neighborhoods, drug dealing is a common and accepted means of supplementing one's income, in many cases, partly to buy more drugs for one's own use. Substance use by the wife may also contribute to domestic arguments that flash over into violence, often involving both parties, and is more likely to result in cases where the woman is the aggressor (Stuart, Moore, Ramsey, & Kahler, 2004).

Illness, Disability, and Pregnancy

Any factor that puts strain on the dyadic relationship may constitute a risk factor for domestic violence, especially where individuals are already predisposed to it. Unfair as it sounds, women who are ill, disabled, or pregnant are more likely to be targets (Hassouneh-Phillips & Curry, 2002; Sullivan & Knutson, 2003), for varied reasons. First, disabled women may not be able to "pull their weight," economically, domestically, or sexually. Second, such women are likely to need extra attention and be perceived as especially demanding during these times. However, in some cases, the enforced invalidism of the wife is actually welcomed by a husband who is into control because, "now she's home where I can keep my eye on her." It is only when the woman recovers and wants to return to her normal lifestyle that trouble may erupt.

The Domestic Violence Cycle

The domestic violence cycle typically begins with the man becoming angry, suspicious, jealous, or resentful about something his wife purportedly has said or done. He attempts to restrict and control his mate who, in turn, may become resentful herself and resort to deception or outright rebellion. This only fuels the man's sense of righteous indignation, which may spark physical violence because "she deserves it" or because he needs to "teach her a lesson." In fact, one of the greatest risk factors for lethal domestic violence is the woman's stated intention to leave the relationship (Aldarondo & Straus, 1994; Wilson & Daly, 1993). Depending on whether the violence is reported, the partner may or may not be arrested. After the storm has passed, many men display apparently sincere signs of remorse, often complete with tears and flowers, asserting some version of the sentiment "It's only because I love you so much and can't bear the thought of losing you" as an excuse for the loss of control. Many women are so taken in by the next few days or weeks' worth of lovey-dovey reconciliation that they quickly forget the bruises and scars and so much want to believe that "he's changed his ways, it'll be all right now."

LAW ENFORCEMENT RESPONSE TO DOMESTIC DISTURBANCES

Of all the calls for service that police officers make, the ones they dread the most are domestic disturbance calls, even though traffic stops remain the single most dangerous type of call for officers. There seems to be an instinctive reluctance to intrude into the physical and psychological private spaces of a person's homestead, but in order for police officers to uphold the law and to protect potential victims, this sometimes becomes necessary.

In fact, as with many crimes, most domestic violence response will take place not in the hands of mental health professionals but within the purview of law enforcement, who are usually the first to be called when an incident erupts (see also chapter 5). Therefore, for those who counsel and treat these victims, an understanding of the law enforcement response to domestic violence is essential. Additionally, because a victim's long-term mental health may be impacted by the nature of the police response, it is vital that responding officers—and the mental health professionals who advise them—understand the basic do's and don'ts of managing these crises.

Police Response to Domestic Calls: Facts and Stats

There must be reasons why most cops loathe and dread intervening in family disputes more than almost any other kind of police work (Blau, 1994; Miller, 2006m; Russell & Beigel, 1990). Part of this no doubt inheres in the extraordinarily interpersonally demanding aspects of such calls. Even if no arrest is made, sorting out and calming down a domestic dispute, essentially performing crisis intervention, mediation, and arbitration, all in the midst of a chaotic scene that may involve adults, children, intoxicated subjects, and potentially hidden weapons, stretches an officer's communication and diplomacy skills to the limit. If an officer is not already somewhat experienced and comfortable in using these skills, this will prove to be a painfully challenging call. As a self-protective psychological defense, many officers consider domestic calls not to be real police work; they may therefore disparage these calls as social work or nuisance calls.

Additionally, intervening in domestic disputes resonates with the personal experiences of many officers, whose own family lives may have been, and/or continue to be, far from idyllic (Miller, 2006m, 2007a, 2007g; also see below). Thus, the personal identification factor is especially strong for this kind of police work: "Jeez, this crazy family sounds like the same kind of fighting that goes on in my house."

Not all concerns are psychological, however. Domestic disturbance calls remain among the most physically dangerous police interventions from the perspective of potential officer injury, and about a third of these calls involve a violent crime. People are typically in an extreme emotional state, often intoxicated, rarely rational, and therefore most prone to suspend judgment and caution and assault an officer. The paradox is that, because many officers regard these as candyass calls, they may be even less likely to take appropriate precautions than they would in responding to a robbery in progress or a suspicious traffic stop. In addition, a domestic disturbance call can easily escalate to an assault, murder, or hostage and barricade situation, thereby posing further danger to officers and civilians.

Overall, the most frequent type of response to domestic disturbance calls is no action taken, often because the responding officers have been able to resolve the situation before physical violence and an arrestable offense have occurred. Alternatively, the situation has spontaneously cooled or one party has left the scene by the time the officers arrive. Of course, when domestic assault has occurred, officers are mandated to make an arrest. Domestic battery tends to be a repeat crime, and as much as a psychologically oriented book like this one would like to say that talking and counseling will resolve such situations and influence a batterer to give up his violent ways, the fact is that arrest of the perpetrator is what usually has the strongest deterrent effect on recidivism. The time for talking is before violence has occurred; once the attacker has made his move, committed his crime, officers must use the necessary force and restraint to take the offender into custody.

In many cases, it is unclear who started the fight, but by the time police arrive, both members of the couple have mauled each other. The use of mandatory arrest policies in case of domestic violence in most jurisdictions has brought growing attention to the role of the female partner in domestic disputes, leading to the arrest of both parties in some cases (Steinmetz & Lucca, 1988). Some victims' advocates have suggested that many of these women are not true abusers themselves, but rather they injured their attackers while defending themselves. However, officers arriving at the scene may not be able to make this distinction and, even if they could, mandatory arrest policies dictate that anyone who has committed an assault—no matter how justified they thought it was at the time—may be subject to arrest, compounding the abuse of at least some of these women (Abel, 2001; Allen, Bybee, & Sullivan, 2004; Hirschel & Buzawa, 2002; Hughes et al., 2007; Martin, 1997).

Unfortunately, those batterers most likely to learn their lesson from such an arrest action are those least likely to be repeat offenders in the first place. That is, they are ordinarily nonviolent, law-abiding, well-educated, and gainfully employed citizens who have something substantial to lose from being arrested and prosecuted for a crime. Typically, for these men, the domestic assault was a one-time overreaction carried out in a distraught state, not a regular, persistent pattern of behavior. For the chronic repeat offender, however, even multiple arrests are not likely to be an effective deterrent; nor will the abuse be stopped by restraining orders or any other measures, short of incarceration of the offender or the spouse extricating herself from the relationship and getting as far away as possible.

Citizen Dissatisfaction With Police Domestic Violence Response

As just noted, once a domestic assault has occurred, officers are mandated to take the necessary arrest action. But, as with almost every aspect of patrol policing (Miller, 2006m; Peak, 2003; Russell & Beigel, 1990), having a good set of interpersonal and communication skills to use in family dispute and domestic violence calls can greatly decrease the potential for escalation and the necessity for making arrests or using physical force in a subject's home. As always, the best form of crisis intervention is crisis prevention (Miller, 2006m, 2007m, 2008). In addition, the tact and sensitivity—or lack of it—with which officers handle domestic dispute calls will resonate within the individual household and with the broader community and will influence citizens' subsequent interactions with the police. Therefore, it would be useful to have some perspective on how citizens perceive local law enforcement responses to their domestic conflict calls.

This kind of constructive criticism was solicited in a study by Kennedy and Homant (1984), who surveyed the reactions of a group of citizens who had called police to respond to a domestic crisis. The study found that citizen dissatisfaction with officer response to domestic violence calls fell into several categories:

Minimizing the situation. Citizens were distressed when responding officers seemed to downplay the seriousness of the assault or the severity of the injuries:

"That just looks like a scratch; it's hardly even bleeding much."
"He only hit you once with the plate? Was it a ceramic or a plastic plate?"

Disbelieving the victim. Citizens felt that officers treated them as if they were lying or exaggerating:

"You sure that bruise is new? It looks like something you might've bumped into a few days ago. Sometimes you can bang your arm and not even realize it."
"Well, if you say he's been beating on you all afternoon, how come you waited till now to call us?"

Uncaring attitude. Victims felt like the officers were "just going through the motions" of taking the report, giving the impression that they had any number of better things to do than to waste their time on this nuisance call. This attitude was conveyed by distracted attention, disinterested or skeptical tone of voice, minimal eye contact, and often cross talk, knowing glances, and joking with other officers or civilians on the scene, sometimes even including the accused perpetrator.

Macho cop. Officers sometimes (defensively?) adopted a tough, no-nonsense, "just-the-facts-ma'am" attitude, without showing a trace of concern or consideration for the distraught emotional state of the victim. In fact, these officers seemed to get annoyed when victims broke down with emotion or failed to give an orderly narrative of events that the officer could record.

Little or no practical information provided. Citizens were dismayed that many officers failed to offer practical information or guidance about victims' shelters, legal and financial support services, procedures for filing complaints, obtaining restraining orders, and so on. Often, when victims asked these questions directly, they received disdainful shrugs or don't-know responses, or officers who were persuaded to yield this information gave the impression that this was one more imposition on their time.

The common thread in these officer reactions seems to be a mixture of distaste for the domestic call itself and contemptuous disregard for the victims. One dynamic behind this may be the defensively macho orientation of many cops who regard victims as losers, no matter where the fault lies, and are thus fearful of their own unconscious identification with the victim. Therefore, they distance themselves psychologically by downplaying the seriousness of the harm and/or denigrating the victim's motives and reactions. As noted above, this disdainful attitude by law enforcement officers may be even more acute in the case of domestic violence calls involving same-sex couples.

However, the Kennedy and Homant (1984) study did find that some citizens expressed satisfaction at responding officers' actions when these actions could be characterized as *small human acts of caring and consideration.* These included an engaged, interested interpersonal style; waiting for the victim to tell her whole story; questioning the victim to make sure the officer understood what she was saying; providing follow-up information and referrals; offering to call social services for the victim; and even making a follow-up call a few days later to check how the victim was doing. Citizens who got this, unfortunately much rarer, form of police response reported overwhelmingly more positive views of their local law enforcement agency. The general lesson for community policing is obvious: Treating citizens with respect and consideration pays dividends in terms of both citizen cooperation and police safety.

Law Enforcement Domestic Calls: Assessment and Approach

Based on the experiences of law enforcement officers and behavioral science practitioners, a number of recommendations have evolved for crisis intervention by police officers during a domestic disturbance call (Garner, 2005; Miller, 2006m; Russell & Beigel, 1990; Sanders, 1997). In addition to offering practical recommendations to officers, this section can provide valuable insight to mental health practitioners on an area of police work that often directly overlaps with their work with victims.

The response to a domestic disturbance call—indeed any police call—typically begins with the dispatcher's communication to available officers. Officers should try to obtain as much information about the disputants as possible, as this will partly determine the nature of their response. Have there been previous calls to this residence? What happened? Are there likely to be weapons in the home? Are drugs and alcohol likely to be involved? Are there children or other vulnerable family members or residents in the home? In general, the more information, the better, so that officers can plan and coordinate their response accordingly.

And planning is important. No matter how routine the call seems, and no matter how often the officers have been through this scenario before, they should always have some sort of front-end and backup plan for the response. At least it should be determined how many officers will respond. For a very simple call, only two responders may be necessary. Where the potential for violence exists, several vehicles and officers may respond. Also, officers should be prepared to call for medical assistance in case of injury. Be aware that a domestic disturbance carries a high potential for escalation, and it should never be treated as a nuisance call.

When officers arrive at the residence, they should first assess the scene from their vehicle. Unless this is an emergency requiring immediate entry, a few minutes spent driving by to check out the surrounding neighborhood may be useful for determining the best approach. They should park a little away from the house, if possible, so the approach and entry don't seem like a sudden blitz. The residence should always be approached with full caution. A discreet peek through the windows may yield valuable clues as to what's going on inside. If the disputants are outside the house or in the street, officers should try to move them inside or onto the property. At the very least, they should be segregated from any onlookers or neighbors who may escalate the situation. When officers announce their presence, they should not stand directly in front of the door. Officers should introduce themselves, using their full name and police title, and make it clear who they are and what they are there for.

Law Enforcement Domestic Calls: Interpersonal Strategies

This is one of the areas where the practical crisis intervention skills of the mental health practitioner and the law enforcement officer overlap (Miller,

1998h, 2006m). Once inside, officers should position themselves between the conflicting parties. If possible, one officer should interview one disputant, while the second officer interviews the other party, with one or more additional officers maintaining vigilance on the scene, watching out for kids, neighbors, and so on. If feasible, the disputants should be separated so that they're out of visual range and earshot from each other. If this is not possible, then only one person at a time should speak. At this stage, third parties should be excluded from the discussion, unless it is clear that the third party is indispensable to figuring out the dispute and/or coming up with a solution. Even then, officers should try to interview the third party separately.

Officers are urged to always maintain the highest level of vigilance and awareness, to always make safety the number one priority by scanning the environment for weapons or even ordinary objects (scissors, lamp, rope) that could be used to inflict injury. If possible, the disputants should be interviewed in relatively safe and "soft" rooms like bedrooms or living rooms, rather than more dangerous and "hard" rooms like kitchens or garages that are likely to contain hard surfaces, sharp instruments, or heavy tools. Vigilance also applies to the officers' own weapon and utilities. Police are trained never to let their attention wander from a suspect's hands and this applies to the disputants in a domestic disturbance. They also observe body language: Is a disputant tensing up in preparation for an attack or shifting subtly to one side of the room in a bid to flee? Officers should always inquire as to who else may be in the house and should always maintain awareness of others entering or leaving the scene.

Officers should use their own body language, tone of voice, and speech content to evoke as calm and nonconfrontational an atmosphere as possible, and emphasize that they are there to help solve the problem. The officers' initial position should be fair but firm:

> "Look, I understand you're both upset, and we're here to help, but if either of you gets violent or commits a crime, we *will* arrest you, okay? So let's see if we can settle this without any more trouble."

The disputants should be asked to sit down, and then, if it looks safe, the interviewing officer may sit down as well, again always remembering to keep an eye open for possible signs of danger. The officers should show the disputants appropriate courtesy and respect by giving them their undivided attention and taking their comments seriously, making written notes, if necessary, and using the other effective interpersonal interview skills.

Obviously, officers should try to ascertain the facts, that is, who made the call, are there restraining orders in force, has a crime been committed, and so on. If no mandatory arrestable crime has yet been committed, they should try to get the parties to resolve their dispute, or agree to separate for the rest of the day, or until the next morning, when they've had a chance to cool off. Often, one disputant or the other will try to get the officers to take his or her side; usually the man if it's another male officer ("You know how these women get—what choice did I have?"), or the woman, if she made the original call ("I called you here to help me—what are you going to do about this?"). Every effort should be made to allow both parties to save face, so one side doesn't feel defeated by the other, which will usually only lead to retaliatory trouble later on.

If the parties have trouble calming down, officers can ask *diversionary reality questions* to tone down the hostility and anger, for example, "How old are your kids? Where do they go to school? They doing okay? What's your son want to be when he grows up?" But as always, it shouldn't be obvious that the officers are trying to change the subject, which may make the speaker feel manipulated and disrespected. Officers should use their judgment.

Law Enforcement Domestic Calls: Mediation and Arbitration Strategies

Like many of the high-tension scenarios that occur in both law enforcement and mental health, domestic disputes can often be addressed using basic mediation and arbitration strategies from the field of conflict resolution (Cooper, 1999; Goldstein, 1977; Slaiku, 1996).

Mediation. Generally, the goal of the *mediation* process is to help disputants solve their own problem rather than trying to solve it for them. In the cases of domestic disputes, mediation would involve the following steps:

> *Step 1.* The officer makes the offer to mediate the domestic dispute, informing the disputants that it is preferable that they solve the problem themselves, but that the officer will help them clarify the issues so that a fair settlement can be reached.
>
> *Step 2.* Each side conveys their version of events. Officers may have to actively solicit suggestions from the disputants as to how to best resolve the crisis.
>
> *Step 3.* The officer restates the key points conveyed by each side, so that everybody is on the same page, understanding-wise, even if there is not yet complete agreement on the details.
>
> *Step 4.* Possible solutions to the domestic dispute are brainstormed and discussed, the officer utilizing shuttle diplomacy, perhaps with the aid of other officers at the scene of the domestic dispute.
>
> *Step 5.* Some agreement is reached, and the officer encourages follow-through to the agreed-upon solution.

Arbitration. If mediation has proven ineffective, or if it is clear from the outset that either or both of the disputants are too angry, agitated, fearful, irrational, or inebriated to productively participate in a mediation, *arbitration* may then be the strategy of choice. This generally involves four phases:

Fact-finding phase. The officer tries to ascertain as much as possible about the situation that led up to the domestic dispute, emphasizing recent triggers rather than long-term relationship factors, unless the latter are pertinent to directly dealing with the present conflict.

Analysis phase. The officer attempts to come to as clear an understanding as possible as to what set off the present conflict and what measures will be most effective for resolving it for now. In the context of a domestic crisis, much of this brainstorming may take place with the collaboration of other officers who are interviewing family members and other parties to the dispute.

Decision phase. The brainstorming officers come up with the fairest and safest decision that will resolve the crisis for now.

Explanation phase. The officer or officers convey their decision to the two parties, emphasizing that this decision is binding, as originally agreed upon by the disputants. In many cases, the alternative to accepting the officers' decision may be more drastic measures, such as arrest of one or both parties, protective removal of children from the home, and so on. It is also important to make recommendations for follow-up services to minimize the chances of a recurring crisis.

Note that although these strategies are framed here in a law enforcement context, many mental health clinicians use an almost identical approach with couples in family therapy to help them clarify and resolve the issues that keep them at odds, even if no actual or threatened violence has ever occurred. Recognizing that the basic underlying principles of effective problem-solving intervention are universal, clinicians should feel free to adopt and utilize whatever adaptations and responsible improvisations of these techniques that are helpful with the patients they work with.

PSYCHOTHERAPY AND COUNSELING OF DOMESTIC VIOLENCE VICTIMS

Many of the strategies for treating victims of all types of crime, as discussed in chapters 6 and 7, may be used to treat victims of domestic violence. However, there are some special considerations with this population.

Crisis Prevention and Intervention

More so than with almost any other type of crime discussed in this book, domestic violence often follows a predictable cycle, as noted above. Therefore, one important intervention involves training your patient to recognize the signs of escalating violence and to take appropriate action. The simple way to remember this is, "When in doubt, get the hell out." However, this may not be as easy as is sounds if the victim has no place to go or if her leaving is complicated by the presence of children, medical disability, financial stresses, and so on. Even in the case of imminent threat, many women will state that they'd rather take their chances with an abusive partner who they at least know, than spend several nights in a public shelter among strangers, many of whom may be less than completely safe or trustworthy themselves.

In such cases, train your patient in as wide a range of conflict defusing deescalation techniques as she is able to assimilate and utilize productively. Role-play these scenarios until she is proficient in utilizing them. The types of strategies chosen will be determined by your comprehensive understanding of the victim's personality, that of her partner, and the overall family dynamics and social situation. For example, some abusive partners may have to be placated, others constructively confronted. It is a serious responsibility of the clinician to ensure that, whatever practical strategy you advise and train your patient to do, the overall priority be her safety. Also, know when it is your responsibility to make a mandated report of child endangerment where this may exist.

Dealing With the Partner

Another, related, difference between domestic violence victims and victims of crimes by strangers is that, at some point, you may find yourself dealing with a distressed and angry partner of your patient. However, despite clinicians' common fears of being accosted by an enraged mate, this type of confrontation has, in my experience and in that of most of my colleagues who do this kind of work, been exceptionally rare. Abusive partners typically want to stay off the radar. In my own case, the few instances where I have been directly challenged by a mate have all consisted of angry phone calls, most just messages on the answering machine and one or two direct angry harangues.

However, vigilance and tact are always required (also see chapter 15). If you are directly threatened, notify the police. In most cases, the abusive partner will be clever enough not to say anything actionable, and, in these cases, be polite and civil in addressing any questions or concerns the caller has, but make it clear that what goes on in the sessions between you and his spouse is confidential. In most cases, less violent partners will simply want to tell their side of the story and then leave you alone. Where the calls become a nuisance, inform the caller that this kind of communication is inappropriate and that it may constitute harassment. Again, most abusive partners will be happy to avoid further legal trouble if at all possible. Be sure to make written notes on all such interactions.

The Marital Relationship

In some cases, you may be treating two people together in marital or couples therapy and, in the course of the sessions, the abusive relationship comes to light. Or, you will be treating the woman, and she discloses the abuse and wants to bring her partner into the sessions to deal with their relationship issues.

In the first case, be sure that both partners want to address the abuse issue. Often, the abuser will either deny the violence or downplay its significance. In the second case, beware of the so-called therapeutic ambush where the woman says her husband is coming in to discuss the domestic abuse, you get prepared to deal with the issue, the husband comes in, you broach the subject and start talking about it, and only then do you realize that this is the first the husband has learned that the family secret has been revealed. The wife was afraid to tell him and was relying on you to be the informer, without letting you know that this was going to be your role. Now you must deal with the anger of the husband who believes that you and his wife cooked up this plot together, as well as your own feelings of having been set up by your patient. These situations, while not irresolvable, are certainly unpleasant and can be avoided by carefully clarifying the goals of any change in treatment plan and the agendas of all concerned.

In the best cases, usually where the abuse is not a long-standing, ingrained pattern, effective couples and family therapy can address the causes of the couple's conflicts, inculcate less violent problem-solving strategies, and help them decide whether there is enough good stuff left in their relationship to make it worth saving.

DOMESTIC VIOLENCE IN POLICE FAMILIES

At one time, this was law enforcement's dirty little secret, although it's not much of a secret anymore. As noted earlier, part of police officers' discomfort in responding to domestic violence calls may be precisely the degree to which it resonates harshly with experiences in an officer's own family. Specifically, in tightly run public safety agencies like police departments, the issue of domestic violence often overlaps with the discussion of administrative discipline (Miller, 2004f, 2006m, 2007a, 2007g), insofar as the officer's department will eventually become involved, however unwillingly, when the problem is persistent.

Police Officer Domestic Violence: Facts and Stats

Recent studies suggest that the incidence of domestic violence among police officers may exceed that of the general population, and the true rate may be even higher because of the reluctance of cops to report fellow officers. The highest rates occur among narcotics and patrol officers, officers working night shifts, those who work more than 50 hours a week, and those who take an excessive number of sick days. Police family domestic violence is a risk factor for police homicide-suicide (Neidig, Russell, & Senig, 1992; Pam, 2001; Violanti, 2007). The repercussions of an arrest and conviction on a domestic battery charge are far greater for a police officer than for the average citizen, because it can mean surrender of his weapon and loss of his law enforcement career.

Therefore, until recently, many departments have maintained a conspiracy of silence around such occurrences, often persuading the complaining spouse that loss of her husband's job would be potentially devastating to the family, and urging the couple to settle things off the record. In other cases, especially where the call is to the home of a senior officer, patrol partner, or member of a special team like SWAT or undercover, there may the palpable, if unstated, threat of ostracism, lack of backup, or general opprobrium for cops who rat out other cops, similar to what occurs with other abuse-of-authority cases (Gallo, 2005; Kruger & Valltos, 2002; Lott, 1999; Miller, 2004f, 2006m; Sanders, 1997). Many small, medium, and large police agencies still have insufficient policies and programs to deal with the problem (Los Angeles Board of Police Commissioners, 1997; Southwestern Law Enforcement Institute, 1995).

However, like other unlawful behavior on the part of officers that is actively or passively abetted, undeterred domestic violence undermines the credibility and effectiveness of the department with both its own personnel and the general public, and sets the agency up for civil and criminal actions relating to negligence and malfeasance (Kruger & Valltos, 2002). And again, like other disciplinary protocols, a program of domestic violence response within police agencies need not be brutal or unfair; indeed, the more equitable and just it is perceived to be, the greater the likelihood it will be implemented and used as needed. Accordingly, the following is an outline of a protocol that addresses the key elements in police officer domestic violence intervention (Gallo, 2005; Kruger & Valltos, 2002; Lott, 1999; Sanders, 1997).

Police Officer Domestic Violence Intervention: Policies and Procedures

As with all departmental programs, success stands or falls with the level of commitment and buy-in by the senior administration. Domestic violence protocols will have little real bite if they are not enthusiastically endorsed by the agency's leadership. Police leaders need to demonstrate by both their words and deeds that unwarranted violence by their officers will not be abided. Many agencies endorse a zero tolerance policy with regard to violent behavior, but as with most such behavioral concepts, zero is not necessarily always an absolute quantity (see chapters 12, 13). Accordingly, departmental policy should spell out as clearly as possible what types of behaviors are not acceptable. Two standards that most departments adhere to are "conduct unbecoming" and "failure to conform to law." Most departments also require officers to make a report if a police call to their own residence has occurred, whether or not arrests were made.

Police leaders should have a good understanding of the dynamics of domestic violence and the magnitude of the problem, both within their own department and in their communities. A commitment to addressing the problem forthrightly in their own departments includes the creation of a culture of disapproval among department leaders, and the allocation of time and resources for adequate training and dealing with incidents.

Training

The key to any credible and permanent strategy for preventing domestic violence is adequate and appropriate training. Training for police officers should cover a comprehensive range of topics, including response, tactics, officer safety, and verbal crisis intervention and conflict-resolution skills. In particular, special training must be provided for officers on how to handle domestic violence calls involving other officers.

Problem Recognition

Astute police supervisors may be able to detect signs of impending or ongoing domestic violence in officers within their own department. The legitimate response to "What happens at home is my business" is "No, it's not, because, (a) if it escalates to an arrestable offense, we lose a good officer; (b) there are liability issues for the department of letting a potentially violent situation go unaddressed; and (c) any kind of family stress that affects our personnel concerns us."

Many of the signals that a domestic violence problem may be brewing or ongoing in an officer's family are generic stress-related symptoms, while others are more specific and may include the following:

- Increased isolativeness of the officer
- Signs of sleeplessness and fatigue
- Signs of alcohol, illegal drug, or prescription medication abuse
- Emotional lability or Jekyll and Hyde personality
- Increased incidence of excessive force complaints on the job
- Talking about the spouse in a particularly derogatory way
- Blaming the spouse for all the officer's problems
- Signs of physical injury that are attributed to accidents but may represent wounds received in physical altercations with the spouse

Investigation and Response to Incidents

Police departments should respond to domestic violence incidents with a comprehensive approach. Kruger and Valltos (2002) recommend that the Internal Affairs Department immediately conduct an initial preliminary inquiry to determine the need for a formal internal investigation. The latter would follow the agency's established protocol for criminal misconduct cases, including suspension of the officer's police powers and reclamation of his or her weapon and police vehicle. Officers should be placed on off-duty status, pending administrative investigation and referral for a psychological fitness-for-duty evaluation (Miller, 2004f, 2006k, 2006m, 2007d).

If the officer is found psychologically fit for duty, administrators might transfer the officer from off-duty to modified-duty, such as noncontact status assignments (the dreaded desk job), until the investigation is complete. If the officer has sustained a criminal conviction related to the domestic battery charge, he will usually be terminated from the department. If lesser or suspended charges ensue, the department retains the right to keep the officer or let him go; if he stays, the officer will be expected to comply with any departmental follow-up measures, as well as with any court orders, that arise from the case.

Not to be neglected is the role of counseling and family therapy, but this resource should be presented as an option, not a requirement or punishment or, worse, a way of deflecting legitimate legal consequences for the officer's actions. Although sometimes a skilled clinician can sufficiently connect with a reluctant, involuntary patient to accomplish some meaningful therapeutic work, in most cases when people are forced to go to counseling or psychotherapy, true progress is rarely made (Miller, 1993a, 1998h, 2006m).

DOMESTIC VIOLENCE IN THE WORKPLACE

When you hire people, you hire their lives.

The area of domestic violence at work represents the perfect area of collaboration among clinical mental health practitioners, organizational psychology and management consultants, and public and private industry executives and managers to set up effective programs for prevention, response, and recovery (Miller, 1997b, 1999c, 2001c, 2008; also see chapter 12).

Domestic Violence at Work: Facts and Stats

Research and practical observation in both the management and psychology fields (Brownell, 1996; Brush, 2003; Duhart, 2001; Friedman, Tucker, Neville, & Imperial, 1996; Hamberger & Holtzworth-Munroe, 1994; Hensing & Alexanderon, 2000; Hoffman & Baron, 2001; Kinney, 1995; Labig, 1995; Leone et al., 2004; Logan, Shannon, Cole, & Swanberg, 2007; McFarlane, Campbell, & Watson, 2002; McFarlane et al., 1999; Meloy, 1997; Nicastro, Cousins, & Spitzberg, 2000; Petty & Kosch, 2001; Riger, Ahrens, & Bickenstaff, 2000; Riger, Raja, & Camacho, 2002; Rothman, Hathaway, Stidsen, & de Vries, 2007; Simon, 1996; Swanberg & Logan, 2005; Swanberg, Logan, & Macke, 2005; Swanberg, Logan, & Macke, 2006; Swanberg, Macke, & Logan, 2006; Swanberg, Macke, & Logan, 2007; Tolman & Raphael, 2000; Tolman & Rosen, 2001; Walker, 1994; Wettersten et al., 2004; Wright, Burgess, Laszlo, McCrary, & Douglas, 1996) have established a number of facts about domestic violence in the workplace:

- Almost half of the U.S. workforce is made up of women. Therefore, spillover from domestic problems is likely to affect a large number of workplaces across the country.
- Each year in the United States, an average of 18,700 workers are assaulted by their intimate partners while on the job.
- Murder is the number one cause of occupational death for women. It is the second leading cause of death for men only because men are more likely to be employed in physically riskier occupations such as construction or emergency services.
- Women are disproportionately represented in some of the riskiest jobs. Most of the service industry, entertainment industry, small retail, and unprotected office jobs are held by women. Women are less likely than men to be able to choose their work hours and so may find themselves working late at night in relatively isolated surroundings,

or conversely, in crowded, noisy environments filled with unsavory characters.

- Abusive husbands or partners harass 74% of employed battered women at work and battered women miss an average of 3 days of work per month due to injuries, embarrassment, depression, or doctor and lawyer appointments. Even women who resolve to get away from the abuser can often change their personal phone numbers and residences far more easily than they can change employment.
- Domestic violence doesn't discriminate: Women in middle-status jobs are as likely to be harassed by partners as those in low-status jobs.
- The risks and costs to businesses of domestic violence spillover in the workplace include lost worker productivity due to absenteeism, physical disability, loss of sleep, fatigue, impaired concentration, anxiety and depression, and disturbed interaction with coworkers and customers. Work schedules may be disrupted due to child care, doctor and lawyer appointments, court appearances, or direct sabotage of work schedules or work products by the abusive partner.
- Women in abusive relationships cost employers more in terms of higher health insurance outlays, increased personnel costs for replacement and temporary workers, and increased security and human resource utilization. There may also be increased legal liability to employers for negligent security, failure to protect the harassed employee, failure to protect other workers, sexual harassment and hostile workplace claims, and so on.
- Unfortunately, when domestic violence continues to adversely affect the company's comfort, safety, and/or bottom line, the most expedient response of the employer is to get rid of the problem by firing the woman.

Recognizing the Warning Signs

Sometimes the signs that domestic violence is spilling over into the workplace are obvious; other times they may be more subtle (Kinney, 1995; Labig, 1995; Logan, Walker, Jordan, & Campbell, 2004; Sullivan, Basta, Tan, & Davidson, 1992; Sullivan, Campbell, Angelique, Eby, & Davidson, 1994; Swanberg et al., 2007). Signs may include any of the following:

Spouse or partner makes threats or other harassing communications to the victim. This may be overt or subtle. Typically, the partner will call numerous times during the day, with tones and attitudes ranging from sweet and conciliatory to rageful and threatening. Until recently, phone contact was the preferred form of communication; these days, harassers are increasingly likely to use e-mail or text messaging—although many will avoid this medium for fear of leaving an electronic paper trail.

Spouse or partner makes threats or other harassing communications to victim's supervisor, coworkers, or customers. Again this can be overt, as in the irately jealous spouse who calls his wife's boss to tell him, "Do you know you have a slut working for you?" Or it can be subtle, as in sending coworkers items from a court order or revealing conversations the spouse has had about work.

Spouse or partner shows up at the workplace. He may ask to see the woman or just hang around the workplace to menace her or conduct surveillance.

Spouse used to work at the same location. A particularly tricky situation occurs when the two partners had been working at the same company—perhaps one even helped the other get his or her job—and then the husband is fired, often for the same kind of obnoxious behavior toward coworkers that he inflicts on his wife at home. Now, he has all the more reason to resent his wife's supposed betrayal of him by continuing to "work for those assholes." She may be afraid to tell him directly that they were probably right to let him go, but she can't just pick up and quit without another job offer. So now the abusive spouse has one more major reason to hate his former workplace and resents his wife for "taking their side." The other problem is that the now-terminated spouse may still have access to the workplace, knows the personnel, and may be familiar enough with the organization to cause major trouble.

Spouse believes the victim's job contributed to problems in their relationship. Whether or not he used to work there, the man may displace all his dissatisfactions and anger onto the woman's job as the primary cause of their difficulties: "You have plenty of time for those strangers, but you don't spend any time with me" (that is, doing the things he wants her to do). She's probably too scared to reveal that, compared to being with him, going to work is a relief because at least the people there treat her with civility. A common problem is seen in marriages where the wife is better educated and has a higher-status job than the husband, which eats at his narcissistic pride: "Who does she think she is, getting on her high horse about her fancy job? Maybe I need to take her down a peg and teach her a lesson." This dynamic also occurs when the wife goes back to school or does anything that the husband believes puts her further out of his league.

Employee is persistently late, frequently asks for schedule changes, or has other attendance problems. Of course, this could be for any number of reasons, from a secret second job, to a personality disorder or psychopathology, to drug abuse (Miller, 2003a, 2008). But managers and coworkers who are familiar with this employee should be able to tell that these behaviors are uncharacteristic of her and take the concerned step of respectfully inquiring into what's wrong (see below).

Employee's work quality has deteriorated, for example, increase in mistakes, missed deadlines, and shallow excuses. This warning sign can be dealt with similar to the previous warning sign. Again, using the employee's past work record as a baseline, employers should be able to determine if the poor work output is a situationally based problem that can be corrected with the right type of intervention.

Obvious signs of physical injury. A prominent black eye or a cast on a fractured limb will usually be a rather unambiguous sign of injury. But many battered spouses will strain the bounds of credulity in denying that this was anything other than an accident. In some cases, the woman is simply not ready to acknowledge to herself that her mate is beating her; in other cases, she fears that letting her job know the truth will get her fired. Often, she's simply embarrassed.

Obvious signs of psychological distress. Some women will be observed or overheard to be crying at their desk, in the ladies' room, or in their car when leaving or arriving at work. Less blatant signs that managers and coworkers can look for include increased isolativeness (probably so others won't see their distress or overhear embarrassing calls), hypervigilance and jumpiness, or overall change in personality and behavior.

What Employers Can Do

Mental health clinicians are in unique position to advise corporate managers in designing programs to respond forthrightly to domestic violence in the workplace, usually in conjunction with corporate legal counsel (Flannery, 1995; Kinney, 1995; Logan et al., 2007; Meloy, 1997; Pierce & Aguinis, 1997; Randel & Wells, 2003; Swanberg et al., 2005; Swanberg, Logan, et al., 2006; Swanberg, Macke, et al., 2006). The guiding principle for managers is: "*When you hire people, you hire their lives.*" Appropriate company response includes several measures:

Encourage disclosure. Employers should strive to create the kind of workplace climate where employees will feel free to come forward to managers with problems that affect their work, even if these are personal (Allen, 2001; Swanberg, Macke, et al., 2006). However, for all of the reasons just mentioned (embarrassment, fear, etc.), battered spouses may be reluctant to disclose this aspect of their personal lives. Then, the manager may have to frame this as an employment issue:

> "Susan, an employee's personal life is just that—personal—unless it directly affects their work performance, their health and safety, or the health, safety, or productivity of other employees. For example, I'd be having this same conversation with you if I thought you had a substance abuse problem that was interfering with your work. Don't worry, I know that's not an issue with you, but it's obvious to everyone around here that your work performance has been dropping and that it's due to something that's going on at home. Again, your personal matters are your own business, but I'm advising you to take advantage of our EAP [employee assistance program] counseling services to get some help for this problem. If there's something you need us to do from a work-related legal standpoint, let's discuss it in confidence and we'll see if it's something we can accommodate. We'll do our best to keep you working productively here if you give us a chance to help you."

Initiate legal action. There is actually a lot that employers can do to keep their workers safe and protect themselves from liability:

- Getting court restraining orders against a clearly threatening husband or boyfriend
- Filing criminal charges if the offending spouse breaks the law by threatening, assaulting, vandalizing, or trespassing
- Filing a civil lawsuit if the perpetrator's actions cost the company lost business, increased security and health care costs, and so on

Usually, a forthright, no-nonsense approach to standing up for the rights of all employees will be sufficient to deter most stalkers and harassers who are only out to do mischief. A no-nonsense approach will also create a legal record for possible prosecution of more serious offenders.

Develop a domestic violence program for the workplace. This will usually be done in the context of an overall workplace violence program (chapter 12) and should contain the following key elements:

- Training and policy seminars, including regular training updates and drills
- Policies and procedures with regard to flexible work schedules and areas, leave-of-absence policies, and off-time
- Security and alarm systems, along with training in their use

- Liaison with local law enforcement, including protocol for summoning help when needed
- Specialized employee assistance and mental health referral services

Indeed, continued employment and self-sufficiency can be one of the most empowering forces that enable women to make the decision to leave an abusive relationship, which in turn will make them better workers (Browne, 1987; Levendosky et al., 2004; Lloyd, 1997; Lynch & Graham-Bermann, 2004; McCabe & Di Battista, 2004; Strube & Barbour, 1984; Wilson, Baglioni, & Downing, 1989). For example, Rothman et al. (2007) found that having steady employment and a self-sufficient income was a crucial factor in abused women's ability to leave their partners. Moreover, these women reported that being employed made them feel competent; reduced social isolation; afforded a distraction from, and an alternate perspective on, their abusive home lives; provided them with physical security, a sense of emotional safety, and a "place to hear my own thoughts"; and gave them a sense of purpose in life. Paradoxically, one advantage that gay and lesbian couples may have in this regard is that neither partner is likely to be as financially dependant on the other as in traditional heterosexual relationships, making it somewhat easier to leave on an economic basis (Letellier, 1994; Lundy & Leventhal, 1999).

Mental health counselors should thus always remember that what happens outside their consulting room is often as important and sometimes more important than what we attempt to accomplish with our patients intrapsychically. Encouraging and providing practical assistance to victims of domestic violence in establishing independent lives can often be the key intervention that pulls our therapeutic efforts together.

CONCLUSIONS

Almost belying the name, domestic violence is a criminal action that often transcends the boundaries of the home and reaches far into the workplace and community. For this reason, a comprehensive and coordinated law enforcement, business administration, and mental health response is needed. And, as we'll see in the next chapter, protecting all employees from violence and harassment on the job can be seamlessly integrated into an overall workplace safety program.

CHAPTER 12

Workplace Violence

A disgruntled [pick one: postal worker, law client, insurance claimant, store customer, hospital patient, factory worker] stormed into his place of business yesterday, killing three people and wounding several more, before turning the gun on himself. Film at 11:00.

You've heard this one before. Often the lead story is followed by interviews with coworkers or associates whose comments almost invariably follow one of two main themes:

> "He was always a little strange, you know, quiet. Kept to himself a lot, didn't get along with too many people, but came in, did his job, and never caused any real trouble. But nobody ever figured him for a stone killer. Man, we didn't see this one coming."

Or:

> "Dammit, I knew it was just a matter of time till something like this happened. This guy was bad news, a ticking bomb, and we all knew it. But there were no precautions or any real kind of discipline at all. We tried to tell management, but they just got annoyed, said there was nothing they could do, and told us not to stir up trouble. When he finally snapped, we were sitting ducks."

Most traumatic events encountered in life—earthquakes, chemical spills, terrorist attacks, plane crashes, street crimes—strike suddenly, without warning, and with little control. Correspondingly, medical, mental health, law enforcement, and administrative efforts typically focus on treating victims, survivors, their families, and other affected persons after the fact.

But one of the cardinal principles of crisis management (Miller, 1998h, 2006m, 2007m) states that: *The best form of crisis intervention is crisis prevention.* For virtually no other type of major tragedy is education, training, and preparation so important in foreseeing and planning for emergencies as in the area of workplace aggression and violence. This chapter begins by describing the measures that organizations can take to prevent or defuse this special kind of crime victimization. Then, special attention is given to what counselors and mental health clinicians can do to help the public organizations and private companies they consult with reduce the risk of this kind of tragedy and respond appropriately when violence does erupt.

WORKPLACE VIOLENCE: FACTS AND STATS

Several decades of research and practical experience (Albrecht, 1996, 1997; Blount, 2003; Denenberg & Braverman, 1999; Flannery, 1995; Johnson & Indvik, 2000; Kinney, 1995; Labig, 1995; LeBlanc et al., 2005; Mantell & Albrecht, 1994; Miller, 1997a, 1997c, 1998h, 1999c, 2000d, 2000f, 2000h, 2001a, 2001b, 2002a, 2005e, 2008; Mitroff, 2001; Namie & Namie, 2000; Neuman & Baron, 2005; Potter-Efron, 1998; Schaner, 1996; Schneid, 1999; Schouten, 2006; Shapiro, Jankowski, & Dale, 2005; Simon, 1996; Vega & Comer, 2005) have established some facts about violence in the workplace:

- Homicide is the number one killer of women and the third leading cause of death for men in the workplace, after motor vehicle accidents and machine-related fatalities.
- You are about twice as likely to be murdered at work than to die from a fall, four times more likely than to be accidentally electrocuted, five times more likely than to go down in a plane crash, and many times more likely than to be killed in a terrorist attack.
- The majority of workplace homicides are done with firearms.
- Most violence is perpetrated by people outside the company, but intracompany violence by employees or ex-employees is not rare, and most people find the prospect of being harmed by a coworker far more frightening than by an outsider, probably because most of us feel that we ought to be safe at work.
- Workplace violence costs American business approximately $4.2 billion a year. To put this in a more personal perspective, it boils down to a conservative estimate of over $250,000 per incident, in terms of lost work time, employee medical benefits, decreased productivity,

diversion of management resources from other productive business, increased insurance premiums, increased security costs, bad publicity, lost business, and expensive litigation costs.

- In terms of the human cost, most workers polled after an incident say that they are psychologically traumatized by the threat of future workplace violence, and a sizable proportion lose work time due to stress disability.

- For every actual workplace killing, there occur over 100 acts of sublethal violence, including fistfights, nonfatal shootings, stabbings, sexual assaults, vandalism, sabotage, bombings, and arson.

- Perpetrators who turn deadly often engage in threats and harassing behaviors before their actions escalate to killing, emphasizing the need for early boundary setting and other preventive interventions.

- Verbal abuse and harassment can be even more destructive to employee morale and productivity than physical assault. Ironically, employees who resort to fisticuffs create a palpable disturbance, cause potentially costly injury, and are an embarrassment to the company; consequently, they are likely to be assertively disciplined. But "mere" verbal threats, curses, snide remarks, and personal property sabotage (one of my patients had rotten food regularly placed in her desk drawer) typically aren't taken as seriously, since they seem to affect few employees or stakeholders outside the direct targets of the nastiness.

- Sexual harassment has become perhaps the quintessential form of interpersonal workplace problems experienced by women (see also chapter 11), and even verbal intimidation or harassment can inflict acute and long-standing psychological and emotional harm.

- Sexual harassment is often a precursor of more overt forms of physical violence, such as assault, rape, or murder in the workplace.

- Complaints about antisocial workplace behavior are often treated by management as nuisances that get in the way of doing business and are thus dismissed with comments like, "Grow up," "Deal with it," "Work it out yourselves," or, "Don't make a big deal about it and maybe it'll go away."

- Ignoring the problems typically emboldens the malfeasor to escalate the abuse to more overtly physical aggression that eventually causes serious damage.

- Alternatively, the persecuted victim, rebuffed by management, feels he has no choice but to take matters into his own hands and retaliates explosively, becoming himself the perpetrator of workplace violence, a dynamic very similar to that noted in many school shootings over the past decade (chapter 13).

THE WORKPLACE VIOLENCE CYCLE

Accounting for individual variations, there appears to be a certain predictable pattern in the evolution of many workplace violence incidents (Denenberg & Braverman, 1999; Kinney, 1995, 1996; Labig, 1995; Mack, Shannon, Quick, & Quick, 1998; Neuman & Baron, 2005; Potter-Efron, 1998; Simon, 1996). The cycle typically begins when the employee encounters a situation (actual or perceived) that he experiences as antagonistic or stressful. This may be a single overwhelming incident or a capping event to a cumulative series of stressors—the proverbial last straw. The worker reacts to this event cognitively and emotionally, based on his predisposing personality, psychopathology, and life experiences. In the typical workplace violence perpetrator, this reaction often involves a noxious stew of persecutory ideation, projection of blame, and violent revenge fantasies.

As these thoughts and emotions continue to percolate, the individual increasingly isolates himself from the input of others and accretes a mind-set of self-protection and self-justification in which a violent act may come to be perceived as the only way out. Blame continues to be externalized and vengeance brews as the worker broods on some version of, "I'll show them they can't do this to me and get away with it." For some individuals, the intolerability of the perceived workplace injustice leads to hopeless suicidality with a retaliatory tinge:

"If they can screw me, I can screw them back—bigtime. Why should other people go on having what they want and enjoying themselves, when I can't? I'll show them they can't do this to me and get away with it. I may be going out, but I'm not going out alone."

The perpetrator fantasizes that after he's gone, his Ramboesque exploits will be reported to millions of people around the world; his name will be a household word. Far from meekly slinking away, our hero will leave this world in a blaze of martial glory—just like in the movies.

The actual means of carrying out this commando action will be dictated by availability of weapons, and, in our society, the easy obtainability of firearms usually makes this the method of choice. The operational plan may be executed impulsively and immediately, or it may undergo meticulous planning with numerous revisions. The final step is the violent act itself, which may occur any time from hours to months to years following the final perceived injustice.

WORKPLACE VIOLENCE PREVENTION

Remember, *the best form of crisis intervention is crisis prevention.* But despite the growing recognition of workplace violence as an occupational problem, denial still appears to be the coping method of choice among American employers. Only a quarter of companies surveyed offer formal training to any employees in dealing with workplace violence and less than 10% offer such training to all employees in the company.

It doesn't have to be this way. In fact, at the start of the twenty-first century, if someone is going to "go postal" on the job that person is probably *least* likely to be a postal worker. That's because, in the past two decades, the U.S. Post Office has undertaken a concerted and effective program to reduce violence at work. By responding in a similarly forthright manner, the retail trade, which in the 1980s and 1990s had accounted for more than one-third of workplace violence deaths, has managed to cut its rate of homicide in half over the past decade.

Companies can do a number of things to reduce the chances of violence at work (Albrecht, 1996, 1997; Blount, 2003; Blythe, 2002; Bush & O'Shea, 1996; Caponigro, 2000; Crawley, 1992; Dezenhall & Weber, 2007; Flannery, 1995; Grote, 1995; Kinney, 1995, 1996; Labig, 1995; Mack et al., 1998; Martinko, Douglas, Harvey, & Joseph, 2005; Miller, 1998h, 1999c, 2002a, 2008; Mitroff, 2001; Nicoletti & Spooner, 1996; Schneid, 1999; Simon, 1996; Yandrick, 1996). They can

- have clear, strong, fair, consistent, and clearly written policies against violence and harassment;
- institute effective grievance procedures;
- maintain a firm security program;
- cultivate a supportive managerial environment that maintains a balance between reasonable employee autonomy and control over their work, and effective supervision and communication when necessary; and
- provide periodic training in resolving conflicts through team building and negotiation skills.

Organizations should have a clearly stated policy of *zero tolerance for violence.* This should be contextualized as a safety issue, the same as with rules about fire prevention or storm emergency drills. Company policies should state clearly that any manner of threatening remark or gesture in the workplace is unacceptable and that anyone who engages in such behavior will face disciplinary action. All threats should be thoroughly investigated, albeit with reasonable sensitivity to all parties. Having official rules that apply to everyone makes enforcement objective and impersonal.

But in order to prevent the workplace from becoming a caricature of some totalitarian, mind-police regime of political correctness, these policies and procedures should leave room for well-informed managerial discretion and basic common sense. Definitions of reportable behavior, with specific examples, should be established, distributed, and role-played, as necessary. Plans should be put in place that specify how and to whom threats and offenses are to be reported, as well as a standardized protocol for investigating threats. Other policy and procedure points include security measures, complaint and grievance procedures, and services available for dispute mediation, conflict resolution, stress management, safety training, and mental health services. Most companies can develop and write up these protocols themselves. Organizations with a large, diverse, and/or complex workforce may want to avail themselves of knowledgeable outside consultants.

Prevention of and Protection From Sexual Harassment

With regard to sexual harassment, companies can take several effective measures (Kinney, 1995; Martinko et al., 2005; Schouten, 1996, 2006; Yandrick, 1996):

- Institute a sexual harassment policy that describes the specific conduct that constitutes harassment and state that such conduct is tolerated neither by the company nor by state or federal law.
- The policy should explain the employee's right to report sexual harassment without fear of retaliation and without having to directly confront the harasser, at least at the time of the initial complaint.
- The policy should contain a grievance procedure that the harassed employee can follow.
- The policy should include the establishment of sexual harassment hotlines for emergency situations; such hotlines are now required by law in at least 30 states.

WORKPLACE VIOLENCE: RESPONSE TO EMERGENCIES

Sometimes, despite the best efforts at prevention, a dangerous situation begins to brew and a violent confrontation seems imminent. Other times, the incident just explodes and personnel have to respond on the spot. Part of the preincident emergency planning should include a contingency for evacuating employees and others and for alerting authorities, but employees and managers still may find themselves trapped in the position of having to stabilize the situation until help arrives.

The following guidelines for handling workplace violence emergencies have been adapted from several sources (Blythe, 2002; Caraulia & Steiger, 1997; Gilliland & James, 1993; Labig, 1995; Miller, 2000c, 2008), along with my own comments and suggestions. As always, these recommendations do not take the place of comprehensive on-site planning, preparation, and training, but they can serve as an interim practical guide to responding to behavior-based emergencies of many types, including workplace violence (see also chapter 13).

Recognizing Warning Signs of Impending Violence

Nonspecific red flags that an employee may be on the verge of losing control include the following:

- Disorganized physical appearance and dress
- Tense facial expression or other distressed body language
- Signs of intoxication or inappropriate use of dark glasses or breath mints to mask alcohol or substance abuse
- Severe agitation, verbal argumentativeness or outright threats, especially to specific persons
- Presence or evidence of weapons

Aside from these general indicators, managers and employees should try to know the people they work with as well as possible so they can be alert to any significant changes in their appearance, mood, or behavior and take action as early as possible to prevent things from boiling over into a violent confrontation.

Defusing a Potentially Dangerous Situation

A potential workplace violence crisis can be thought of as occurring in several stages, each with its own set of recommendations for defusing danger. Like all protocols, don't think of these as an unvarying sequence of discrete steps but rather as general categories of response that can change course or blend into one another, depending on the person and the circumstances (Caraulia & Steiger, 1997; Labig, 1995).

In the *anxiety phase,* the employee is becoming increasingly overwhelmed and agitated, and the response that is most needed at this stage is support. The focus of the intervention should be on how the employee feels and what his concerns are. This involves rapport building and active listening, the mainstay of crisis intervention.

"You seem upset about something, Fred. Whatever's going on, I hope you'll let me help you out."

In the *defensive phase*, the employee comes to feel increasingly trapped and out of options. The response needed here is a directive one in which the employee is shown a safe and dignified way out of the danger zone. Helpful techniques involve encouraging and modeling self-control, redirecting anger, using calming body language, giving limited choices, and gently but firmly setting limits.

"I know you're angry about the last suspension, but I don't want you to do anything that's going to hurt yourself further. C'mon, take a deep breath and let's step into the atrium and talk this out. Or do you want to go down to the cafeteria and get a cup of coffee? I'm buying."

In the *acting-out phase,* the employee has already lost some control. The appropriate response is containment. Until the cavalry gets there, focus on the employee's immediate behavior, set clear and reasonable limits, and use calming speech and body language. If the employee has not yet been violent, and security or law enforcement have arrived, you may sometimes be able to use them to leverage cooperation from the employee.

"Okay, Fred, I hear you, you made your point. Let's pull this thing back, okay? We can replace the computer but I need you to put down the fire extinguisher and do whatever the security people tell you till we get this thing sorted out. I called the authorities here because I don't want you or anyone else to get hurt."

In the *tension-reduction phase,* the crisis has largely passed and the employee should be ready to accept help in reducing his level of anxiety and anger. Assuming no serious harm was done and the employee is not actually in custody, the appropriate response is a supportive type of rapport that is helpful, understanding, and calm. Reinforcing a controlled and face-saving ending to the potentially dangerous episode is often the best insurance that it won't be repeated, even if the employee's behavior eventually results in disciplinary action or termination.

"I'm glad we were able to settle this, Fred. It took guts to do the right thing. We're going to let the medics check you out and the police ask their questions, and then, when the dust settles a little, we're going to figure out what to do next, okay?"

Handling a Violent Episode

When the situation looks like it's getting beyond the point where it can be defused adequately, then safety comes first. The rule is *When in doubt, get the hell out.* Pay attention to the environment and to potential dangers, make a mental note of possible escape routes, and think about how to call for outside help. If you find yourself absolutely trapped in a potentially dangerous situation, heed the following guidelines (Blythe, 2002; Caraulia & Steiger, 1997; Flannery, 1995; Gilliland & James, 1993; Labig,1995), supplemented by adequate training and practice.

> *Initial action.* If possible, don't become isolated with a potentially dangerous employee or customer, unless you have made sure that security precautions have been taken to prevent or limit a violent outburst. But sometimes an interview or disciplinary session begins benignly enough, only to abruptly start spiraling out of control. If this happens, casually interrupt the interview to call and request something, while actually calling for help. That's why it's important to have a prearranged signal for just such an emergency. Some authorities recommend directly telling the subject you are summoning help in order to maintain credibility in the interaction and because this may actually reassure some subjects who are feeling out of control. Other subjects may panic and attack you if they think you're calling for backup. Assess the situation and use your judgment.
>
> *Body language.* Don't behave in ways that could be interpreted as aggressive or threatening, such as moving too close, staring, pointing, or displaying provocative facial expressions or postures. Try to stand at an oblique angle facing the employee: not directly in front of him, which could be interpreted as a challenge, and not behind him, which may signify a possible sneak attack. Observe the general rule of standing two quick steps away from a dangerous subject. Some authorities recommend asking the employee if you can sit down, as this may constitute a less threatening figure. Then encourage him to be seated as well. If you're already standing, and it looks safe, try to slowly and unobtrusively maneuver yourself toward a doorway or other point of quick exit and always be scanning the environment for points of escape, but be careful not to be too obvious about this, which may antagonize the subject. Always move slowly and keep your hands where they can be seen.
>
> *Communication style.* Keep the employee engaged in conversation about his feelings or about a specific problem, but avoid egging him on. Venting should not escalate to ranting. Keep the conversation going, pace it,

and modulate your voice. Don't shout, put a sharp edge on your voice, or use threats. Conversely, don't mumble or speak hesitantly so that the employee has trouble understanding you, which he may find irritating. Give the employee your undivided attention and use empathic listening skills, such as simple restatement of the employee's concerns to show you're getting it.

Use common sense and your own judgment, but generally don't attempt to logically reason with a subject who is under the influence of drugs or alcohol or is clearly irrational or psychotic. The purpose of your communication is not to try to talk him out of his gripes or delusions: You won't. Conversely, don't pretend to agree with the subject's distorted point of view because the inherent deceptiveness and insincerity of this gesture may further infuriate him. Rather, show empathy and concern for his real or imagined plight and suggest alternative ways of resolving the crisis.

Another principle of crisis communication is *When in doubt, shut up.* Use silence as a tactic and let the employee talk, as the more energy and adrenalin he expends, the sooner he will fatigue and the easier it will be to control the situation. However, avoid seeming like you're ignoring the employee and be sure to answer when spoken to. Also, if his own speech seems to be agitating himself further, use verbal and nonverbal calming techniques to ratchet down the tension level while continuing to let him talk.

> **Communication content.** Don't argue, give orders, or disagree when not absolutely necessary. Don't push your own authority or blather on in an officious, know-it-all manner. Conversely, don't be overly placating or patronizing and don't condescend by using childish responses that are cynical, satirical, or insulting. Be careful with attempts to lighten the situation with humor. Persons under extreme stress tend to be very literal and concrete, and even well-intentioned levity may be misinterpreted as mocking or belittling his plight.

Don't make promises you can't keep, except possibly to buy time in an emergency situation. Avoid complex "why" and "what" inquiries that put the employee on the defensive; rather, use simple, direct, close-ended, yes-or-no questions. Calmly and simply explain the consequences of further violent behavior without provocation or condemnation. Set limits and give choices between two alternatives: "I want to talk with you about this, Fred. Do you want to sit down here or go outside for a smoke?" Try to deescalate slowly, moving from step to step toward less agitated behavior.

Scene control. Whenever there's a commotion, people may flock to the scene, either to help or just gawk. Don't allow a number of interveners to interact simultaneously with the employee in multiple dialogues, as this can be confusing and irritating. Have one intervener take charge. If this person is clearly ignored or rejected by the subject, try to find someone who can establish better rapport. Any physical restraint or take-down procedures should be carried out by personnel with specialized training in this area. Don't allow an audience to gather around the employee, cheer him on, insult him, or shout at him from a distance; this includes the media. Anyone who has no business being there should leave immediately. If professional crisis negotiators or law enforcement officers show up at the scene, brief them as thoroughly as possible and then let them take charge.

Guns and Weapons

In many cases of workplace violence, the subject is armed (Schaner, 1996). An employee may have brought a weapon to the scene with the clear intention of using it or kept it with him during his conversations with his boss or coworkers, "just in case." In other situations, a customer may have a dispute with the company and brought along a weapon for backup, or it may just represent a robbery attempt. In any of these cases, some recommendations apply (Dubin, 1995; Flannery, 1995), to be supplemented by adequate training and practice, when abruptly faced with an armed life-and-death confrontation.

The first thing to do upon seeing the weapon is acknowledge it with a neutral and obvious remark, for example, "I see the gun." Maintain your distance, keep your hands visible, and move slowly. Never tell the subject to drop the gun or attempt to grab it, as he may have another weapon concealed or may simply overpower you. As rapport develops, and if the subject appears ambivalent about using the weapon, request that he point it away while you talk. Appeal to his sense of competence and control: To avoid an accident, ask if he will at least decock the gun (revolver) or put the safety catch on (semiautomatic pistol). If he flat out refuses, let the topic go and just be cautious.

If the subject seems willing to surrender the weapon, don't ask him to hand it over, but rather have him unload it, place it down in a safe, neutral corner, and back away. Some authorities recommend that the intervener then slowly pick up the gun and neutralize it, being careful not to point it at the subject, as this may give him an excuse to pull another concealed weapon or otherwise attack you. However, any contact with the weapon on your part can be dangerous because you don't know whether he'll suddenly change his mind and think you're trying to attack him. Therefore, to avoid being baited into going for the gun, wait until the subject has put it down safely, then ask him to calmly walk out of the room with you, leaving the weapon behind.

One of the principles of crisis negotiation is that the more time that passes without the subject's firing the weapon or otherwise injuring anyone, the lower the overall likelihood of violence occurring (Gilliland & James, 1993; McMains & Mullins, 1996; Miller, 2005c, 2006m). Initially, however, you should comply with whatever reasonable and safe demands the armed subject may make ("Sit over there." "Get my supervisor on the phone." "Hand over the money.") and take special care to avoid agitating him further. Continue to talk to the subject (unless he tells you to be quiet), reasonably empathize with the perceived grievance or his feelings about it, and acknowledge that he's in control of the situation.

Try to appear calm, but not nonchalant or cocky and not intimidating, confrontational, or argumentative. Encourage the armed subject to talk out his concerns, but remember the difference between venting and ranting: The former serves to blow off steam, the latter can cause the pot to boil over. Employ the relevant defusing strategies discussed above (and reinforced by your training) until the crisis is safely and successfully resolved or qualified professionals have taken control of the scene.

WORKPLACE VIOLENCE RECOVERY

Sometimes the worst case scenario happens and a violent incident stuns and horrifies the workplace. People may be killed, others physically wounded, some held hostage, and many emotionally traumatized. It is in the aftermath of such a dramatic episode that executives, managers, and the mental health clinicians they consult with typically engage in the most intensive collaboration to facilitate the recovery of affected personnel and the company as a whole (Miller, 1997a, 1997c, 1998h, 1999c, 2000d, 2000f, 2001a, 2001b, 2002a, 2005e, 2008).

Plans, Policies, and Procedures

A particularly fruitful collaboration among executives, managers, and mental health professionals concerns proactively setting up policies and procedures for responding to the aftermath of a workplace violence incident. Many of these originated in specialized settings such as mental health clinics or law enforcement agencies and have been developed and adapted for the corporate world by psychology and management experts (Albrecht, 1996, 1997; Blythe, 2002; Caponigro, 2000; Dezenhall & Weber, 2007; Flannery, 1995; Kinney, 1995, 1996; Mantell & Albrecht, 1994; Miller, 1999c, 2008; Mitroff, 2001; Yandrick, 1996).

Media and public relations. A specially designated media spokesperson should brief the media and, more importantly, shepherd them away from grieving employees, family members, and eyewitnesses. A firm, forthright, proactive, and sincere approach to providing information is preferred, from someone in a high position within the organization or, alternatively, a qualified outside public relations spokesperson or firm. Companies should always be prepared to offer a concerned and honest answer to the question, "What is this organization doing for the survivors and the victims' families?"

Employees and families. Someone should be designated to notify the victims' families of the incident and be ready to offer them immediate support, counseling, and other services (also see chapters 8, 9). Personnel managers should arrange time off for grieving and traumatized employees as appropriate. Following the initial stages of the incident, the mental health clinician should help managers and supervisors find ways for the employees to memorialize slain victims.

Law enforcement, physical security, and cleanup. Someone should be assigned to immediately check, protect, and/or restore the integrity of the company's data systems, computers, and files. A representative should be designated to work with local law enforcement. The crime scene should be kept intact until law enforcement has gone over the area. A cleanup crew for the site of the attack should be available, pending approval from law enforcement investigators. Exquisite sensitivity to surviving staff's feelings about "cleaning up the mess, like nothing happened" is crucial, and such cleanup operations should be conducted in as respectful, even solemn, a manner as possible.

Legal measures. In-house legal counsel or the company's outside law firm should be notified about the incident and, if necessary, asked to respond to the scene. They should advise company executives and managers as to appropriate actions immediately following the incident and in the weeks and months ahead. Always remember that the greater the sincere concern shown by the company for its employees, families, and stakeholders, the lower the level of contentious litigation is likely to occur in the months and years to come.

Mental health mobilization. In the best case, planning will have included detailed preparation and practice drills with the company psychologist or outside mental health consultant. In most cases, it simply means that the mental health clinician has become sufficiently familiar with the organization to know how to gather critical information and respond promptly and effectively at the time of a crisis. Unfortunately, in many organizations, postincident mental health services are farmed out to generic EAP counselors who, competent enough to handle routine mental health issues, have little or no training in posttraumatic stress syndromes or corporate crisis intervention.

Company representatives should know how to contact their mental health professionals immediately, and arrange for the clinicians to meet first at top levels of the organization for executive briefings, and then schedule meetings with anyone in the organization who needs to talk about what happened. A critical incident debriefing area (see below) should be established for the responding mental health professionals. Optional crisis intervention services should be made available for all potential workplace violence victims, not just immediate survivors or employees. A follow-up schedule should be arranged for the clinicians to return to the site for further services as needed or for referral of employees to their private offices or clinics for follow-up counseling.

Restoring Order: Posttrauma Crisis Management

In the immediate aftermath of a workplace violence incident, available personnel must begin the process of accounting for slain, injured, and surviving employees while awaiting the arrival of posttrauma professional service providers. Company officials must communicate the message that all personnel and family members will be provided the utmost care and concern. Mental health consultants should advise managers and executives that many of their employees will be destabilized, demoralized, and disoriented, and that they will be looking to company authorities to restore order and their sense of confidence and psychological equilibrium. This is a critical time. Failure to demonstrate constructive grief leadership following a crisis can leave a corrosive stain on the morale of the company that will be hard to expunge. The following are steps that mental health consultants can assist companies in taking that are designed to facilitate the expression of concern and restore order following a workplace violence trauma:

Demonstrate concern and caring for those who have been harmed by the trauma. The clear message that employees and other organizational stakeholders need to hear is that management is going to do everything humanly and administratively possible to care for those affected by this tragedy.

Within the limits of privacy and security, *open up communication channels and control rumors.* Describe what actions the company is taking to assist in recovery and what measures are being developed to reduce the risk of this kind of trauma happening again.

Assess the organization's personnel and business requirements in order to restore business performance. Inform employees what it will take to get back to normal and approximately how long it will take.

Following the immediate and short-term crisis interventions, *arrange for the posttrauma mental health team to return* to the workplace on a periodic basis to counsel and debrief employees as needed.

Conduct a thorough postincident investigation. Remember another principle of crisis intervention: *20/20 hindsight = 20/20 insight = 20/20 foresight.* Questions asked during the postincident investigation may concern the nature of the perpetrator, his relationship to the organization and with coworkers and supervisors, his history of disciplinary action or termination, his role as a customer or other outsider, the actions that led to his dissatisfaction as an employee or customer, any restraining orders or other legal actions and their enforcement, the workplace stressors that may have been involved, financial pressures, drugs, alcohol, mental illness, or personality disorders, any warning signs that should have been heeded, and the company's overall security and threat assessment procedures.

In general, if there is any positive outcome that can emerge from a workplace violence incident, it is what can be learned in order to reduce the chances of the same kind of tragedy happening in the future. To the extent that this is accomplished, a greater sense of control and safety will allow the traumatized company to heal itself and get back to business.

Role of Executives and Leaders

This sense of control and safety begins with a strong message from top management that emphasizes the company's willingness to take appropriate responsibility, address the causes of the incident in a forthright manner, provide services for all who need them, and pursue every necessary step and reasonable action to ensure, as much as humanly and organizationally possible, that something like this never again catches the company unprepared. Indeed, all successful managers, at any level, manifest the qualities of true leadership in both ordinary and critical circumstances (Miller, 2006g, 2006m, 2008).

WORKPLACE VIOLENCE: PSYCHOLOGICAL EFFECTS

Here is where the mental health clinician can have the greatest impact on corporate crisis intervention, both in terms of direct clinical services and in a consultative role (Miller, 1998h, 1999c, 2008).

Workplace Violence Response Patterns and Syndromes

Individuals affected by workplace traumatic events may include injured employees, employees remote from the scene, witnesses, family members, first responders such as police or paramedics, stakeholders such as suppliers or customers that knew the victims, or any others connected to the trauma (Kinney, 1995, 1996; LeBlanc & Barling, 2005; Mantell & Albrecht, 1994; Neuman & Baron, 1998, 2005).

According to one model (Kinney, 1995), employees can be conceptualized as falling into three general groups following a trauma:

> **Recover quickly.** Many individuals will show a relatively rapid, spontaneous recovery, seemingly without the assistance of any type of mental health intervention. Some of these seemingly stoic souls, however, may be internalizing their pain and grief, only to unload their suppressed emotional burden at a later date.
>
> **Require modest psychological counseling.** These individuals may need some mental health assistance in order to regain their previous level of confidence, security, and safety but are unlikely to become long-term patients.
>
> **Develop serious psychological disorders.** These may include PTSD (chapter 2), severe anxiety or depression (chapter 3), or somatoform disorders (chapter 4) that require more extensive psychotherapy and/or other clinical services.

Some authorities (Flannery, 1995; Mantell & Albrecht, 1994) have identified three basic stages of reaction in the aftermath of a workplace violence incident, which appear to bear some similarity to the stages of response to many kinds of disasters.

> **Stage one: Shock, disbelief, and denial.** This stage of the workplace violence response begins immediately after the incident and may last anywhere from minutes to hours to days, occasionally for weeks or even months. In severe trauma cases, people may wander about, stunned and dazed by the event they have just endured. This reaction usually dissipates over time, shading into the remaining stages.
>
> **Stage two: Cataclysm of emotions.** Here, the victims may run a gauntlet of different feelings as they try to come to terms with their experience. This stage can last for a few days or linger for years and can include feelings of vengeance directed against the perpetrator of the violence; anger against the company for failing to protect them; rage against God, fate, society, or the criminal justice system; and self-blame for failing to take the proper action, misperceiving the obscure warning signs, or just being in the wrong place at the wrong time. Survivors may experience fear and terror; suffer from phobias and panic attacks as they

attempt to return to the workplace; and develop hypervigilance, intrusive imagery, withdrawal, sleep disorders, and health problems. They may experience grief, sorrow, survivor guilt, self-loathing, confusion, and depression as they return to the workplace and are reminded of fallen coworkers by worksite grief anchors, such as a desk, workstation, locker, photos, nameplates, media accounts, anniversary dates, and so on.

Stage three: Reconstruction of equilibrium. By this time, the survivors have finally started to regain their emotional and mental balance. They have a new outlook, not just about what happened, but about themselves and how they have coped and will continue to cope. There are still good days and bad days, but the movement is definitely in the direction of recovery.

Posttraumatic Stress Disorder in Workplace Violence

When the serious psychological impact of the workplace violence event persists beyond one month, employee victims may develop full-blown PTSD. The basic symptoms and clinical parameters of PTSD have been described in chapter 2, and PTSD symptoms seen in victims of workplace violence may have their own particular form and rationale (Flannery, 1995). Traumatic events destroy one's sense of reasonable mastery and personal control. Some victims assume a stance of overcontrol, trying to avoid ever being vulnerable again. Others try to regain control by blaming themselves for what happened. The implicit assumption is that if the victim did something to put himself in harm's way, then he can somehow change this so that it will never happen again; blaming the company, supervisor, or coworkers is an analogous process. Still others give up completely and descend into drugs and alcohol. They seem to have developed the assumption that because they were unable to avert the violence at work, they are unable to control anything in their lives.

Disruption of caring attachments and basic human trust is related to the fact that workplace violence is perpetrated by other human beings. To make matters worse, other employees may distance themselves from the surviving victims in order to avoid "contagion" or to self-protectively search for some aspect of the victim's behavior that "caused" the violence. This reinforces the employee-victim's withdrawal and produces a vicious cycle of alienation and recrimination.

A sense of meaningful purpose in life is disrupted in the wake of workplace violence. Victims don't feel safe, no longer regard daily life at work or home as predictable or controllable, and lose their motivation to carry on. The deliberate, conscious threat to or destruction of human life by others is frightening and demoralizing, and it raises the existential problem of evil that must be addressed before the victims can once again begin to invest their time and energy in work, family, and recreational activities (Flannery, 1995).

Impact of Mass Violence at Work

Most recent studies of workplace violence have focused on dramatic events, such as mass shootings (Classen, Koopman, Hales, & Spiegel, 1998; Fergusson & Horwood, 1987; Hough et al., 1990; North, Smith, McCool, & Shea, 1989; North et al., 1999; North, Smith, & Spitznagel, 1997; Schwartz & Kowalski, 1991; Smith, North, McCool, & Shea, 1990; Trappler & Friedman, 1996). These studies have documented considerable psychological impact on victims, witnesses, and families. As noted several times in this book, this impact is influenced by various factors, including degree of exposure to the traumatic agent as well as personal characteristics such as demographics and psychiatric history.

Gore-Felton, Gill, Koopman, and Spiegel (1999) studied the psychological effects of a 1993 mass shooting at an office building in San Francisco. In this incident, 14 people were shot and many employees were trapped in the building for several hours. Within 8 days of the shooting, one-third of the 36 employees who worked in the building where the shootings took place were found to meet clinical criteria for acute stress disorder (ASD; see chapter 2). It was largely these employees who went on to develop PTSD later.

In 1991, a gunman drove his truck into the front of a crowded cafeteria in Killeen, Texas, and began shooting customers indiscriminately, many at point-blank range. After being wounded by police, the gunman fatally shot himself. He killed a total of 24 people, including himself. North, Smith, and Spitznagel (1994) examined acute traumatic stress symptoms in men and women who were present during the mass shooting. Over 80% of those who witnessed the violence reported experiencing intrusive recall of the traumatic event, and one-half to three-quarters of these individuals experienced hyperstartle responses, insomnia, and nightmares.

On May 5, 1992, during closing arguments of a divorce proceeding in the local courthouse of the small upscale suburb of Clayton, Missouri, right outside St. Louis, the estranged husband pulled two revolvers from his briefcase and shot his wife and both parties' lawyers. He fired at the judge, missing him, and then strode through the back hallway, firing at several people. By the time police shot and wounded the gunman, his wife lay dead and five others were wounded. The whole episode lasted less than 10 minutes.

Johnson, North, and Smith (2002) studied the aftermath of the Clayton courthouse shooting by interviewing employees who were present that day. They found that one-fourth of the study participants had a diagnosable psychiatric disorder after the courthouse shooting incident. However, three-quarters of this affected subsample had histories of preexisting psychiatric disorder, which was believed to be a risk factor for an adverse posttraumatic reaction (see chapters 2 and 3). Only 10% of the sample developed a new psychiatric disorder they had not experienced prior to the incident, and half of these represented classic PTSD syndromes.

Despite the relatively low rates of psychiatric disorder after the courthouse shooting, mental health services were mobilized and abundantly used. Nearly half the sample received some form of mental health services, which may have reduced the rates of psychopathology. In fact, although almost all respondents reported some degree of psychological distress from the incident, most reported relatively good levels of functioning by the time of the study and described relatively minor long-term effects of this incident on their lives. This argues for the importance of timely mental health intervention (see below).

Johnson et al. (2002) speculate that the higher rates of PTSD following the Killeen, Texas, massacre may relate to the larger scope and greater intensity of that incident, with 24 fatalities and the associated terror and horror for victims trapped by a gunman shooting them at point-blank range for a period of a quarter of an hour. In comparison, the Clayton courthouse shooting involved one fatality, a shorter period of action (less than 10 minutes), and less intense exposure (few individuals even seeing the gunman). It is also possible that individuals regularly frequenting a courthouse are more mentally prepared for the possibility of such an event, or at least more used to being in the presence of assorted rough characters and thus might experience fewer psychological problems afterward.

Finally, differences in community characteristics might also be expected to affect the response of individuals to these mass murder events. The southern, small-town community environment of Killeen, Texas, might be expected to provide greater social support to the victims, but this did not appear to be sufficient to overcome the traumatic effect of this devastating incident and so did not translate into lower rates of psychopathology at those sites, compared to the Clayton courthouse incident that took place in the heart of the greater St. Louis metropolitan area, but appeared to involve an overall lesser degree of traumatization.

PSYCHOLOGICAL INTERVENTIONS
FOR WORKPLACE VIOLENCE

Therapists and counselors may be directly involved in providing services to surviving victims of workplace violence, their coworkers, and families of surviving or slain victims. Although the principles of counseling and therapy are similar to those discussed in other chapters of this book, some special challenges and considerations apply to providing mental health care in the workplace context.

Benefits of Organization-Based Workplace Violence Interventions

For one thing, although most authorities emphasize the advantage of early identification and treatment of workplace trauma and other PTSD syndromes, many companies, agencies, and insurance carriers are still reluctant to make psychological referrals after a traumatic incident at work, fearing that such actions will lead to expanded claims against them or excessive outlays for treatment and disability benefits. In fact, actual experience documents the opposite: Prompt and appropriate psychological care of traumatized employees can reduce the number of stress claims and the cash amount of legal settlements, because responsible action makes a positive statement about the company's commitment to employee well-being. Further, with proper intervention, the affected employees are less likely to develop costly substance abuse, chronic pain, somatization, or other traumatic disability syndromes (Albrecht, 1996; Denenberg & Braverman, 1999; Everstine & Everstine, 1993; Flannery, 1995; Martinko et al., 2005; Miller, 1998h, 1999c, 2001a, 2001b, 2002e, 2008; Schneid, 1999; Yandrick, 1996).

Model Psychological Intervention Programs for Workplace Violence

In the past few years, a number of preventive and reparative trauma treatment programs have been developed for the psychological management of workplace violence. These have been developed for diverse needs and populations, including responding to a wave of terrorist robberies at financial institutions in the Netherlands (Brom & Kleber, 1989), dealing with American workplace accidents and violence (Everstine & Everstine, 1993), handling the stressors sustained by law enforcement and emergency services personnel during critical incidents (Mitchell & Everly, 1996), managing workplace violence in the health care setting (Flannery, 1995), and addressing the trauma of bank robberies in the United States (Jones, 2002). In reviewing these model programs, think about which ones, or what combination of protocols, might work most effectively with the company or organization you contract with or consult to.

Organizationally Supported, Clinician-Guided Approaches

Brom and Kleber (1989) outline several principles of intervention that underlie their program. To avoid the potentially stigmatizing singling out of individuals, assistance of traumatized employees is standardized, and all involved personnel participate. Assistance is formulated as an official program within the organization, with a clear delineation of staff roles and responsibilities. Management assigns a skilled staff member or clinical consultant who is in charge of victim assistance, has no direct association with the career of the traumatized employees, and is not bound to report on the employees.

In this model, the clinician's function is solely to support the traumatized employees immediately after the event and in the longer term recovery period. Organizations develop clear policies and procedures with regard to the temporary absence of traumatized employees and, if necessary, the transfer of an employee to another position within the organization without penalty or repercussions.

Everstine and Everstine's (1993) program is similar. Treatment of traumatized employees is carried out by mental health professionals with specialized training and experience in crisis intervention and trauma therapy. All employees are encouraged to participate, but those who are particularly resistant to the group process may be referred for individual counseling or psychotherapy. The treatment services are individualized to meet the needs of each particular employee and his or her job environment. Where return to the original worksite is not possible, retraining and reassignment are implemented.

According to this model, when a traumatic event occurs at the workplace, it is management's responsibility to take decisive steps toward facilitating stabilization and recovery. For example, time should be set aside for employees to discuss and work through their reactions to the event. Employees should be given as much factual information as possible about the incident, as well as the condition of coworkers (within the limits of privacy) to mitigate dangerous rumors and restore a sense of control. Employees who are in the hospital or recuperating at home need information and support as well, and efforts should be made to prevent them from being alienated from their fellow workers.

Workplace superstitions about bad luck often take the form of unaffected workers avoiding or actively ostracizing the trauma survivors for fear that the victims' ill fortune could rub off on them or because the victims are defensively regarded as somehow responsible for their fate, similar to the circumstance surrounding some sexual assault and other crime victims (see chapters 1, 2, 8, 10). These potential sources of conflict may be defused in group meetings, restoring needed cohesion and workplace support (Everstine & Everstine, 1993).

Critical Incident Stress Debriefing (CISD)

Critical incident stress debriefing or CISD (Mitchell & Everly, 1996) is a structured group intervention that was originally developed for law enforcement and emergency services personnel but that has been adapted for use in a wide variety of settings, including workplaces, disaster management, health care settings, and the military (Clark, 2007; Dyregrov, 1997; Everly, Flannery, & Mitchell, 1999; Miller, 1995b, 1998h, 1999g, 1999k, 2000a, 2005d, 2006f, 2007k, 2007m; Mitchell & Everly, 1996). The CISD process is designed to promote the emotional processing of traumatic events through the ventilation and normalization of reactions, as well as preparation for possible future crises. A CISD debriefing typically is a peer-led, clinician-guided process, although the individual roles of clinicians and peers may vary from setting to setting. The staffing of a debriefing usually consists of a mental health clinician and one or more peer debriefers, that is, fellow workers who have been trained in the CISD process and who may have been through critical incidents and debriefings in their own careers.

A typical debriefing takes place within 24 to 72 hours after the critical incident and consists of a single group meeting that lasts 2 to 3 hours, although shorter or longer meetings may be dictated by circumstances. Group size may range from a handful to a roomful, the determining factor usually being how many people will have time to fully express themselves in the number of hours allotted for the debriefing. Where large numbers of workers are involved, such as in mass disaster rescues (see chapter 14), successive debriefings may be held successively over the course of several days to accommodate all the personnel involved.

The formal CISD process—often referred to as the Mitchell model, after its chief originator (Mitchell & Everly, 1996)—consists of seven key phases, designed to assist psychological processing from the objective and descriptive, to the more personal and emotional, and back to the educative and integrative levels, focusing on both cognitive and emotional mastery of the traumatic event:

1. *Introduction.* The introduction phase of a debriefing is the time when the team leader—either a mental health professional or peer debriefer, depending on the composition of the group—gradually introduces the CISD process, encourages participation by the group, and sets the ground rules by which the debriefing will operate. Generally, these involve confidentiality, attendance for the full session, unforced participation in the discussions, and the establishment of a noncritical atmosphere.

2. *Fact phase.* During this phase, the group members are asked to briefly describe their job or role during the incident and, from their own perspective, provide some facts about what happened. The basic question is: "What did you do?"

3. *Thought phase.* The CISD leader asks the group members to discuss their first and subsequent thoughts during the critical incident: "What went through your mind?"

4. *Reaction phase.* This phase is designed to move the group participants from a predominantly cognitive mode of processing to a more cathartic, emotional level: "What was the worst part of the incident for you?" It is usually at this point that the meeting gets intense, as members take their cues from one another and begin to vent their distress. Clinicians and peer-debriefers keep a keen eye out for any adverse or unusual reactions among the participants.

5. *Symptom phase.* This begins the movement back from the predominantly emotional processing level toward the cognitive processing level. Participants are asked to describe cognitive, physical, emotional, and behavioral signs of distress that appeared (a) immediately at the scene or within several hours of the incident; (b) a few days after the incident; and (c) continuingly, even at the time of the debriefing: "What have you been experiencing since the incident?"

6. *Education phase.* Continuing the move back toward intellectual processing, didactic information is provided about the nature of the stress response and the expected physiological and psychological reactions to critical incidents (see chapter 2). This serves to normalize the stress and coping responses and provides a basis for questions and answers.

7. *Reentry phase.* This is the wrap-up, during which any additional questions or statements are addressed, referral for individual follow-ups are made, and general group bonding is reinforced: "What have you learned?" "Is there anything positive that can come out of this experience that can help you grow personally or professionally?" "How can you help one another in the future?" "Is there anything we left out?"

This is not to suggest that these phases always follow one another in an unvarying, mechanical sequence. I've found that in practice, once group participants feel comfortable with the debriefing process and start talking, there is a tendency for the fact, thought, and reaction phases to blend together. Indeed, as Mitchell and Everly (1996) recognize, it would seem artificial and forced to abruptly interrupt someone expressing emotion just because "it's not the right phase." As long as the basic rationale and structure of the debriefing are maintained, the therapeutic process will usually ensue. Indeed, on a number of occasions, previously silent members have spoken up at literally the last moment, when the group was all but getting up to leave. Clinician team leaders typically have to step in only when emotional reactions become particularly intense, or where one or more members begin to blame or criticize others.

Assaulted Staff Action Program (ASAP)

Building on the work of Mitchell and Everly (1996), Flannery and colleagues (Flannery, 1995; Flannery, Fulton, Tausch, & DeLoffi, 1991; Flannery, Penk, Hanson, & Flannery, 1996; Flannery et al., 1998) have designed a comprehensive, voluntary, peer-help, systems approach, called the *assaulted staff action program* (ASAP), for health care staff who are assaulted by patients at work. The program provides a range of services:

- Individual critical incident stress debriefings of assaulted staff
- Debriefings of entire hospital units
- A staff victims' support group
- Employee victim family debriefing and counseling
- Referrals for follow-up psychotherapy, as indicated

The ASAP team structure is comprised of 15 direct-care staff volunteers. To depathologize the process and maximize its appeal, the approach is conceptualized as psychoeducational, rather than as formal clinical counseling or psychotherapy per se. The ASAP has three supervisors, and the ASAP team director is responsible for administering the entire program and for ensuring the quality of the services.

When combined with preincident training and stress management, the ASAP program has reportedly proven effective in ameliorating the psychological impact of patient assaults on employees and in significantly reducing the overall level of violence institution-wide. In facilities where it has been applied, the program has proven to be cost-effective in terms of reduced staff turnover, less use of sick leave, fewer industrial accident claims, and less medical expense as overall assault rates have declined. Indeed, the authors make the practical, bottom-line point that the costs associated with the entire program are far less than that of one successful lawsuit.

Flannery (1995, 1996) recommends the following basic steps in implementing an organization's own ASAP:

1. Develop administrative support for the program
2. Tailor the model for the individual facility
3. Recruit the team members
4. Train the team
5. Field the completed service

Each step generally takes about 1 month, so teams can be online within about 6 months.

Enhanced Debriefing Model (EDM)

Jones (2002) has developed a specialized debriefing model for employee victims of bank robbery trauma, who, he believes, may suffer the additional stress and trauma associated with repeated exposure to workplace triggers and cues. This *enhanced debriefing model* (EDM) incorporates a structured, time-limited, group-based intervention much like CISD, but EDM places special attention on workplace support in the recovery process. Another aspect of this model is its emphasis on consultation and training of managers before an incident occurs, although, as we've seen, most CISD-based models, including ASAP, emphasize proactive training.

The EDM program begins in a consultative mode by providing an appraisal of workplace support and making suggestions designed to increase organizational cohesiveness, especially during the critical moments immediately following the trauma. For example, EDM may help the managerial staff of an organization identify possible nonsupportive aspects of the work environment that may interfere with victim recovery. The importance of work environment support in the recovery process is emphasized to the organization through ongoing consultation with human resource directors and managers.

Based on numerous individual and group interventions I've carried out with survivors of workplace violence, I can't stress enough the importance of organizational support and commitment to the process of helping traumatized employees. In one of the worst cases I can remember, a bank branch grudgingly arranged for a staff debriefing after a holdup, only because the service was mandated by their managed care contract. The branch managers clearly regarded the whole thing as a waste of time that cut into the employees' work hours. The most uncomfortable back room in the storage and lunch area was found for the debriefing, which was frequently interrupted by other employees coming in and out to get coffee or use the bathroom. Entering coworkers (who had not been involved in the robbery) gawked at the seated debriefees and a few made audible sarcastic comments about "free time." Needless to say, the participants wanted the whole thing over with as quickly as possible, and little therapeutic work was accomplished.

The best case I can remember, in terms of company support, involved a hostage and shooting crisis perpetrated by a disturbed customer of a medium-sized investment firm, which resulted in two deaths and several injuries. Almost immediately, the firm's president suspended business as usual, arranged for temps to cover the basic needs of the company, offered his home to be used for almost round-the-clock debriefings of the almost 100 employees, and provided food, beverages, and in a few cases, bed and board to employees who were too upset to drive home. He and the senior management staff offered any kind of practical help they could to survivors and their families, personally checked on proper funeral arrangements for the slain employees, visited the employees who were in the hospital, and generally shared in the grief and recovery of the members of their staff. Far more than any specific clinical services I could provide, this natural, unselfish, human response to tragedy within the ranks on the part of senior staff—the true definition of *leadership*—helped this firm to heal quickly and move on. In leading the process of recovery, the staff showed respect for their slain comrades but also honored their memories by productively continuing their work.

CONCLUSIONS

The design and maintenance of behaviorally safe workplaces represents a vital collaboration between industry and the mental health professions. Employers must learn to take all threats to worker safety seriously and take action to deal with those threats. They must encourage all employees, men and women, to report any breaches of personal or company security. Violence prevention should be right up there with fire prevention as a corporate safety issue. Companies must have measures in place to deal with disciplinary matters, safe hiring and firing, escalating crises, ongoing emergencies, and aftermath effects. These measures will reduce the risk of avoidable tragedies. Just as importantly, companies that encourage a fair and honorable corporate culture are more likely to earn the respect and loyalty of their employees. These employees will be more productive, and higher productivity means greater profitability. Finally, appropriate response to a workplace violence incident can often make the difference as to whether a small- to medium-sized company or local branch can survive and continue doing business. Mental health clinicians have a vital role to play in advising, consulting, and providing direct clinical services to public organizations and private companies of all types. And if safety is a critical issue for working adults, how much more so does this apply to the safety of our children in their workplace, the schools?

CHAPTER 13

Bullying and School Violence

W e've just seen that most working adults have a reasonable expectation of safety at their job sites. Children's job is to go to school—shouldn't they have the same expectation? As many of this book's chapters have so far made clear, most violent crimes are perpetrated by people the victims knows. For domestic violence victims, it is their mates; for workplace violence victims, it is often their coworkers; and for children, it is typically those they spend the most time with during their day, their schoolmates. Thus, the school environment exerts a powerful impact on the cognitive, emotional, and behavioral development of children (Bluestein, 2001).

PEER VICTIMIZATION: TERMS AND DEFINITIONS

Peer victimization is the experience of being a target of the aggressive behavior of other students or other children who are not siblings and not necessarily age-mates (Hawker & Boulton, 2000; Olweus, 1993, 1994; Ross, 1996).

Bullying can be defined as the illegitimate use of sadistic and/or coercive power by children or adults against another person. Bullying is defined as a specific type of aggression in which (a) the behavior is intended to harm or disturb; (b) the behavior occurs repeatedly over time; and (c) there is an imbalance of power, with a more powerful person or group attacking a less powerful one (Nansel et al., 2001).

Punking is a relatively new term that describes the practice of verbal and physical violence, humiliation, and shaming usually done in public by males to other males. Punking is commonly used by adolescent boys and is often described interchangeably with bullying (Phillips, 2007).

PEER VICTIMIZATION AND BULLYING:
THE LEGAL DIMENSION

Historically, the practice of peer victimization among children has often been delegitimized and rationalized as "roughhousing" or "boys will be boys" (Phillips, 2007). Ironically, the kinds of intimidation and harassment that would get an employee fired at almost any job are routinely tolerated by school authorities when they occur between students. In many of the cases of school violence studied, the perpetrators had been harassed or persecuted in some way by other students, and their efforts to have their plights resolved by school authorities were rebuffed or ignored. Of course, a far greater number of bullied students suffer in silence.

In addition to the human costs, school violence of any kind, like workplace violence (chapter 12), can have legal repercussions. *Stoneking v. Bradford Area School District, 1988* found that if a school is aware of dangerous and unlawful activities on its premises and takes insufficient action to address them, it may be found liable because of students' rights to liberty under the 14th amendment. However, school officials may be protected from liability if they can demonstrate due diligence in preventing crime on campus.

As bullying began to be increasingly regarded as unacceptable, federal and state governments moved to prohibit it, using Title IX of the 1972 Federal Education Amendments, which prohibits harassing behavior in schools and school-sponsored contexts. Under Title IX, harassment includes a pattern of behavior or a single incident, perpetrated by anyone, that creates an intimidating or hostile environment in which the targeted person cannot work or learn. Additionally, the Equal Protection Clause of the 14th Amendment of the United States Constitution has been used to protect against bullying, stating that schools are responsible for equally protecting all students and that all citizens are due equal protection under the law. Lastly, states such as Washington have instituted anti-bullying acts that are enforced statewide in schools (Phillips, 2007).

Ironically, although much more stringent legislative regulation exists for school safety than workplace safety (chapter 12), workplaces have been much more proactive than schools in developing antiviolence programs, which is why this chapter applies many of the workplace principles to the school setting. Perhaps this disparity exists because, in most corporate settings, incidences of violence affect the bottom line to a far greater extent than in most public schools.

TYPES OF SCHOOL BULLYING AND HARASSMENT

Nansel et al. (2001) studied 15,686 U.S. youths in grades 6 through 10 and found that 26% of the boys reported bullying others up to once a week, whereas 21% of boys reported being bullied regularly. These statistics translate into millions of boys participating in bullying either as a bully, a victim, or both. In addition to this direct participation, millions of youths and adults participate through witnessing these behaviors. Unlike girls, however, who could recall details of their harassment, boys experienced these practices so often that many had difficulty remembering their first experience.

Some experts in school violence have classified bullying and harassment into several overlapping categories, the most common of which will be reviewed here (Bjorkgvist, 1994; Crick et al., 1999; Hawker & Boulton, 2000; Olweus, 1993; Ross, 1996):

Individual bullying basically involves one-on-one aggression, usually when one kid just has it in for another. This is probably the most common kind of bullying that occurs in schools and neighborhoods.

Group bullying is also relatively common and involves a bunch of kids ganging up on the victim; the phenomenon is known as *mobbing* in the European literature. Often, only one member of this gang may actually commit an aggressive act, with the rest of the cohort cheering him on. On other occasions, however, several members of the group may join in the violence. In such cases, there is always the danger that the aggression will escalate to serious injury or even death of the victim.

Direct bullying involves the direct aggression of one child to another. Examples include hitting, shoving, tripping, and destruction of the victim's property.

Indirect bullying is carried out through a third party or in some way that conceals the identity of the aggressor. This may include secret sabotage of the victim's belongings, homework assignments, reputation, and so on.

Relational bullying is behavior that damages peer relationships and acceptance within the social group. This is the preferred method of girls who bully and, in many cases, can be as psychologically devastating to the ostracized victim as any physical injury.

A related and more general concept is *verbal victimization,* in which the student's status is attacked or threatened with words, and which can be exceedingly vicious and damaging to a student's psyche and self-image.

TYPES OF BULLIES

A combination of research (Coloroso, 2003; Shafii & Shafii, 2001) and practical experience has produced a rough consensus as to a typology of bullies:

Antisocial bully: "I'm the boss." This is the bully on a power trip. Clinical evaluation would no doubt reveal diagnostic features of conduct disorder (House, 1999; Mandel, 1997), which is the childhood version of antisocial personality disorder. These are the kids who simply get off on wielding power over others. They are not troubled in the classic psychosocial sense; in fact, they show a distinct lack of care or conscience about anything but their own gratification. Many of these kids can be quite charming and crafty and able to play innocent with adults. Because of their charismatic power, they often attract acolytes and badass wannabes, who then become the bully's cheering section, encouraging his depredations for the vicarious power rush.

Distressed bully: "Feel my pain." This type of bully most closely fits the stereotype of the troubled kid. There is typically an edgy, dysphoric cast to this child's personality: He may suffer from a mood disorder, ADHD, or borderline or paranoid personality disorder. He is less likely than the antisocial bully to go looking for trouble, but his irritable, mistrustful attitude and impulsive, hair-trigger temper may cause him to lash out at anyone he suspects of disrespecting him or otherwise getting on his nerves. He may feel remorse after such an outburst or he may attempt to justify it. This type of bully is sometimes called the *bully-victim* because he is likely to assume both roles at different times and with different students. He is also more likely to suffer multiple types of abuse in school, at home, and in the community (Holt, Finkelhor, & Kantor, 2007).

Situational bully: "Having a really bad day." Most of the time, this kid will keep to himself, but when stressed, he tends to project his anger at a target of convenience. The sheer unpredictability of his behavior may make him even more shunned by his peers because they never know when he's going to be a nice guy and when he's going to "go off."

TYPES OF VICTIMS

Consistent with the clinical reality that there are not always pure victims and pure villains, a general victim typology has emerged from the study of bullying (Coloroso, 2003; Shafii & Shafii, 2001) and from practical experience.

Anxious/depressed victim: "Why me?" This is the poor soul, nerd, or geek who is usually at the bottom of the social pecking order and is often the prime target for bullies, first, because of his weakness and submissiveness and, second, because the poor soul typically has few peers who will stand up for him. This victim spends an inordinate amount of time just trying to stay out of the bully's way. Often these victims suffer in silence for years and may develop a variety of serious physical and psychological disorders (see below).

Martyring/rescuing victim: "On a mission." These victims seem to wear their victimhood like a badge of honor and derive a grim sort of satisfaction from garnering sympathetic attention to their plight. Often, they overlap with the victim-bystander type discussed below or the bully-victim described above. They seem to be on a mission to highlight the bully's aggression and are less likely to run and hide than the anxious-depressed victim.

Provocative victim: "Gimme your best shot—I dare you." This often overlaps with the above type. This is the victim that seems to be "asking for it." In a roundabout, passive-aggressive way, this victim achieves a kind of victory over the bully by showing that he can take it and, what's more, that he will always bounce back and ask for more. Furthermore, his ability to evoke an aggressive response gives this student a paradoxical form of control over the behavior of a physically stronger person. In many cases, school peers don't know what to make of this kid. On the one hand, he seems crazy by acting like a glutton for punishment; on the other hand, he accrues a kind of grudging respect for standing up to the bully, even without directly retaliating. Ironically, because of the low payoff in terms of their own sense of power and control, bullies usually gravitate to someone else who presents a less willing but more obsequious victim.

TYPES OF BYSTANDERS AND WITNESSES

In most cases, the power rush that bullies get from their aggression necessitates an audience, some willing, others conscripted. Accordingly, there has evolved a typology of bystanders (Coloroso, 2003; Shafii & Shafii, 2001).

Victim-type bystander: "Better you than me." Bullies often have more than one chosen victim; in fact, there may be a hierarchy of victims, with members of this reluctant fraternity changing rank order at the bully's whim. Some in the group standing around, witnessing the aggression, may be former or current victims themselves and are only too glad to have someone else taking the thumps for now—even if they feel a little guilty about it. Others who have thus far escaped the bully's depredations may feel it's only a matter of time until his attention turns to them.

Bully-type bystander: "Power without the heat." This is the wannabe bully, the kid who may not be bad enough or tough enough to be a schoolyard predator himself but clearly gets off on identifying himself with the alpha aggressor. He'll be in the crowd, cheering the bully on, or at least encouraging him by his presence. Some of these kids retain their sidekick role, while others graduate to fully bully status themselves.

Avoidant bystander: "Don't ask, don't tell." This is the bystander who makes every effort to distance himself from the fracas because he just doesn't want the hassle. This type often overlaps with the victim-type bystander, except that the avoidant bystander has so far managed to stay under the bully's radar and wants to keep it that way.

Chameleon-type bystander: "Hey, whatever." This kid will do whatever he thinks it will take to avoid being a victim himself. If the bully needs a cheerleader, he'll cheer. If he can get away with lamming out, he'll flee. If there's an antibully coalition forming (see below) and he thinks it will be better for him to be in their camp, he'll switch allegiances. He has learned to adapt and survive by morphing his behavior into whatever the situation requires.

BULLYING: CAUSES, RISK FACTORS, AND PROTECTIVE FACTORS

Someone once said that "life is basically a fifth-grade class." Most social animals, from fish to birds to mammals to primates to people, have hierarchies and pecking orders, and the extremes of this are seen in the dynamic relationship among bullies, victims, and bystanders (Coloroso, 2003; Phillips, 2007; Shafii & Shafii, 2001). Several factors play a role.

Individual factors include biological traits of temperament, personality traits and disorders, and psychopathology. They also include factors of resilience and self-confidence to assertively stand up to aggression while not unnecessarily making oneself a target. Empirical research has shown that certain types of maladjustment, such as loneliness, depression, anxiety, and low self-esteem, are positively associated with such peer relationship difficulties as submissiveness, social withdrawal, and unpopularity with peers. These peer relationship difficulties are themselves risk factors for continued peer victimization (Hawker & Boulton, 2000).

School factors include the formal policies and programs that are in place for dealing with bullying, harassment, and peer violence (see below), as well as the general atmosphere of the school administration with regard to supporting student disclosure and standing behind students who are being victimized, as opposed to taking a hands-off, let-them-work-it out attitude.

Cultural factors reflect the fact that schools are often a reflection of their communities and the larger surrounding society, and the behavioral climate at school will be influenced by the religious, social, and family values of the surrounding community, which in turn contribute to school spirit, community connectedness, and morale. For example, a school climate that constructs, encourages, or supports an ideal norm of masculinity as constituting a Hollywood caricature of macho strength, power, and control can expect a heightened incidence of students solving problems through physical aggression (Gilligan, 1997; Kimmel, 1996; Phillips, 2007).

EFFECTS OF BULLYING

Studies have shown school victimization to exert a variety of deleterious effects on students' physical and mental health (Hawker & Boulton, 2000; Holt et al., 2007; Johnson, 1989; Kaltiala-Heino, Rimpelae, & Rantanen, 2001; Miller, 2002b; Mynard, Johnson, & Lohan, 2002; Nansel, Overpeck, Haynie, Ruan, & Scheidt, 2003; Nansel et al., 2001; Olweus, 1993; Pitcher & Poland, 1992; Rigby, 2003):

- Lowered self-esteem
- Increased loneliness and isolation
- Anxiety and panic attacks
- Depression and suicidal thoughts
- PTSD
- Increased number of doctor visits
- Psychosomatic symptoms and stress-related illnesses
- Greater use of tobacco and alcohol
- Reduced school attendance
- Impaired academic performance

Only rarely do disturbed, desperate students resort to violence (see below), but when they do, it often highlights systemic problems that have occurred for a long time—a strong parallel with workplace violence (chapter 12).

SCHOOL PROGRAMS FOR MANAGEMENT OF BULLYING: THE P.A.S.S. MODEL

From a review of the literature (Bender & McLaughlin, 1997; Coloroso, 2003; Hawker & Boulton, 2000; Olweus, 1994; Pitcher & Poland, 1992; Ross,

1996; Shafii & Shafii, 2001) and my own experience (Miller, 2000g, 2002b, 2003c, 2004d, 2004e, 2007e, 2007f), I have designed a model program for combating bullying, harassment, and peer aggression in schools, which I have termed the *P.A.S.S.* model.

> *P = POLICY.* This consists of educational programs and written policies regarding bullying, harassment, and peer victimization. As with workplace violence and workplace safety (chapter 12), a structured program is essential in order to achieve student, faculty, family, and community buy-in for the concept and practice of school safety.
>
> *A = ACTION.* This is the practical application of the policy and procedures phase noted above. These measures include a structured program for reporting and investigating threats and incidents, training in peer mediation and conflict resolution, and, where necessary, direct intervention with students, parents, and law enforcement.
>
> *S = SUPPORT.* This ensures needed backup services such as mentoring and extracurricular activities, as well as mental health referral and consultation.
>
> *S = SUPERVISION.* This provides oversight to the program in the form of periodic review of program effectiveness, with recommended modifications, as well as periodic monitoring of individual students who may be at high risk for being either bullies or victims.

STUDENT STRATEGIES FOR HANDLING
SCHOOL BULLYING: THE D.I.C.E. MODEL

Again, from a review of the literature (Bender & McLaughlin, 1997; Coloroso, 2003; Hawker & Boulton, 2000; Johnson, 2000; Olweus, 1994; Pitcher & Poland, 1992; Ross, 1996; Shafii & Shafii, 2001) and my own experience in working with schools and counseling individual students (Miller, 2002b, 2003c, 2004d, 2004e, 2007e, 2007f), I have designed a model protocol that educators and counselors can teach students to use (with proper training and practice) to combat bullying, harassment, and peer aggression in schools, which I have termed the *D.I.C.E.* model.

> *D = DOCUMENT* incidents of bullying and harassment. Note the date, time, location, and people involved, including the bully(ies), victim(s), bystanders, and other people around. Be as detailed as possible but be unobtrusive about doing it. Even the mere fact of recording this information often gives these kids a modicum of empowerment and control.

I = *INFORM* teachers, family, friends, or anyone you trust. This is often the trickiest part because many kids, including victims, may fear the stigma of being a snitch far more than they fear the bully's wrath. For many kids, this is a personal decision, and teachers, parents, and counselors cannot force a child to divulge being the victim of a bully unless there is an issue of direct child endangerment, in which case it may become a matter of mandated reporting of abuse by teachers or clinicians.

C = *CONFRONT* bullies and bystanders in a constructive way. The operative word here is *constructive,* which I define as any strategy that will reduce the frequency or intensity of interpersonal aggression. Some of these will be described below.

E = *EMPOWER* yourself with pride-building activities and peer support. Victimization feeds off low self-esteem and powerlessness. Find things you're good at. Find people who like you and will support you. Develop a crew, a set of friends you can count on (see below). Of course, for many children, this may be easier said than done.

HANDLING A BULLYING ENCOUNTER: WHAT KIDS CAN DO

Despite all the preparation and policies, a bullying confrontation may take place and there are some practical recommendations for students who find themselves caught in this situation. Always remember that the overriding guiding principle of all of these interventions is *safety first.* These strategies should always be used to defuse and deescalate a confrontation, perhaps with some saving of face but never just to win the confrontation for its own sake, which may only serve to escalate violence or set oneself up for later retaliation.

Educators and counselors should use the following outline as a general guide and feel free to be as flexible and creative as they can, accounting for the personalities of the individuals involved and the general culture of the school. Needless to say, training should be reinforced through sufficient rehearsals and role-plays, perhaps enlisting an outside professional to come into the school to conduct the training. The elements of this program consist of the following (I haven't come up with a catchy acronym for this, yet):

Personalize your response. The most effective intervention strategy will be the one that jives with the student's core personality and individual characteristics. Trying to act tough when you're not or attempting to use humor when that isn't your natural inclination will only seem contrived

and may backfire. Develop individualized strategies that seem most natural and comfortable for you.

Have a crew. Isolation is the handmaiden of victimhood. Develop an
insulative social circle. Like all predators, bullies tend to look for the
weakest members to cull from the herd. This is not to encourage your
friends to put themselves in danger—in fact, they don't actually have
to do anything—but often, the mere presence of a solid group of kids
who won't tolerate the bully's aggression against one of their crew is
enough to make him stalk off and try to find an easier target.

Sidestep. If you see trouble coming, try to get out of its way. Ideally, you
shouldn't have to hide and skulk through the halls, but don't know-
ingly and unnecessarily put yourself in a position where a confrontation is likely to erupt. For example, at assembly, don't sit right in the
bully's line of sight. If you share the same class, sit behind the bully if
possible. If you have to verbally interact, try to be neither overly deferential or challenging. Become a less attractive target.

Deflect. In a few cases, you may be jumped suddenly by the bully or
his cohorts, but in most cases, the encounter starts with a verbal exchange. Learn to use a variety of noninflammatory quips to deescalate
the situation, allowing the bully to save face but affording you some
little dignity in the process. This may take some creativity, so practice
and rehearse with your counselor-coach. For example:

BULLY: Hey, faggot, where you going—to cooking class?

STUDENT: Math, brother, math. Gotta cook up some equations so I can
get to basketball practice.

Use constructive humor. This is an extension of the above. Be careful here
because most bullies are very concrete and will interpret any joking as
an attempt to humiliate them, so try to use humor which is self-effacing
yet not self-abasing, for example:

BULLY: Yeah, go to math, Einstein. Only a four-eyed faggot would be
running to that class.

STUDENT: Hey, us four-eyed faggots gotta use our brains so we can get all
the smart babes.

Confront with realistic consequences. With a bully determined to provoke
a physical confrontation, sometimes, the direct approach may be the only
effective one:

BULLY: Well, I tell you what, faggot. You want to get to that faggot class, you gotta get past me.

STUDENT: You sure you want to do this? You know you already got two suspensions and, if you touch me again, I'm reporting it and so are all these people [which is why it's good to have a crew], which means this time, you get expelled and it goes to the police. So, hey, you decide if it's worth it.

For some bullies who feel they have something to lose, this may work. Others just won't give a damn and are only interested in saving face for the moment in front of their cheering section. Know your customers.

Get out of danger zone. Remember, the overriding rule is, safety first. So if there's no other choice, beat a hasty retreat and keep yourself safe. Most people won't disrespect you from refusing a fight that you can't possibly win.

HANDLING A BULLYING EPISODE:
WHAT ADULTS CAN DO

As stated above in the discussion of the P.A.S.S. model, for an antibullying program to work, and for the kids to buy in to the effectiveness of the strategies described above, they have to know that the administration will back them up. They also have to know that if the faculty and other responsible adults see trouble brewing, they will step in to intervene and not leave the kids floundering. Many schools have actual police forces or security services on campus, but sometimes a teacher or other adult may have to act quickly until these professionals get to the scene. In fact, there may be legal repercussions for failing to do so. The following recommendations apply to the adults in charge.

Assess for danger: Safety first! Scan the surroundings and make sure your intervention won't do more harm than good. If possible, call for backup in the form of additional faculty, security, or police. That's why it's essential to have a plan in place for these contingencies.

Separate the disputants. If trouble is brewing but has not yet boiled over, make every effort to gently but firmly get the antagonists out of earshot and visual range of each other. If more than one adult is present, have someone talk to each kid separately. If it's just you, you may have to use a little shuttle diplomacy to get the two sides to back off.

Determine the nature of the dispute: Bullying or otherwise. Kids are kids and not every confrontation constitutes peer victimization. Sometimes a heated argument can break out between students that doesn't actually involve one kid taking advantage of the other. At other times, the dividing line is not so clear. If this appears to be just a spirited debate among equals, encourage the parties to walk away and cool off, because you're obligated to discourage any kind of confrontational encounter that could escalate to a physical fight, but it's important to know when not to make a mountain out of a molehill.

Reaffirm rules and state consequences. In a firm, authoritative way, remind the disputants of the school rules of conduct and the consequences of failing to follow them. If either of the parties is under special probation or other conditions, remind him of this fact out of earshot of other students to avoid unnecessary embarrassment, but make it clear that the rules will be enforced.

Offer to mediate or arbitrate at a later time. If no actionable offense has yet been committed, offer to help the disputants resolve their disagreement, whatever that may be. The typical response will be, "No thanks, we'll work it out," in which case commend them on their efforts and remind them of the consequences of further fighting.

Make sure each side understands and can articulate rules and consequences. To avoid ambiguity and later claims of, "I don't remember you saying that," or, "I didn't know you meant that," have the disputants repeat to you a summary of what you've just discussed: "Just to make sure we're all on the same page, tell me in your own words what we just discussed." Make emendations to the narrative as necessary until the student gets it right. In most cases, it is probably not a good idea to make the disputants shake hands and try to pretend they're now friends, which may only foment further resentment. Better to keep them separated and just allow the situation to cool off.

Take administrative or disciplinary action, if necessary. If either or both of the disputants won't deescalate the situation or if the disagreement progresses to fighting, call security, campus police, or local community police, and take whatever action is appropriate, from suspension to arrest.

Support peer intervention. Make sure students understand that the school administration will stand by students' efforts to lawfully and nonviolently back up victims of bullies and that their efforts to report incidents and prevent violence will be firmly supported. One of the best ways to do this is by arranging for school-wide antibullying training to institutionalize this support.

The importance of administrative buy-in for such peer support intervention programs cannot be overemphasized because, especially in schools with high baseline levels of aggression, half-hearted and insufficiently supported implementation of such programs not only will fail to reduce the incidence of bullying, harassment, and peer aggression over the academic year but students will become more reluctant to get involved in any constructive school program (Cowie & Olafsson, 2000; Scarpa & Haden, 2006). Basically, if the school administration isn't serious about violence prevention, the bullies, victims, and other students will soon come to regard the program—and any other school-sponsored activities, such as safe sex or antidrug campaigns—as a joke.

PSYCHOTHERAPY AND COUNSELING WITH VICTIMS OF BULLYING

In contrast to the literature on crime victim therapy in other domains, less has been written about treating children and adolescents who have been, or are currently, the victims of bullying and peer aggression. Yet, these are often some of the most traumatized patients we will see in clinical practice. Unlike the brutal but time-limited impact of victims of a sexual assault, mugging, carjacking, workplace violence incident, or even a military battlefield casualty, peer aggression may be chronic and ongoing and the student has to go back to school every day. Thus, intervention must combine the practical antibullying strategies outlined above with more supportive esteem-building modalities to allow the student to retain, or regain, his self-respect and, at the same time, focus on his or her schoolwork.

In this regard, I have found a recently described treatment program (Stein et al., 2003) useful as a clinical template to pull together, consolidate, and summarize many of the therapeutic strategies described in this book in order to apply them directly to treating victims of bullying and peer violence. I outline this program here, along with my own comments, suggestions, and modifications based on my experiences in utilizing these and related concepts in clinical practice.

Stein et al. (2003) describe a standardized cognitive–behavioral group intervention protocol that is claimed to significantly decrease symptoms of PTSD and depression in students who are exposed to violence and that can be effectively delivered on school campuses by trained school-based mental health clinicians. Called the *Cognitive–Behavioral Intervention for Trauma in Schools* (CBITS), the program consists of a 10-session group format that was designed for use in an inner-city school mental health clinic with a multicultural population. The session formats are as follows:

Session 1. The first session introduces the group members and provides a description of confidentiality rules and group procedures. The treatment model is explained using stories and illustrations. The students are invited to discuss their reasons for participating in the group, specifically, the kinds of stresses or traumas they have been experiencing in the school setting.

Session 2. The students are educated about common reactions to stress and trauma. They are then trained in the relaxation response and other arousal control techniques (chapter 6) to reduce anxiety and afford a sense of control over their bodily reactions. Most kids are fascinated by the idea that they can actually control something their own body does, and they typically get into these behavioral medicine exercises with great enthusiasm. The students are then trained in imaginal exposure to the traumatic events, in this case the bullying and peer violence scenarios, and are encouraged to utilize the arousal control strategies to counteract their feelings of fear and shame. This exercise is practiced over the next several sessions, as treatment proceeds.

Session 3. The students are introduced to the principles of cognitive therapy by way of a discussion about the relationship between thoughts and feelings. They are trained to monitor their feelings states by use of a *fear thermometer.* They are then taught basic cognitive therapy techniques (chapter 6) for combating negative thoughts and asked to assess what effect this has on the fear thermometer. I have found that kids especially like the thought-stopping strategy and come up with all kinds of creative symbols for doing this.

Session 4. The students are taught how to combat negative thoughts, an application of the cognitive restructuring technique described in chapter 6. The tricky thing here is deciding what qualifies as a negative thought. Some students may want to banish any conceivable memory of their traumatic bullying experience, which can disrupt the effort to inculcate the very kinds of adaptive antibullying verbal and behavioral strategies described above. Therapists will usually have to customize the meaning of negative thoughts for each student, depending on his or her personality, degree of traumatization, and stage in the treatment process, but the guiding principle should be to control thoughts that are maladaptive and destabilizing, while retaining enough cognitive capacity to utilize practical coping skills.

For example, to counter the ruminative thought,
"I'm just a wimp. I'll always be pushed around."

Don't use:

"I won't think about it; I'll just concentrate on my schoolwork."

But try:

"Of course, my brain gets zonked when a bunch of much bigger kids gang up on me. But I'm learning how to deal with things so they don't get to that point. Then, I won't have to be afraid as much and I can focus better on my schoolwork."

Session 5. No matter what, the students still have to go back to school. So in this session, the students learn to deal with maladaptive avoidance responses by developing useful coping skills. They are taught how to construct a fear hierarchy and are trained in the use of psychophysiological self-control strategies, as well as practical coping skills, for each successive challenge in the hierarchy. They are also asked to begin utilizing these strategies in their natural environment, essentially learning to desensitize themselves to the fear-producing environment of the school surroundings. In addition, they are encouraged to utilize the practical coping techniques they've learned, should an incident arise.

Sessions 6 and 7. These sessions focus largely on exposure to stress or trauma memory through imagination, drawing, and/or writing. This is actually the phase that is most akin to traditional psychotherapy per se, as the students work through the personal issues that relate their victimization and its impact on their self-worth, family identity, peer relationships, and so on. This is also the most individualized portion of the therapeutic program, and clinicians are encouraged to use their skill and ingenuity to help these kids come to grips with the effects of the peer victimization on their development as students and as people.

Session 8. This session provides an introduction to social problem solving. Students are taught various strategies for nonviolent conflict resolution and other interpersonal problem solving skills. I've found this to be especially effective for the martyring and provocative-type victims who, until now, may not have known how to gain attention other than by passive-aggressive and obnoxious behavior. I typically combine this with broader social skills training to allow these students to maximize their ability to make friends, enlist the cooperation of teachers and family members, and thereby solidify a growing supportive social network.

Session 9. This session continues practice with social problem solving and introduces a *hot seat* exercise in which the students take turns role-playing improvised scenarios. This is especially useful because these students are the experts in what type of interpersonal challenges they'll have to face each day as they return to school.

Session 10. By continuing to present a wide variety of role-playing scenarios, as well as applying the skills learned in their natural environment, *relapse prevention* is reinforced. Finally, a *graduation ceremony* cements and ritualizes the progress made and provides realistic optimism for the future.

Note that, although Stein et al. (2003) present their program as a standard sequence, which was necessary for their empirical study of its effectiveness, in clinical practice you can be as flexible and creative as your patients require. I have found that the program can be adapted to an individual format (probably the most common in most mental health clinicians' practices) and the session stages can be varied, compressed, extended, or reordered, depending on the needs of the students. It can also be open-ended, with students invited to come back for booster sessions as needed. Finally, this program can be incorporated into ongoing therapy for broader individual, family, and social issues that affect these children.

SCHOOL VIOLENCE

Jonesboro. Littleton. Columbine. Virginia Tech.

School violence is not really *back* in the news because it never really left. Eclipsed by the national preoccupation with terrorism (chapter 14), recent campus mass violence incidents remind us that most killers of Americans are still our own citizens and that many of these murders take place where we expect them least, our schools. This section will provide some insight into the psychology of this modern form of mass murder and provide some practical recommendations for preventing, responding to, and recovering from school violence. These recommendations can be utilized by law enforcement, education, and mental health professionals.

DEMOGRAPHICS AND CLINICAL EFFECTS OF SCHOOL VIOLENCE

According to the National School Safety Center (Bender & McLaughlin, 1997), school violence continues to pose significant problems for society:

- Mass violence, involving high-powered weaponry and multiple casualties, are still rare events on school campuses. Excluding mass violence, almost three million crimes are committed on or near a school campus each year, comprising 11% of all reported crimes in America.

- The number of children who carry guns to school on a daily basis is estimated to range from 135,000 to 200,000.
- The *incidence,* or frequency, of youth violence as a whole has been decreasing since the 1970s; however, during the same period, the *severity* of juvenile violence has dramatically increased, including a greater number of homicides, involving more potent weapons.
- In addition, students are committing violence at increasingly younger ages.

The psychological ripple effects of school violence extend far beyond the incidents themselves. For example, in the first year following the Columbine High School shooting, there were a disproportionately high number of vehicular accidents, suicide attempts, assaults, and student deaths (Johnson, 2000). A study of children's acute responses to a sniper attack on an elementary school playground showed that the children exhibited traumatic responses similar to those of adults. One hundred and fifty-nine school-age children were interviewed approximately one month after the event. Children with less severe degrees of exposure (i.e., who were not in the playground at the time of the attack) rarely evidenced acute posttraumatic symptoms as compared to the highly exposed children (Pynoos et al., 1987).

SCHOOL VIOLENCE PERPETRATORS

For all the media attention given to school violence, very little empirical work has been done regarding the psychology of this kind of youthful mass murder. Accordingly, much of what we know about school violence perpetrators has been extrapolated from studies of other types of mass murder, especially older perpetrators of workplace violence (chapter 12), who have been studied for several decades, as opposed to school shootings, which are a more recent societal phenomenon (Johnson, 2000; Miller, 2002b; Pitcher & Poland, 1992).

To put things in perspective, high-profile multiple murders on school campuses, horrific though they may be, are still relatively low-frequency events. As we've just discussed, much more common are the everyday instances of bullying, harassment, and nonlethal violence that occur on school campuses across the nation and the world. These, too, can be psychologically traumatizing and may set the stage for episodes of explosive retaliatory violence.

Indeed, analysis of the mass school shootings of the past decade highlight the grimly intimate association that often exists between bullying and harassment and school mass violence. In these events, the cycle of violence typically begins when the student undergoes an event or series of events that he perceives as the last straw in a cumulative series of humiliations. Based on the student's predisposing personality and psychological dynamics, his reaction will consist of some combination of persecutory ideation, projection of blame, and violent revenge fantasies. As thoughts and emotions stew, the student isolates himself from the input of others and enters a mode of self-protection and self-justification in which a violent act may come to be perceived as the only way out. As with workplace violence, the actual commando-style mission may be executed impulsively and all at once, or it may undergo numerous revisions and months of planning. The violent act itself may be carried out alone or with the collaboration of like-minded compatriots. In most cases, the episodes end with the death of the perpetrators, either by their own hand or by responding law enforcement authorities.

PREVENTING SCHOOL VIOLENCE

Academic administrators who remain unmoved by the human costs of school violence might want to consider the potential legal and financial liabilities. As noted above, in *Stoneking v. Bradford Area School District, 1988*, the court found that, if a school is aware of dangerous and unlawful activities on its premises and takes insufficient action to address them, it may be found liable under the 14th amendment, unless it can demonstrate due diligence in trying to prevent crime on campus. Accordingly, the following recommendations are adapted from a large body of work in the area of workplace violence (also see chapter 12) that can be productively applied to the academic setting (Denenberg & Braverman, 1999; Kinney, 1995; Johnson, 2000; Labig, 1995; Miller, 1998h, 1999c, 2001a, 2001b, 2002a, 2008; Namie & Namie, 2000; Pitcher & Poland, 1992; Ross, 1996; Schouten, 2006).

Clear Policies

Schools should have clear, strong, consistent, written policies against bullying, intimidation, and harassment. They should have effective security programs; a standardized, confidential, and user-friendly reporting system; a supportive faculty; open channels of communication; and training in verbal negotiation and conflict resolution skills. Schools must have a clearly understood policy of *zero tolerance for violence*. Although this sounds simple, it needs to be given a lot of thought because a policy that is overly lax or overly restrictive can damage the program's credibility. Antiviolence measures should be contextualized as a safety issue, the same as with rules about fire prevention or disaster drills. Plans should be in place that specify how threats are reported and to whom, as well as a protocol for investigating threats.

Safe Discipline

As in the workplace, many acts of violence relate to the perpetrator feeling he was treated unfairly by the faculty, the administration, or other authorities; some of this relates to confusion over the very zero-tolerance policies cited above. Schools should develop an individualized disciplinary program that strikes a balance between a too heavy-handed approach that might discourage reporting and participation, and a too lenient approach that gives the impression of ambivalence and lack of control. Discipline should occur in stages, with a clear policy and rationale for each action taken, from reprimand, to suspension, to expulsion, to prosecution. School officials should not be afraid to pull rank where student safety is concerned.

Safe Suspension or Expulsion

If disciplinary or corrective measures prove ineffective, suspension or expulsion from school should be clear and firm without being inhumane. This should include a systematic process of documentation as to the precise behaviors and rule violations that have necessitated these actions. The student and his family should be treated with reasonable respect but should understand that the action is final and will be backed up. The student should be informed of any counseling or other services offered by the school for the transition period. For behaviors that constitute criminal acts, school officials should report these to local law enforcement or their own school police if they have them.

RESPONDING TO SCHOOL VIOLENCE

Sometimes, despite the best efforts at prevention, a dangerous situation begins to brew and a violent incident becomes a distinct possibility. Or the incident just erupts explosively and personnel have to respond immediately. In either case, the effectiveness of the response will be determined by how thorough the pre-incident planning and training have been.

Warning Signs of Impending Violence

It is always best for school officials to know their individual students, but generic warning signs include deterioration or changes in dress, speech, facial expression, increased agitation, anxiety, isolation and/or depression, evidence of substance use, or preoccupation with violent events in the media. Almost always, the student's peers will know something is up way before parents or teachers do, which is why a safe and confidential reporting system is so important.

Policies and Procedures for School Violence Response

Schools should develop a preventive plan to decrease the likelihood of violence. This may include peer mediation, community tutoring programs, community disciplinary committees, specialized training for teachers, curricula that espouse and model nonviolence, and other measures. In addition, schools should implement a crisis response protocol in case violence erupts, including policies and procedures for communication, evacuation, notification of law enforcement and emergency services, and so forth.

Planning and training for defusing potentially violent episodes should be developed, put in place, and reviewed periodically. Elements of such a protocol include initial actions to take when danger begins to escalate, codes and signals for summoning help, chain of command for handling emergencies, appropriate use of verbal control strategies and body language, scene control and bystander containment, tactics for dealing with weapons, and hostage negotiation procedures.

The following are some specific recommendations mental health consultants can provide to educators for responding to a potential or actual violent crisis in school (Bender & McLaughlin, 1997; Johnson, 2000; Pitcher & Poland, 1992). Readers will note the similarities in principle and application to the protocols for handling workplace violence (chapter 12) and violence in the mental health care setting (chapter 15). As always, these recommendations should be supplemented by appropriate training, and many schools (and workplaces) offer formal training in crisis response.

Preventing a Potentially Violent Episode

Teachers and other school officials should keep their eyes and ears open for signs of potential confrontation. Try to get a bead on the student rumor mill. Without violating student privacy rights, keep tabs on known troublemakers; try to be aware of their schedules and whereabouts during the school day. Consider leaving doors open or ajar during classes to hear any trouble inside or outside class. Use a *teacher buddy system,* in which each teacher is paired with the instructor across the hall, and the paired teachers routinely do a quick visual check with each other at regular intervals during their classes.

Have a firm but reasonable *weapons search policy:* transparent bookbags, open lockers, metal detectors—whatever makes sense for your school. Alert the principal to any rumors of potential violence or weapons violations, along with your estimate of how serious those rumors may be. If you are teaching a class and become aware of a disturbance or even hear gunfire from somewhere on the premises, shut your door and let no students in or out until you are informed of further action to take; again, leaven this recommendation with your own judgment and common sense. Consider outfitting teachers with dedicated cell phones or in-house walkie-talkie units to establish quick communication in case of a rapidly unfolding crisis.

Managing a Potentially Violent Situation

Teachers or other school officials may encounter a potentially violent situation that is starting to develop. In some cases, this may involve a student with a weapon. If security or law enforcement cannot be immediately summoned—or until they arrive—there are a number of things that the mental health consultant can advise teachers to do that may minimize the chance of a threatening incident escalating to serious violence, especially if there are weapons involved.

To begin with, remember that your best asset is your good judgment and mature behavior. Stay calm and model emotional control. Most commonly, dangerous altercations with weapons in school will begin with a "show-off" weapon display. If you witness such a pose and no one has yet been injured, avoid confrontational tactics, threats of punishment, or statements regarding consequences. This is the time to keep things calm to avoid injury. Subtly and nonobviously, try to isolate the threatening student, for example, by asking him to come to another location to discuss the matter. In cases where it appears the threatening student is showing off to make a point, assure him that you will listen to his side of things if he puts down the weapon so "everybody can concentrate on what you have to say." In other cases, there may be no particular side he's on or point he wants to make; the student is just on a power trip and the weapon is his ticket to grandeur.

Try to keep other students from either challenging the weapon-wielding student or egging him on with encouragement. Often, a threatened student will feel the need to stand up to the student with the weapon in order to save face. Then, the first student feels he has no choice but to attack the disrespecter. Try to deescalate these brewing confrontations; usually the best strategy is to get the threatened student out of there. If other faculty are on the scene, enlist them to try to move other students out of the area, even as you try to get the weapon-wielding student to move to a more isolated area. In some cases, a trusted student peer may have some positive influence on the aggressive student, but this can be risky unless you know both parties well. In general, anything you can do to calm the situation and keep everybody safe is preferable.

Managing a Hostage Crisis

In school settings, it is quite possible that a dangerous confrontation may result in students and teacher finding themselves trapped in a classroom or other area, de facto hostages to a weapon-wielding student who won't let them leave (Miller, 2005c, 2007b). In such a circumstance, again, try to stay calm. Ask the student if you can talk without him pointing the weapon at you. Make it clear that as long as he doesn't do anything aggressively threatening, nobody will try to escape or attack him. If he appears ambivalent about using violence, gently broach the subject of letting some of the students go, perhaps the girls or any handicapped students that may be present. Convey to the other students the importance of keeping as calm and still as possible. Continue to talk with the student in a steady voice, assuring the student that the problems can be addressed without violence.

If possible, unobtrusively maneuver yourself behind furniture or other objects that could deflect an attack or block bullets from a firearm. Always be looking—again, without being obvious about it—for places to dive or jump. As long as no violence is occurring or appears imminent, avoid heroics and keep a safe, nonintimidating distance. Keep your hands clearly visible and avoid all abrupt, sporadic movements. If the student offers you the weapon, suggest that he unload it, place in on a surface away from people and walk out of the room with you. Make sure you instruct students and others in the room to keep away from the weapon. If and when law enforcement arrive, let them take over and follow their instructions.

Handling a Violent Episode

If the student starts firing the weapon, the priority is to save lives. If you can escape through a door or window, do so and instruct or help students to do the same. If no exit is possible, hit the floor and instruct the other students to do likewise. Seek cover behind furniture. Much depends on the situation. Some authorities recommend that if there is one gunman and many students, rushing the perpetrator with books or chairs may disorient him and knock him down long enough to disarm or disable him. In some cases, this may work; in other cases, it may get more people killed—there is no one answer that applies to all situations. Follow your training and your best judgment. Remember, the goal is not to save the day, it's to save lives.

When they arrive on the scene, law enforcement may attempt to make a tactical entry. This may first come to your attention in the form of the sting of tear gas, the shock of flash-bang grenades, or the sound of gunfire. Instruct your students to stay down until police officers pick them up off the floor or instruct them to move. Bear in mind that entering officers may not immediately be able to separate the good guys from the bad guys and may restrain everybody for safety until they can get it sorted out. Follow law enforcement's instructions until everyone is out safely.

RECOVERING FROM SCHOOL VIOLENCE

The crisis is far from over when the police and media leave. Students or faculty may have been killed, others wounded, some held hostage, and many psychologically traumatized. Like workplaces (chapter 12), schools should proactively establish policies, procedures, and training for responding to the aftermath of a violent incident (Miller, 2002b, 2003c, 2007e), and the plan should include the following elements.

Law Enforcement, Physical Security, and Cleanup

A school representative should be designated to work with local, regional, and/or federal law enforcement. Within the limits of safety, the crime scene should be kept intact until investigators have gone over the area. There should be someone assigned to immediately check, protect, or restore the integrity of the school's data systems, computers, and files. Physical cleanup of the area, pending approval from law enforcement, should be conducted in as respectful a manner as possible.

Mental Health Mobilization

This includes a prearranged plan for school representatives to contact local mental health professionals immediately, arrange for the clinicians to meet first with school officials for updates and briefings, conduct crisis counseling with affected students, faculty, and families, and arrange follow-up schedules for mental health clinicians to return to provide psychological services as needed.

Student and Family Interventions

Another designated school official should notify the victims' families of the incident and be ready to offer them immediate support, counseling, and referral services. The school should arrange time off for grieving and traumatized students and faculty. After the initial stages of the incident have passed, mental health clinicians should help students and school officials find constructive ways of memorializing the victims.

Media and Public Relations

A media spokesperson or public information officer should be designated to brief the media and shepherd them away from grieving students, family members, and faculty. School officials should cooperate with law enforcement authorities as to the timing and content of news releases.

Legal Issues and Postincident Investigations

These measures include notifying the school's legal counsel, who should be asked to respond to the scene, if necessary. Investigatory questions include the nature of the perpetrator(s), their relationship to fellow students and faculty, history of disciplinary action or suspension, specific circumstances or institutional stressors that may have led to the incident, the role of mental illness or substance abuse, any warning signs that should have been heeded, and a thorough review of the school's overall security, threat assessment, and critical incident response protocols.

In summary, if any good can come out of a school violence episode, it will be in the form of improved policies and procedures that adopt a best-practices model to the prevention, response, and recovery to and from any kind of institutional mass violence. This kind of proactive effort can save lives, improve student health, and reduce costs and liabilities from both everyday school bullying and harassment and more uncommon lethal mass violence.

PSYCHOLOGICAL INTERVENTIONS FOR SCHOOL VIOLENCE VICTIMS

Several large-group, school-based postdisaster interventions for children and adolescents that have either been developed for school violence or can be productively applied to such incidents have been reviewed by Abueg, Drescher, and Kubany (1994). Weinberg (1990) describes a large-group intervention program to help adolescents deal with school traumas such as accidents or suicides in which grief and loss issues predominate. Students meet in a school assembly, which fosters a familiar, supportive atmosphere. Healthy grief is described and emotional expression is encouraged. Students who appear especially upset, are identified as particularly at risk, or attempt to leave the group meeting are met either individually or in small-group sessions.

A school-based approach explicitly modeled on the critical incident stress debriefing (CISD) protocol (Everly et al., 1999; Miller, 1999g; Mitchell & Everly, 1996) is described by Johnson (1989). This adaptation for children and adolescents involves a postcrisis group debriefing protocol that incorporates five stages:

1. An *introductory phase,* in which the goals and purposes of the group are spelled out.
2. A *fact phase,* in which the children each describe what happened to them in the disaster.
3. A *feeling phase,* in which the children may express the emotions and reactions they have had in response to the crisis.
4. A *teaching phase,* in which the group leader educates the children as to the nature of stress symptoms and the course of recovery.
5. A *closure phase,* in which the children are encouraged to develop some plan of action to facilitate improved coping in the future.

Johnson (1989) emphasizes that the group's sense of security and normal routine needs to be reestablished at the conclusion of the debriefing. Even class debriefings, designed to help students adjust in a familiar environment, can be upsetting. To the extent possible, a sense of continuity should be provided by a return to some semblance of a normal schedule of activities. After the debriefing process has fulfilled its therapeutic purpose, the group leader lets the students know that the time has come to resume a normal routine.

Another CISD model of intervention for use in the schools is presented by Ritter (1994). This approach encourages schools to act proactively to establish a working relationship with CISD teams in the local community so that, in case of a crisis, the system can spring into action. Schools have utilized CISD team resources effectively in connection with student suicides, homicides, hostage incidents, natural and manmade disasters, motor vehicle deaths, and sports event deaths. Protocols for the effective use of CISD-type resources require flexibility, cooperation, and coordination of local and regional debriefing resources. They also may require additional expenditures to coordinate different groups and individuals and bring them all up to speed on such topics as trauma, death and dying, grief, the CISD process, and other therapeutic and psychosocial interventions.

Harris (1991) describes a family-based crisis intervention model designed for use within 1 week following a traumatic disaster. Initial sessions are designed to elicit open expression of feelings and the development of rapport with the therapist. Cognitive restructuring (chapter 6) is used, when appropriate, to correct distortions and irrational thinking on the part of the family members. Next, practical issues requiring immediate attention are identified. Communication skills are taught and social support is fostered. Families are encouraged to take concrete, positive problem-solving action to create a sense of movement and progress toward goals.

Vernberg and Vogel (1993) describe a disaster intervention protocol that may be productively applied to episodes of mass violence in schools. Intervention strategies are divided into four phases.

1. The *predisaster phase* primarily involves incorporating mental health services into local or regional disaster plans.
2. Interventions in the immediate *impact phase* of the disaster include ensuring support for help providers at affected sites, gathering and disseminating accurate information, and making initial contact with children who have been affected by the traumatic disaster event.
3. *Short-term adaptation phase* interventions include classroom strategies that allow emotional expression and cognitive processing of the traumatic events through group discussions, drawing, play therapy, and other appropriate outlets. Interventions during this phase also include family approaches such as providing information and education, absenteeism outreach, and brief family therapy. It also includes individual modalities, such as one-on-one debriefing, individual psychotherapy, and pharmacological approaches, where appropriate.
4. Finally, *long-term adjustment phase* interventions include more extensive individual and family psychotherapy, as well as the use of communal rituals and memorials.

Throughout the process, as in most of the other well-run intervention programs discussed in this chapter, there is an emphasis on providing the maximum degree of adaptive recovery and normalization with a minimum of therapeutic intrusion and overload; however, it is also important to identify those at-risk children and families at each stage who may require more intensive and extensive treatment and support (Miller, 2002b).

CONCLUSIONS

Employees shouldn't have to be afraid to go to work, and students shouldn't have to fear going to school. As with workplace violence, the most effective interventions for school violence are those that are most preventive. However, having a program in place to deal with every phase of a possible incident will increase the overall sense of safety and confidence in the educational setting that allows learning to take place. Indeed, bullying and harassment have been described as a form of *schoolyard terrorism,* while domestic violence (chapter 11) has sometimes been termed *intimate terrorism.* Yet, in the new world of the 21st century, mental health clinicians may be increasingly called upon to deal with terrorism of a much broader and more frightening kind.

CHAPTER 14

Victims of Terrorism

Terrorism is as old as civilization and has existed ever since people discovered that they could intimidate the many by targeting the few. However, terrorism has achieved special prominence in the modern technological era, beginning in the 1970s as international terrorism, continuing in the 1980s and 1990s as American domestic terrorism, and apparently coming full circle in the 21st century with mass terror attacks on U.S. soil by foreign nationals. Arguably, the two culmination points of domestic and international terrorism in the past decade have been Oklahoma City and the World Trade Center. Many experts believe that the worst is yet to come (Bolz, Dudonis, & Schultz, 1996; Keller, 2002; Mueller, 2005).

THE NATURE AND PURPOSES OF TERRORISM

The word terrorism derives from the Latin *terrere,* which means "to frighten." A terrorist act is rarely an end in itself but rather is intended to instill fear in whole populations by targeting a small, representative group. Mao Tse-tung reportedly spoke of "killing one to move a thousand." A major difference in the case of mass terrorism like the World Trade Center and the much-feared potential nuclear terrorism of the future may be the terrorists' desire to wreak maximum destruction as an end in itself, going far beyond the symbolic value of the act and turning it into a veritable war of annihilation (Miller, 2006d, 2006e).

Only in the past decade has terrorism become a significant fact of life for Americans. Accordingly, the body of clinical psychological literature on terrorism has lagged behind that of other types of traumatic events. However, as practicing clinicians, we need to realize that good psychotherapeutic technique and wisdom are generalizable skills that may productively be applied to the treatment of a wide range of traumatic disability syndromes (Miller, 1993a, 1998h).

Terrorist attacks, such as Oklahoma City and the World Trade Center, combine features of a criminal assault, a disaster, and an act of war (Hills, 2002). Hence, much of what follows combines therapeutic approaches culled from the more extensive literatures on treating victims of criminal assault, homicidal bereavement, natural and man-made disasters, war and political violence, workplace homicide, and school shootings, much of which will be already familiar to readers of this book. In this sense, those impacted by terrorist attacks are the ultimate crime victims, and many of the concepts and strategies you've mastered with other victims will aid you in assisting this special population, with the adaptations and extensions discussed in the following pages (Miller, 2003d, 2003e, 2004a, 2005a, 2005b, in press-b).

PSYCHOLOGICAL REACTIONS TO TERRORIST ATTACKS

Terror: The Ultimate Traumatic Event?

In essence, terrorism is the perfect traumatic stressor, because it combines the elements of malevolent intent, extreme harm, and unending fear of the future. Indeed, the very purpose of terrorism fully meets Criterion A of the *DSM-IV-TR* (APA, 2000) diagnostic classification of PTSD, that of injuring or threatening self or others, and involving "the experience of intense fear, helplessness, or horror" (see also chapter 2).

Bolz et al. (1996) have identified several elements that are almost universal in modern terrorist activities, and that thereby make terrorism a prime traumatic stressor:

> *Violence as an instrument of persuasion.* Basic to the definition of terrorism is the use of violence as a method of influence, persuasion, or intimidation. In this sense, the true target of the terroristic act extends far beyond those directly affected. The Murrah building in Oklahoma City is bombed to make a point about the intrusive federal government. A Spanish passenger train is blown up to effect withdrawal of that country's troops from the Middle East. The goals here are to use threats, harassment, and violence to create an atmosphere of fear that will eventually lead to some desired behavior on the part of the target population and/or its leaders.

Targets chosen for maximum effect. The targets and victims of terrorism are selected for their maximum propaganda value, ensuring a high degree of media coverage. A great deal of thought may go into the symbolic value of the attacks, or the victims may simply be targets of opportunity. This approach may backfire if the goal is to garner public sympathy, and if noninvolved innocents are killed along with the symbolic targets. Alternatively, if the aim is to inflict as much horror and panic as possible, then indiscriminate slaughter may serve only too well. Traditionally, the aim of most terrorist acts has been to achieve maximum publicity at minimum risk, yet the recent spate of suicide bombings in the Middle East and elsewhere shows that fanatical devotion will often trump personal caution, and this lack of restraint even for self-preservation is what makes suicide terrorists so frightening.

Use of unconventional tactics. A major distinction between a terrorist and a soldier or guerrilla is that terrorists use irregular and unconventional military tactics, especially employing secrecy and surprise (sneak attacks) and targeting civilians, including women and children. As noted above, if the goal is to inflict maximum fear and intimidation, then it makes sense to choose locations that contain the largest number of innocent victims. These types of glaring acts are also the most likely to garner media attention.

Absolutist loyalty and ideology. Intense loyalty and allegiance to the cause of the organization characterizes most terrorist groups. The ability to commit otherwise unspeakable acts—not to mention giving one's own life—necessitates an absolutist belief that these acts are done in the cause of some overarching, worthy purpose. The very relentlessness of the terrorists' mission of destruction makes their acts all the more frightening and destabilizing for victims because they understand that there is little that will deter the extremists until they get what they want.

Schmid (2000) has differentiated two types of terrorist victims: *Focused terrorism* has specifically chosen victims. These might be political figures or members of a specific group against which the terrorists are acting. *Indiscriminate terrorism,* in contrast, is directed against random victims who are not specifically selected and are innocent targets of opportunity. One of the most frightening aspects of this latter type of terrorism is that its victims are most often persons who have no direct connection with the terrorists and no involvement in the issues or ideological activities that motivate the terrorist incident. They are essentially innocent targets of opportunity.

Another aspect of mass terrorism is its effect on those who are not directly harmed in the incident but whose lives and fortunes are secondarily affected by it (Kratcoski, Edelbacher, & Das, 2001). For example, attacks on airports or cities can result in losses of millions of dollars to the many persons whose livelihoods depend on travel or commerce. Governments or localities victimized by terrorist attacks must divert otherwise-needed funds for defense, security, medical aid, and other services. Additionally, as much as citizens may be victimized and intimidated by the terrorists themselves, government agencies' efforts to control the terrorism may impose restrictions on the citizens' abilities to move about freely or compromise basic freedoms and human rights. All of these have been prominent concerns following 9/11.

Toxic, Radiological, and Biological Terrorism

Chemical and biological warfare and terrorism are not new, either. Medieval soldiers threw plague-ridden corpses over the walls of besieged cities. Colonizers of the American West gave smallpox-impregnated blankets to Indian tribes. In World War I, lethal gas was commonly referred to as a "terror weapon." However, in modern industrial society, the fear of potential exposure to hidden harmful agents has achieved an almost mystical quality. Even in ordinary industrial or commercial use, exposure to hazardous substances is often a traumatic event (Baum, 1987; Baum & Fleming, 1993; Baum et al., 1983; Miller, 1993c, 1995c, 1998h; Solomon & Thompson, 1995). Being poisoned has a frightening connotation that goes deep into the collective psychological and cultural unconscious of humankind. It conjures up fears of diabolical possession, the casting of evil spells, moral and spiritual uncleanness, ostracism and banishment from the community, and—especially in the context of terrorism—insidious contamination and conspiracy. Further, in the case of toxic and radiological agents, the fears of contamination can extend to future generations.

In planning for such possible chemical and biological attacks, military and civilian planners are apparently taking such potential *toxic stress casualties* quite seriously (Romano & King, 2002). The widespread panic, confusion, and demoralization that might result from such an attack would multiply the casualties occurring from direct exposure to the substances themselves, as well as strain limited medical resources in dealing with them. In fact, the U.S. Army Medical Department notes that, historically, two such "mental stress cases" have typically occurred for every actual chemical injury (Stokes & Bandaret, 1997). This analysis suggests several possible origins for these cases:

- *Normal physiological stress symptoms* (chapter 2) may be mistaken for exposure to chemical weapons agents. Even soldiers specifically trained to recognize signs of chemical poisoning often mistake symptoms of physiological arousal for those of actual exposure. How much more susceptible, then, would ordinary untrained civilians be to this type of symptomatic misattribution?

- *Unrelated illnesses or syndromes*—allergies, headaches, gastritis—could be mistakenly attributed to the feared chemical or biological agent, creating further diagnostic confusion and psychological disability. In cases of severe conversion disorder (chapter 4), the purported toxic exposure could become the focal point for patients' psychological conflicts and distress, causing them to become unshakably convinced of their own mortal peril. Even with actual exposure to the agent, the degree of contact might be minimal and the risks slight, but fear could magnify the psychologically disabling distress, especially when no safe dose has been established.

- *Iatrogenic (treatment-related) or self-inflicted casualties* may result from medically prescribed or self-administered medications or other substances—ranging from misuse of antidotal agents such as atropine and diazepam, to prescribed narcotic drugs for pain of physical injuries, to various home remedies concocted by desperate victims, to alcohol and hard drugs of abuse—may produce disagreeable or disabling symptoms that may be mistaken for, or added to, the symptoms of toxic exposure. For example, military doctors have reported that self-administration of two types of nerve agent antidote autoinjectors can produce headache, restlessness, and fatigue; these symptoms can be exacerbated in a tired, dehydrated, or stressed person.

- Individuals with no known actual toxic exposure may *malinger or fabricate symptoms* (chapter 4) in order to obtain otherwise unavailable medical, financial, or other resources and services.

Psychological Responses to Mass Terror Attacks

Aside from Oklahoma City, the World Trade Center, the Madrid train bombing, Asian nightclub attacks, bus bombings in London, and the ubiquitous daily suicide attacks throughout the Middle East, there have so far been very few examples of the kind of mass terror attacks that are feared for the future. Accordingly, most of what we know about psychological responses to mass trauma comes from the study of natural and man-made disasters (McGinn & Spindell, 2007; Miller, 1998h; Miller et al., 1997; Norris et al., 2002a, 2002b; Norwood, Ursano, & Fullerton, 2000; Ursano, Fullerton, & Norwood, 1995). The latter, such as dam ruptures and nuclear power plant meltdowns, probably come closest to terroristic attacks in the sense of being caused by human beings through the misuse of technology. The difference, of course, is that in the case of a Bhopal or a Chernobyl, the damage to multiple innocent lives came from human error or, at worst, callous negligence. Tragic as that may be, it is still a far cry from the willful and malicious intent to do harm that characterizes terrorist attacks.

Characteristics of Disasters

As noted above, mass terror attacks share features with disasters. Disasters are traditionally divided into two broad categories:

Natural disasters are those that are the product of errant nature: hurricanes, floods, avalanches, wildfires, earthquakes.

Technological disasters involve the misworks of man: shipwrecks, plane crashes, building collapses, toxic spills, nuclear reactor leaks. In some cases, the dividing line is not so clear.

Definitional distinctions aside, major disasters share a number of characteristics with mass terror attacks that clearly place both in the category of shared traumatic events (Abueg, Drescher, & Kubany, 1994; Aldwin, 1994; McGinn & Spindell, 2007; Ursano, Fullerton, & Norwood, 1995):

- There is typically little or no warning that the event is about to occur, and even when supposedly adequate warning exists, citizens often display a stupefying capacity for denial and minimization. Thus, by the time the threat is unmistakably clear, it is often too late for effective action.
- Disasters generally occur in a relatively short time frame. By the time the full extent of the threat is realized, the worst may be over, yet the aftermath must still be dealt with.
- Disasters typically involve extreme danger, including loss of life. At the very least, people lose something of value, whether it is their home, treasured keepsakes, their livelihood, their friends or family members, or their sense of a secure and predictable world.
- Disasters are psychologically overwhelming and provide very little chance for people to exert any kind of meaningful personal control. Helplessness magnifies the traumatic effect of disasters. Conversely, engaging in rescue or relief efforts—doing *something* other than sitting around waiting for the next crisis to occur—is typically associated with significantly lower levels of psychological trauma, even if the efforts are exerted after the peak of the disaster itself (Hobfoll, Hall, et al., 2007).
- Disasters happen to many people simultaneously, and it is not unusual for disaster victims to feel like the whole world is coming to an

end. On the positive side, the fact that many community members share similar traumatic experiences may facilitate later therapeutic disclosure of fearful thoughts and feelings regarding the trauma. In addition, the community may pull together and provide a higher than usual level of social support for victims, which may be psychologically beneficial to those most in need (McGinn & Spindell, 2007; Walsh, 2007).

The Disaster Response: Clinical Features

Some observers have noted that the behavioral and psychological responses seen in disasters frequently have a predictable structure and time course (Ursano, Fullerton, Bhartiya, & Kao, 1995; Ursano, Fullerton, & Norwood, 1995; Ursano, Kao, & Fullerton, 1992). For most individuals, posttraumatic psychiatric symptoms are transitory. For others, however, the effects of a disaster linger long after the event, rekindled by new experiences that remind the person of the past traumatic event. In cases of mass terror attacks, this hypervigilant dread is magnified by the sense that it may never be really "over" and that "the worst is yet to come."

Research shows that the overall magnitude and severity of a disaster is the single best predictor of both probability and frequency of postdisaster psychological disability—the so-called dose effect of traumatic exposure (Abueg et al., 1994; Green, 1991; McGinn & Spindell, 2007; Ursano, Fullerton, & Norwood, 1995)—with some studies suggesting that 10% to 30% of highly exposed individuals develop posttraumatic symptomatology. The greatest risk is for persons exposed to life threat, grotesque scenes or activities (e.g., handling human remains), or similar situations evoking intense, overwhelming revulsion or fear (Ursano & McCarroll, 1990). Intrusive thoughts and memories seem to be the most frequently reported posttraumatic symptoms following natural disasters, with avoidance symptoms—feelings of numbness, social withdrawal, and shunning of trauma-related situations or reminders—tending to be less common (Abueg et al., 1994).

PTSD per se is not the only psychological disorder associated with disasters (Ursano, Fullerton, Bhartiya, et al., 1995; Ursano, Fullerton, & Norwood, 1995). Major depression, generalized anxiety disorder, adjustment disorder, and substance abuse also have been diagnosed in individuals exposed to a disaster. Grief reactions are common after all disasters. Single parents may be at a high risk for developing psychological disorders, because they often have few resources to start with and they commonly lose some of these already meager social supports after a disaster. Over time, when resources remain limited and employment and postdisaster financial resources are scarce in the community, there is often a sharp increase in domestic violence and child abuse (chapter 11).

Anger as a reaction to bereavement in the aftermath of a disaster—especially a man-made one—is often complicated by the natural desire to apportion blame and responsibility (Solomon & Thompson, 1995). In the case of mass terror, the offender may be clearly identifiable, or—more frighteningly—may be shrouded and ill-defined. In such cases, survivor anger may be free-floating and unfocused, and may be displaced onto rescue workers, medical personnel, community officials, or anyone deemed even remotely responsible for, or connected with, the mass terror event, the failure to predict or prevent it, or the lack of sufficient helping services in the aftermath (Hobfoll, Hall, et al., 2007; Lindemann, 1944; Raphael, 1986).

Phases of the Disaster Response

Research and clinical study have shown that in many natural and technological disasters, people's responses often follow a predictable course (Cohen, Culp, & Genser, 1987; Weiner, 1992). Recent events have shown this pattern to apply to mass terror reactions (Hobfoll, Galai-Gat, Johnson, & Watson, 2007), but further study is necessary before conclusive generalizations can be made.

> *Phase of impact.* In this immediate postdisaster phase, victims experience a growing fear as the impending threat becomes known. This may pass over into paralyzing terror as the full realization of the danger unfolds. In cases of sudden attack, there may be no preparation at all. In many cases, numbing depersonalization, a kind of psychic anesthesia, may permit the person to go on automatic, partially ignore his or her pain and fear, and take some constructive action during the disaster.
>
> *Phase of heroism.* The impact phase shades over into the phase of heroism, in which disaster victims make intense and valiant efforts to protect and save whomever and whatever they can. They often work feverishly, nonstop, for hours or even days at a time, propelled by grit and adrenalin, sometimes valorously distinguishing themselves in ways they never thought possible. However, if the emergency lasts too long, exhaustion, frustration, and disappointment eventually overcome them, especially if they feel their efforts have been in vain.
>
> *Honeymoon phase.* After the acute danger has subsided, the survivors peek out from their bunkers, and the honeymoon phase begins, typically lasting days to weeks. The survivors survey the damage, exchange reminiscences and war stories, and generally share in the elation

of having survived the ordeal. A range of emotions may prevail, from somber mourning of the dead and reflection on the tragedy, to a veritable carnival atmosphere where survivors pat each other on the back, share remaining snacks and drinks, and look forward to imminent rescue, recovery, and rebuilding.

Phase of disappointment. But all too often the reprieve doesn't come soon enough. Or it is half-hearted, disorganized, or misapplied—too little, too late. The survivors, waiting and waiting for the relief they feel they've earned, become disillusioned and bitter in this next phase of disappointment. The communal spirit begins to fray as survivors bicker over dwindling resources. Tempers flare, people sicken, and many survivors sink into depression.

Phase of reorganization. Hopefully, in most cases the lack of response does not persist for too long. In the phase of reorganization, the survivors come to realize that recovery is at least partially in their own hands. They begin to rally around the task of rebuilding their lives, or at least remaining as comfortable as possible until real help can arrive. Some remaining animosity and resentment may mar this renewed spirit of cooperation, but mostly the survivors gamely hold on and look toward the future. In many of these cases, the posttraumatic stress reaction may be delayed for months until it is safe to let down one's guard, to drop the numbed psychological survival mode and allow one's true feelings to surface.

Individual Responses to Disasters

Whether the disaster is natural or technological—and, in the latter case, accidental versus deliberate—may affect the victims' appraisal of, and psychological response to, the catastrophic event (Baum, 1987; Baum & Fleming, 1993; Baum, Fleming, & Singer, 1983; Solomon & Thompson, 1995). Realistically, we don't expect to have control over the forces of nature. So as tragic as the effects of floods and earthquakes may be, perhaps we're better able to resign ourselves by adopting a philosophical, will-of-God kind of attitude. But disasters caused by human folly or negligence are different. Here we often feel that there's been a violation of the trust we implicitly place in those who are supposed to protect us, as in the case of radon-contaminated housing tracts or nuclear reactor meltdowns.

But even disasters caused by callous neglect or incompetence may be easier for victims to deal with than destruction emanating from the direct intention to do evil that characterizes terrorist attacks. One instructive study comes out of the first World Trade Center terrorist bombing in 1993 (Difede, Apfeldorf,

Cloitre, Spielman, & Perry, 1997). The most distressing aspect of those survivors' ordeal was the shattering of their fundamental beliefs about themselves (invulnerability, immortality), the world (predictability, controllability, safety), and other people (trust, safety, isolation) that had previously shaped their lives. Many were angry that their fabric of belief in a just world had been rudely shredded. All felt isolated, in the sense that others could not possibly understand what they had gone through. Concerns about death and questions about the meaning and purpose of their lives haunted many survivors. Subjects who had suffered previous traumas experienced a recrudescence of symptoms from those past events, along with the current traumatic reactions. Several subjects moved out of the New York area to start over.

A more recent American Medical Association study of the more devastating 2001 World Trade Center attack found 11% of all New Yorkers to show symptoms of PTSD 2 months following the incident, almost three times the national average. A surprising finding was that the degree of PTSD distress was most strongly related to the amount of TV coverage watched. This suggests that potentially vulnerable victims may have attempted to use the acquisition of information through television as a coping mechanism, but instead they ended up retraumatizing themselves (Kalb, 2002).

One universal risk factor for more severe reactions appears to be exposure to death and the presence of dead bodies and human remains. One component of this is the raw intensity of the exposure, for example, sights, smells, and sounds of the wounded and dying; proximity to the bodies; or actual physical contact with the dead. Personalization and identification with dead victims—"that could have been me"—appears to be a particular risk factor for later psychological disability. For example, subjects directly exposed to the dead were found to subsequently show aversion to eating meat as well as compulsive handwashing. In most cases, these symptoms abated after several months (Lindy, Grace, & Green, 1981; McCarroll, Ursano, & Fullerton, 1993, 1995; McGinn & Spindell, 2007; Raphael, 1986; Ursano, Fullerton, Bhartiya, et al., 1995; Ursano & McCarroll, 1990). In other cases, the most traumatically stressful aspect of a disaster is the legal wrangling that ensues as victims and their families seek compensation, justice, or just some straight answers (Underwood & Liu, 1996).

PSYCHOLOGICAL INTERVENTIONS FOR TERRORIST CRISES

Qualified mental health clinicians have an important role to play at all phases of a terrorist attack, from the immediate crisis, to the evolving scope of the trauma, to the short- and long-term recovery efforts.

Hostage Crises

Although mass terroristic destruction claims the headlines, many forms of domestic and international terrorism involve abduction and hostage taking. Those whose occupations or lifestyles potentially expose them to this kind of terroristic threat need proper psychological training and preparation to deal with these crises.

Strentz (1987) points out that certain psychological traits and behaviors seem to characterize those hostages who survive their ordeal versus those that do not, or those who may survive physically but who succumb to overwhelming psychological trauma.

Survivors of hostage crises typically are able to retain faith in a positive outcome. They are able to maintain a superior attitude and somehow psychologically rise above the situation, while at the same time containing any hostility they may feel toward their captors. They use fantasy to imagine a future where they will be free and also are able to rationalize the situation in terms of odds of a successful outcome. During the ongoing hostage crisis, they control their outward appearance and behavior and keep to routines. They make an effort not to stand out and they try to blend with their comrades. If possible, they try to use flexible thinking and humor as coping devices.

Succumbers typically show an opposite pattern: They are overwhelmed with feelings of abandonment, self-pity, and despair. They dwell on the worst aspects and outcomes of the situation. If angry, they make it known, thereby drawing negative attention to themselves. They suspend normal activities, and manage to stand out in any of a variety of counterproductive ways, for example, behaving obsessively, acting out of control, or being either excessively resistant or compliant.

Strentz (1987) points out that resistance to hostage takers is invariably dangerous. Effective resistance or quick escape requires strength, specialized knowledge, and skill to succeed. Any half-hearted or ill-conceived defensive measures will only make a bad situation much worse, so the basic recommendation is to comply with any reasonable requests that don't put you in immediate peril.

Strentz (1987) recommends several successful coping strategies for getting through a hostage crisis and coming out alive and in reasonably good psychological condition. These apply not just to terrorist hostage situations but also to such crises during workplace violence (chapter 12), school violence (chapter 13), and mental health crises (chapter 15):

Have realistic faith in yourself and the authorities. An American hostage taken by foreign or domestic terrorists should never regard him- or herself as forgotten, no matter how long the abduction lasts. The FBI opens a case on each American national who is abducted, and if a hostage understands this, it can help mitigate the impulse to succumb to feelings of being isolated or abandoned. Most domestic police forces have trained hostage negotiators and crisis response teams whose mission it is to see that civilian hostages are rescued alive. Indeed, law enforcement hostage negotiation has an impressive 95% success rate in resolving crises without loss of life or serious injury (McMains & Mullins, 1996; Miller, 2005c, 2006m, 2007b; Slatkin, 2005).

Contain your hostility toward your captors. While fear is the typical dominant emotion among hostages, some captives may become angry, but any hostile reactions to your captors must be suppressed. Most people are probably familiar with the *Stockholm syndrome* in which increased time and interaction between the captors and captives creates a bond between them that may inhibit violence. The term *London Syndrome* describes the opposite behavior of unproductively provoking one's abductors. During the Iranian Embassy siege in London, the Iranian Abbas Lavasani refused to compromise his dedication to the Ayatollah and continuously and passionately argued the righteousness of the Islamic revolution. Despite the pleas of fellow hostages for him to keep quiet, he continued to pontificate loudly and was finally killed by his captors. Lesson: A hostage situation is not the place to make your point, especially if you're the hostage.

Avoid overcompliance. At the other extreme is the person who stands out by being overly polite and helpful, or by doing more than the abductors require. At best, such a person sets themselves up to be exploited and may incur the resentment of fellow hostages. At worst, such an irritatingly obsequious attitude may induce contempt in the hostage takers, leading to special abuse. Reportedly, the only hostage in the United States to be shot at a deadline by a hostage taker was a female bank teller who was overcompliant. As a general rule, do what you're told to by the hostage takers, but do it slowly and purposefully, and try not to convey a sense of either extreme fear or overenthusiasm. Allow the terrorists to do things wrong and make mistakes—don't volunteer to help unless you are ordered to do so and then only do the minimum. By the same token, avoid being seen as deliberately obstructing the hostage taker's goals and actions, which risks retaliation.

Control your outward appearance and behavior. Of course, it's hard to act cool and calm when your life is in peril, but a stable and controlled demeanor conveys a sense of confidence that helps to calm your own inner turmoil and may even help settle a jittery terrorist down. If you project a façade of mature, professional, and decisive behavior, without coming off as a threat or a pest, the chances are better that your abductors will respond with a degree of grudging respect, or at least leave you alone.

Take a superior attitude. A self-empowering inner attitude of superiority and rising above will help you get through the hostage crisis, as long as you keep this attitude to yourself and don't express it in hostile words or actions toward your abductors.

Rationalize your abduction. No matter what the circumstances of the hostage crisis, don't waste emotional energy blaming yourself or obsessing over what you should or shouldn't have done. Focus on the fact that you are alive, accept that you are a captive for the time being, have faith in the authorities to do what they can to free you, take whatever steps you can to get through the crisis safely and sanely, and plan for the time when you'll be free again.

Fantasize to fill empty hours. In many hostage situations, which may last hours or days, boredom is the real enemy. Any way you can pass the time or escape mentally through fantasy will help the ordeal go by more easily. Just be careful not to let these fantasies drift into wistful reminiscences or longings that may lead to despair.

Keep to routines. Use routine activity to occupy your mind and prevent unproductive depressing rumination. Just be sure not to do anything that will irritate your captors or draw unnecessary attention to yourself. Examples of routine activity include physical exercise, prayers, intellectual games, or other activities.

Strive to be flexible and keep your sense of humor. "I'm being held hostage, my life is in danger, and I'm supposed to laugh about it?" Good point. The key here is not comedy but the ability to use irony and cognitive flexibility as coping devices, such as assigning your captors humorous names, goofing on their speech or actions, and relishing their screwups. The important thing is to keep your bemusement to yourself: The last thing you want is for your captors to think you're mocking them.

Blend with your peers. If you are comfortable in a leadership role or have particular skills that can improve the situation, you may choose to take a leadership position and so help others to survive with dignity. But bear in mind that some terrorists will select leaders for special abuse. Also, when other hostages are released, the hostage leader may be retained as a special bargaining chip. All things being equal, your chances of surviving are higher when you blend in with the crowd.

Serve others. Helping to take care of the other hostages serves several functions, such as occupying time, binding anxiety, and providing a life-affirming and uplifting experience to give yourself a much-needed sense of control. Again, always be mindful of not making yourself stand out as a leader or spokesperson of the group, but do what you can to be of service to your peers.

On-Scene Mass Casualty Intervention

In mass terroristic attacks, surviving victims may be multiplied by dozens, hundreds, or thousands. In such cases, mental health interventions will resemble those used in many kinds of mass disaster situations.

Physical Care and Safety

We mental health clinicians like to think of ourselves as specializing in psychological forms of treatment, but what disaster victims usually need first is down-to-earth, practical provision of basic services. Somebody's got to help clear the debris and hand out the sandwiches before we can even think of getting survivors to pay attention to stress management lectures and coping-skills groups. One way to look at this is to remember that, in times of disaster, physical care is psychological care, and initial postdisaster interventions must focus on establishing safety, providing nourishment and medical care, and affording protection from the elements, not to mention from continued or subsequent attacks (Hobfoll, Galai-Gat, et al., 2007; Kinston & Rosser, 1974; McGinn & Spindell, 2007; Ursano, Fullerton, & Norwood, 1995; Walsh, 2007).

Information and Education

Once mass terror survivors feel they're out of immediate danger, once they've been fed, clothed, bandaged, and sheltered, then they usually want answers. Lack of accurate information is itself potentially traumatic, and may be physically harmful if wild rumors result in panic or deprivation of services. Key points of information include the nature and effects of the terrorist event itself and the progress of any ongoing or forthcoming response and relief efforts.

It is important to reestablish communication networks in the traumatized community as soon as possible. Newspapers, official bulletins, television, the Internet, and especially radio can provide information as well as emotional help. Rumor management is an important task of community leaders and an area in which mental health personnel can assist. Fears of loss and separation should be addressed by establishing reliable communications, including casualty identification and notification procedures. Basic information should be provided about sanitation and medical care (McGinn & Spindell, 2007; Ursano, Fullerton, & Norwood, 1995; Walsh, 2007).

Moving to the psychological realm, victims of disaster appear to benefit from basic, understandable education about the onset and course of posttraumatic symptoms. The key is to normalize the traumatic stress experience while discouraging an alarmist expectation of severe psychological disability to come. Victims should know what to expect but not be talked into unnecessary distress (McGinn & Spindell, 2007; Ursano, Fullerton, & Norwood, 1995; Walsh, 2007).

Community Responses

For many mental health workers, mass terror and disaster psychology requires a shift from the traditional individualistic focus on psychopathology. Ursano, Fullerton, and Norwood (1995) have adapted preventive medicine's epidemiological model in infectious disease and toxicology as the paradigm for psychological disaster intervention. This model includes determining the individual's level of exposure to emotion-laden stimuli, such as gruesome scenes or the experience of having family members killed or injured. It also involves identifying individuals at higher risk for traumatic disability and monitoring behavioral and psychological responses over both the short and long term.

Mental health consultation to the community can facilitate recovery and limit disability following a catastrophic event (Pitcher & Poland, 1992; Ursano, Fullerton, & Norwood, 1995). In the wake of a terroristic disaster, the mental health consultant attempts to identify high-risk groups and behaviors, foster recovery from acute stress, decrease the prevalence of serious disorders, and generally minimize pain and suffering. Both acute and long-term effects of the disaster must be considered. Initial interventions include consultation to the affected community's leaders, clinicians, teachers, clergy, law enforcement, and other care and service providers to maximize their understanding of the responses to trauma and disaster.

Because many mass terror victims can't or won't present themselves to traditional mental health services, psychological care must be organized around outreach programs in the community. Identifying high-risk groups is thus one of the most important aspects of disaster consultation (McGinn & Spindell, 2007; Pitcher & Poland, 1992; Ursano, Fullerton, & Norwood, 1995; Walsh, 2007). The consultation team in the affected community must integrate smoothly into the disaster environment at a time when outsiders are often experienced as intrusive.

Death Notification and Body Identification

Chapter 8 provides a detailed description of death notification and body identification protocols for families of homicide victims that can be adapted for families of victims of terror attacks who may be subject to what has been termed *ambiguous loss* (Boss, 1999, 2002; Boss, Beaulieu, Wieling, Turner, & La Cruz, 2003).

To recapitulate, where no body has been recovered, be clear about this. If there is hope that remains may yet be found, state this, but try to be as realistic as possible about the chances. Notify the family of whatever identification procedures may be occurring, for example, DNA-matching, and direct them to the proper authorities. In the absence of definitive remains, offer the family the choice to utilize so-called symbolic remains, for example, the urn of ashes from Ground Zero that was offered by the City of New York to each family of a missing person after 9/11. Enhance the meaning of symbolic remains by encouraging memorialization activities for the missing family members that allow them to pay their respects in a meaningful way (Boss et al., 2003; Walsh, 2002, 2007).

Short-Term Crisis Intervention Protocols

After the acute emergency has passed, the kind of interventions that take place in the next few post-trauma days can make an important difference to the long-term mental health of survivors (Litz, 2004). Two of the most widely used models of short-term mental health crisis intervention are critical incident stress debriefing (CISD) and the National Organization of Victim Assistance (NOVA) program.

Critical Incident Stress Debriefing (CISD)

CISD is a structured group intervention designed to promote the emotional processing of traumatic events through the ventilation and normalization of reactions, as well as preparation for possible future crisis experiences (Everly, Flannery, & Mitchell, 1999; Miller, 1998h, 1999g; Mitchell & Everly, 1996). The program was outlined in chapter 12 in connection with workplace violence and has been applied productively to the treatment of both direct victims and rescue service workers following terrorist attacks. One caveat, however, is that CISD and other stress debriefing approaches not be viewed as stand-alone modalities but be integrated into a coordinated system of follow-up care (Hobfoll, Galai-Gat, et al., 2007; McGinn & Spindell, 2007; Miller, 1998h, 2006m, 2007m).

NOVA Model of Group Crisis Intervention

The *NOVA* offers another model for group crisis intervention (Stebnicki, 2001; Young, 1988, 1994). This model uses a similar protocol to that of the

CISD model but is consolidated into three phases of intervention, which can typically be accomplished in one 90-minute session. The strategies and approaches used to facilitate group debriefings allow crisis responders to work with large groups of both primary and secondary survivors. NOVA has adopted the term *group crisis intervention* rather than *group debriefing* because the term *debriefing* is often used in military and law enforcement contexts, potentially creating confusion among civilian survivors of traumatic incidents.

Group crisis interventions often take place at or near the site of the critical incident. Strategies in this model allow group facilitators to consider group size as well as sociocultural aspects of the population being served. Separate peer groups should be held with direct victims and survivors who were closest to the traumatic epicenter. Those who were more indirectly affected by the critical event, such as rescue teams, trauma counselors, or other crisis response personnel, should be debriefed in a separate group (Regehr & Bober, 2004). Timing of the group crisis intervention is also important, as some groups may respond best within hours of the crisis, while others may need several days to decompress sufficiently for therapeutic intervention to take hold.

The NOVA model contains three basic intervention phases:

1. *Safety and security.* This first phase usually begins with introductions of the group facilitator(s), as well as setting the groundwork for a therapeutic environment based on trust, safety, confidentiality, and personal disclosure. The goal of this phase is to provide a safe environment for survivors to release intense emotions after a traumatic event.

2. *Ventilation and validation.* The second phase allows survivors to ventilate and review physical, emotional, and sensory experiences they associated with the critical incident. Some key questions that the group facilitator(s) may use during this phase include "Where were you when this incident happened?" "Who were you with?" What did you see, hear, smell? "What did you do next?" "How did you react at the time?" This phase of the intervention provides an opportunity for survivors in the group to become aware that others have had similar experiences. This is also an opportunity to educate the survivors on common emotional reactions to extraordinary stressful and traumatic events, reinforcing the belief that they are not going crazy and that other people in the group have similar feelings and emotions. During this phase, survivors should be provided with factual information regarding the traumatic event that has taken place to dispel any misinformation and counter any myths or rumors. A second set of

questions that would be beneficial in this phase includes "Since the time of the event, what are some of the memories that stand out for you?" "What has happened in the last 48 hours?" "How has this event affected your life?"

3. *Prediction and Preparation.* The final NOVA phase should be a time for group members to cultivate seeds of hope for the future. Survivors should be encouraged and instructed on how to prepare for future emotions and identify any critical life areas that would hinder their recovery. Indeed, taking practical, constructive action is increasingly being identified as important for coping with overwhelming trauma (Hobfoll, Hall, et al., 2007). This is also a time for survivors to identify resources and supports that will facilitate coping and healing. The third series of questions that group facilitators may pose includes "After all that you have been through, what do you think will happen in the next few days or weeks?" "Do you think that your family, friends, and community will continue to be affected?" "Do you have any concerns about what will happen next?"

Psychological Intervention With Children and Families After Mass Casualty Terrorism

Even though children are rarely the direct targets of terrorist attacks (Miller, 2003d, 2006d, 2006e), they are deeply affected by this kind of trauma, which disrupts the world around them (Hoven, Duarte, & Mandell, 2003). Interventions with children and families following a mass terror attack are similar to the modalities discussed in chapter 13 in connection with school violence, the difference perhaps being the scale of the event and the number of people affected.

The stresses on families, particularly the persistent postdisaster problems of lost income, employment, and housing, result in increased feelings of powerlessness and loss of control, which often lead to increased rates of child and spouse abuse (chapter 11). This is why the provision of information, education, and basic services, although not usually thought of as therapy per se, is often an indispensable part of improving the mental health of families after a disaster (Schecter & Davis, 2007; Ursano, Fullerton, & Norwood, 1995).

Accordingly, interventions with parents and their families should be directed at assisting the child to regain a sense of safety, validating the child's emotional reactions rather than discouraging or minimizing them, strengthening the sense of security and control in the family environment, anticipating and providing additional support during times of heightened distress (such as anniversaries of the event), and minimizing secondary stresses (Johnson, 1989; Pitcher & Poland, 1992; Schecter & Davis, 2007; Ursano, Fullerton, & Norwood, 1995).

Young children may ask the same questions repeatedly until they are able to process and understand all the information. Therapists should advise adult caregivers to be patient and respond to the child's questions, in an age-appropriate manner, as many times as necessary (Spungen, 1998). Contrary to the impression of many adults, children often have a more sophisticated notion of the concept of death than is first appreciated (Yalom, 1980). Because children of the same age may differ widely in terms of their psychodevelopmental maturity, adults should take their cue from the cognitive level and personality of the individual child (see chapter 9).

Due to a combination of developmental factors and response to traumatization, children may have particular difficulty in verbalizing their reactions to the traumatic bereavement. Individual group therapies with children, therefore, necessarily need to be more participatory and experiential. Worksheets, games, play therapies, skits, puppet shows, music, storytelling, and art modalities should be integrated into the therapeutic program for traumatized children (Beckmann, 1990; James, 1989; Spungen, 1998).

Children should be included in memorialization activities, albeit at an age-appropriate level. They should be part of both the planning process and presentation of memorial services. Children may write poems or stories, draw pictures, create a scrapbook, plant a tree, or create some other memorial. This can be done either as an individual or family project, or both (Sprang & McNeil, 1995; Spungen, 1998; also see chapters 9 and 13).

Individual and Group Treatment Modalities for Children Following Terrorist Attacks

Several large-group, mostly school-based postdisaster interventions for children and adolescents may productively be adapted for cases of mass terroristic trauma.

Stewart et al. (1992) describe an intervention following a hurricane that used both large and small groups in a single 2-hour session, designed to lower levels of disaster-related distress and enhance social support among students. The intervention incorporated physical activity and group-enhancing activities. The didactic portion helped explain to students the relationship between unmet needs and stress and also attempted to normalize stress-related symptoms.

Vernberg and Vogel's (1993) program was described in chapter 13 in connection with school violence. To recapitulate, their disaster intervention protocol divides intervention strategies into four phases. The *predisaster phase* primarily involves incorporating mental health services into local or regional disaster plans. Interventions in the immediate *impact phase* of the disaster include ensuring support for help providers at affected sites, gathering and disseminating accurate information, and making initial contact with children who have been affected by the traumatic disaster event. *Short-term adaptation phase* interventions include classroom strategies that allow emotional expression and cognitive processing of the traumatic events through group discussions, drawing, play therapy, and other appropriate outlets. Interventions during this phase also include family approaches such as providing information and education, absenteeism outreach, and brief family therapy. It also includes individual modalities, such as one-on-one debriefing, individual psychotherapy, and pharmacological approaches, if appropriate. Finally, *long-term adjustment phase* interventions include more extensive individual and family psychotherapy, as well as the use of communal rituals and memorials.

Several individual and group treatment protocols for children have recently been developed specifically to address post–terror attack trauma in this vulnerable population.

Hoagwood et al. (2007) describe the *Child and Adolescent Trauma Treatments and Services Consortium* (CATS) established by the New York State Office of Mental Health in response to the 9/11 terror attacks in New York. This involved a 15-session, manualized treatment protocol for encouraging interpersonal engagement, skill building, processing trauma and bereavement, and improved family relationships. Liberal use was made of narrative therapy, and the program offered certificates of completion at termination.

Schechter and Davis (2007) describe the establishment of a *Kids Corner* in the downtown New York area following 9/11. This dedicated room provided a kid-friendly environment—complete with arts and crafts, toys, snacks, books, work tables, and an adjoining family consultation area—where children and families could feel relatively safe and comfortable expressing themselves and processing what they were going through.

Specifically, Schechter and Davis (2007) offer the following recommendations for therapists and counselors who may have occasion to treat children after a terrorist attack (many of these will seem familiar from our discussions in chapters 9 and 13):

- Listen to the child in a way that validates the importance of what he or she has to say.
- Help the child to articulate, in an age-appropriate fashion, what it is he or she wants to express, so everyone will be clear about what the child is thinking and feeling.

- Utilize nonverbal forms of communication, such as art, music, and play therapy.
- Support healthy attachment bonds with living family members and with the memory of deceased loved ones. Help the child to mourn constructively at an age-appropriate level.
- Within realistic boundaries, help the child imagine and anticipate how things will get better, for him- or herself, the child's family, and the community.

Schechter and Davis (2007) also provide recommendations for therapists and counselors who work with the families of children traumatized and possibly bereaved by a terrorist attack (also see chapter 9):

- Normalize and validate the parents' reaction to their own losses, as well as their children's reactions to the terroristic trauma and the disruption of life it has entailed.
- Help parents understand what their children are going through by providing accurate, authoritative information about stress and coping and how they differ between children and adults. This should be both from a general perspective and also from your insight about the individual child and family you're working with.
- Provide the family with practical strategies for coping with their own distress and helping their children cope with theirs.
- Discourage unproductive media viewing of the event, which can serve to retraumatize children and some adults, as well.
- Without prematurely pushing or forcing it, encourage a return to as normal a lifestyle as circumstances allow.

COMMUNITY AND SOCIETAL RESPONSES TO TERRORISTIC TRAUMA

By definition, mass-casualty terroristic disasters are community events, and there is much that community leaders can do to offer support and increase therapeutic and social morale. Interventions require building relationships within the community through police, mental health professionals, teachers and school administrators, business managers and executives, and spiritual and religious groups.

Community Responses

Symbols are an important part of the recovery process. Commendations and awards to rescue workers and to those who have distinguished themselves are important components of the community recovery process. Memorials to the victims of the terroristic disaster are part of the healing process and should be encouraged. Leaders are powerful symbols in and of themselves. Local and regional leaders should be encouraged to set an example of expressing their own grief in a healthy and mature way, in order to lead the community in recognizing the appropriateness of constructive mourning (Ursano, Fullerton, & Norwood, 1995).

Walsh (2007) cites Landau and Saul's (2004) four recommendations for enhancing community resilience following a major catastrophe:

1. Strengthen social support, coalition building, and information and resource sharing to enhance social connectedness, and build or reinforce a sense of community (also see Hobfoll, Galai-Gat, et al., 2007).
2. Help survivors construct a collective group narrative, a communal storyline that gives meaning to the experience and helps memorialize it as an event that was overcome (Hobfoll, Hall, et al., 2007).
3. Work toward reestablishing normal routines and a sense of returning to the land of the living.
4. Where appropriate, assist survivors in arriving at a positive vision of the future; in other words, encourage realistic hope.

More broadly, the recognition of a disaster by outside authorities, such as the governor or president, is also an important part of recovery. When a distressed community is acknowledged, its members feel less alone and more in communion with the world at large. This support—"we're with you"—is a necessary component of the healing process. Such outside support networks offer the hope of additional resources as well as emotional support. Interventions require building relationships within the community through police, mental health professionals, schools, teachers, and administrators, as well as spiritual and religious groups. The mental health consultant, who may at first feel like an outsider, fills some of these same functions, serving as an indicator of the larger world's concern, providing hope for the return to normal or seminormalized life, and allowing a brief respite from the ongoing issues of disaster stress and recovery (Kratcoski et al., 2001; Stebnicki, 2001; Ursano, Fullerton, & Norwood, 1995).

National and International Responses

Oklahoma City was an Oklahoman crisis, but it was also an American tragedy. September 11, 2001, was an attack on New York and Washington, but it was also a national crisis and an international trauma with worldwide consequences for the mental health and stability of the whole planet's inhabitants. In cases of mass terrorism, the mental health response may well have to involve international coordination and cooperation (Kratcoski et al., 2001).

According to the United Nations Commission on Crime Prevention and Criminal Justice, a comprehensive victim services program must include immediate crisis intervention; short- and long-term counseling; victim advocacy; protection and support during the investigation and prosecution of terroristic and other violent crimes; adequate training for allied professionals on victim issues, violence prevention and intervention strategies; and public education and awareness raising on victim issues (Kratcoski et al., 2001).

A UN Voluntary Fund for Victims of Terrorism has been proposed but has not yet been established. In the interim, an immediate clinically grounded, community-based response to victimization is needed; this should include a mental health plan for disaster and terrorism victims to provide immediate and long-term services. A mechanism should be established for providing readily available crisis intervention services whenever and wherever they are needed in terrorism incidents (Kratcoski et al., 2001).

Finally, from the perspective of justice, laws must be enacted to specifically set penalties for terroristic crimes and to provide for the swift apprehension, extradition, prosecution, and sentencing of the offenders and their supporting and sponsoring parties.

CONCLUSIONS

We have entered a perilous age. Not since the days of the Cuban missile crisis and the Mutual Assured Destruction doctrines of the cold war have Americans felt so personally threatened. Skilled, trained, and experienced mental health clinicians will be vital resources in combating the psychological disruption of our society in the wake of future terrorist attacks. The intended effect of terrorism is, after all, psychological, and from individual therapy to mass interventions involving tens of thousands, the potential contribution of psychology to mitigating the worst effects of this assault on our national psyche can be immeasurable. Readers of this book who have honed their clinical skills in treating different kinds of crime victims will find many of these skills in high demand if and when the next crisis hits. To keep those skills sharp, and the motivation to use them fresh, we also need to know how to take care of ourselves and our colleagues.

CHAPTER 15

Our Own Medicine

*Counseling and Psychotherapy of Mental
Health Professionals*

Whether dealing with multiple victims of a mass terror attack or single individuals struggling with the various and sundry outrages committed against
them, doing crime victim counseling and psychotherapy is not for wimps;
it's tough, demanding work that can take an exhausting toll on practitioners.
If that weren't enough, crime victim therapy can be a dangerous profession,
especially when caseloads include severely disturbed patients or those with
disordered, vindictive, and/or potentially violent peers or family members.
Therapists and counselors may be threatened, sometimes stalked and harassed, occasionally assaulted and injured, and a few of our colleagues have
been killed (Miller, 1998c, 1998h, 2000c, 2000j, 2007k).

STRESSES AND CHALLENGES OF CRIME VICTIM THERAPY

The traumatic experiences and reactions of crime victims can rub off on
clinicians. Therapists who work with crime victims often begin to feel overly
concerned about their own safety and seek greater security measures. Some authorities believe that the most effective therapists are also the most vulnerable
to this *mirroring* or *contagion effect,* in that those who have enormous capacity
for feeling and expressing empathy tend to be most at risk for burning out
(Figley, 1995); however, I don't think heightened vulnerability to burnout is
a necessary correlate of therapeutic empathy and skill. On the contrary, therapists who have the greatest degree of true empathy, as long as it is combined

with a sense of autonomy and personal resilience, often make the most skilled helpers (Miller, 1993a, 1998h).

Compassion Fatigue, Vicarious Traumatization, and Burnout

Nevertheless, clinicians who work on a regular basis with traumatized patients and people in crisis may be subject to special stresses. These professionals are regularly surrounded by the extreme intensity of trauma-inducing events and their aftermaths, and can be easily drawn into this vortex of emotional intensity. Figley (1995) identifies several reasons why trauma therapists are especially vulnerable to what he terms *compassion fatigue.*

First, empathy is a major personal resource for trauma workers to guide and counsel the traumatized. While the process of empathizing with the trauma victim and family members helps to understand their experience, in the process, therapists may be traumatized themselves.

Second, many trauma therapists have experienced some traumatic event in their own lives, and this unresolved trauma may be activated by accounts of similar traumas in patients. There is thus the danger of the crisis worker's overgeneralizing from his or her own experiences and methods of coping and overpromoting those methods with patients. Examples of this phenomenon may occur in the work of domestic violence and sexual assault counselors.

Finally, special stresses are involved in working with traumatized children, where the identification, empathy, and sympathy factors are always high (James, 1989; Johnson, 1989; Miller, 1999d, 2003e).

As the therapist begins to lose his or her objectivity and overidentify with patients, depression and apathy may develop. Reactively, the therapist may start to find him- or herself "not giving a damn" about patients—or anyone else. Therapists may be relieved when difficult patients cancel sessions (Moon, 1999). Crisis clinicians may walk around in fear and dread of their beepers and cell phones going off, announcing the next emergency they must respond to. The stress effects may spill over into the therapist's family life as he or she becomes more withdrawn and emotionally unavailable (Cerney, 1995). Alternatively, other therapists may become trauma junkies, increasingly reinforced by the lurid thrill of working with such dramatic cases, but in the process sacrificing their clinical objectivity and effectiveness (Yassen, 1995).

McCann and Pearlman (1990) coined the term *vicarious traumatization* to describe the transformation that occurs within the therapist as a consequence of overly intense and/or overly prolonged empathic engagement with patients' trauma experiences and their sequelae. These effects usually don't arise solely from one therapy relationship but accumulate across time and number of helping relationships. The age, sex, personal trauma history, length of time doing trauma therapy, size of trauma patient caseload, and current stresses of the therapist may interact with exposure to multiple patient narratives of suffering to contribute to trauma-related symptoms in the therapist (Elliott & Guy, 1993; Follette, Polusny, & Milbeck, 1994; Pearlman & MacIan, 1995).

The *burnout* literature (Ackerly, Burnell, Holder, & Kurdek, 1988; Deutsch, 1984; Gilliland & James, 1993; Pearlman & MacIan, 1995; Robinette, 1987; Rodolfa, Kraft, & Reiley, 1988) suggests that being younger or newer to trauma work is associated with higher levels of burnout, as is working in a hospital setting, where more severely injured or disturbed patients are likely to be seen. As in any field, a certain selection process seems to operate in terms of personality structure, temperament, and cognitive style, so that there emerges a delicate balance, in terms of clinical effectiveness, between being too fresh and callow versus being too encrusted and emotionally shriveled (Miller, 1993a, 2003a).

Special Challenges of Trauma Therapy and Counseling

Talbot, Dutton, and Dunn (1995) describe some of the distinctive features that make trauma and crisis work stressful for psychotherapists and that can be directly applied to the work of mental health professionals who treat crime victims:

> *Urgency and immediacy of the response.* The crisis response is often of an outreach or in-the-field nature, which means that the therapist has little or no control over many aspects of the situation: when it happens, where it happens, who will be there, and what services will be required. Typically, there is little or no advance notice, scant time to prepare, limited time for individual interventions, lack of space, and unfamiliar or dangerous surroundings. As we've seen in chapter 5, often we must take our crime victims when and where we find them, outside the comfort zone of our office or other clinical setting, and frequently off the page of our schedule book. In a crisis, the crime victim counselor needs to be able to work speedily and effectively to stabilize the situation and to prepare the victim for more extensive interventions later on.
>
> *Volume and intensity of the work.* The cumulative volume of crime victim work, both in terms of the number of people requiring attention in numerous successive crises and the extremely intense engagement required with each patient in any one crisis or therapeutic session, can exert a debilitating effect. As noted in chapter 5, emotional intensity is almost always high and victims are often in a regressed and decompensated state. Some victims may themselves perceive therapeutic

interventions as intrusive and become resistant or hostile. Clinicians accustomed to structured therapeutic interactions may find themselves feeling overwhelmed when confronted by trauma victims whose needs are largely for basic empathy and containment. Often there is nothing to do but listen, and even this may be an extremely difficult task under chaotic circumstances. Also, there is often little or no history regarding the precrisis or premorbid functioning of the victims. The crisis often occurs within an organizational context, such as law enforcement and the criminal justice system, which makes particular demands on first responders or investigators, and which may be at odds with the needs and wishes of the victim or the clinician (Talbot et al., 1995).

Threatening patients. Koopman, Zarcone, Mann, Freinkel, and Spiegel (1998) surveyed staff in a university psychiatric clinic who had received threats made on the telephone and in person by a patient who was an outpatient at the facility. The patient threatened to kill several administrative personnel as well as himself. Two weeks later, questionnaires were sent out to employees. The researchers found that greater acute stress symptoms were present among persons who reported more exposure to a threatening patient, viewed the episode with the patient as threatening, and served as a clinic administrative staff person (i.e., had more of an opportunity of a face-to-face interaction with the threatening patient compared to nonclinic administrators).

Effects of Crime Victim Work on Clinicians

The stresses of crisis intervention can affect mental health clinicians in a number of ways. In the aftermath of their interventions with victims of armed bank holdups, Talbot et al. (1995) report finding themselves often feeling isolated, angry, tense, confused, powerless, hopeless, anxious, emotionally exhausted, and overwhelmed with responsibility. Patients' problems seem alternately insignificant or insurmountable, and the clinicians may begin to lose perspective and to overidentify with their patients. Clinicians may intellectualize, becoming overly rigid and inflexible in their thinking. Using denial as a protective strategy, clinicians are often unaware of the way in which the work has affected them, and the recollection among different emergencies becomes blurred.

These clinicians often feel exhausted, increase their alcohol intake, suffer somatic symptoms such as headaches, gastrointestinal complaints, and sleep disturbances with nightmares, experience increased sensitivity to violence in general, and become emotionally demanding of family and friends. They become increasingly tense and distractible, expecting the phone to ring at any moment announcing yet another crisis or emergency (Talbot et al., 1995).

Transference, Countertransference, and Therapeutic Boundary Issues

Therapeutic interactions with traumatized crime victims are by no means always appreciated or accepted, especially at the beginning of treatment. Well-intentioned therapists may be surprised to encounter patients' transferential perceptions of them as sadistic persecutors and torturers. In a countertransferential twist, therapists may experience disgust, revulsion, despair, terror, and helplessness as they now become the victims and their patients assume the roles of tormenters and persecutors, causing therapists to feel all the more inadequate and inept. In other cases, countertransference feelings can lead the therapist, under the guise of giving comfort, to repeat the trauma of the previous experience—to retraumatize the patient (Cerney, 1995). For example, the therapist may find herself taking an overly rigid or punitive stance or tone with some patients.

Countertransference issues are of particular importance in work with crime victims because they tend to revolve around frightening aspects of the therapist's life that are often unconscious and difficult to deal with, such as fears of violence, abandonment, helplessness, degradation, maiming, and death. Many traumatized patients are in such pain and are so skilled at communicating it that therapists may accede in good faith to patients' inappropriate requests. In fact, what these patients really need is a therapist who can maintain appropriate boundaries and thereby prove that they, the patients, are not the perpetrators or collaborators, that they are not responsible for and do not deserve their victimization, as they may have inferred or deliberately been led to believe from the reactions of others (Cerney, 1995).

Cerney (1995) has delineated some of the transferential situations encountered in trauma therapy that are frequently seen in work with crime victims.

Projective identification. Here, the patient experiences feelings of being persecuted by the therapist. When these persecutory feelings become unbearable, the patient tends to project them outward, often with such intensity that the therapist internalizes the feelings to the point of identifying with them, and then acts accordingly, like a persecutor, even though that is not her usual style. The therapist may become rude, insulting, and cruel to the patient, often aware of this reaction but bewilderingly unable to change it. Other motives may include the therapist's need to dissociate herself from the patient's plight. Either way, the patient again undergoes the trauma of being victimized, and the therapist's self-perception of being a kind, understanding professional may be severely damaged (Catherall, 1995; Cerney, 1995).

Overidentification. This is often the therapist's countertransferential response to the patient's transferential projection. Here, the therapist overidentifies with the crime victim's pain, rage, and desire for revenge, especially when the therapist comes from a similar developmental, sociocultural, or experiential background as the patient. This therapist reaction may serve to intensify the patient's feelings rather than helping him to work through and beyond them, which is necessary for trauma resolution. On the other hand, if the patient comes from a different background, the therapist may tend to minimize, negate, or invalidate aspects of the patient's experience. The affront to the sense of self experienced by therapists of traumatized crime victims can be so overwhelming that, despite their best efforts, therapists begin to exhibit the same characteristics as their patients. That is, they experience a change in their interactions with the world, themselves, and their families. They may begin to have intrusive thoughts, nightmares, and generalized anxiety. At this point, therapists themselves clearly need supervision and assistance in coping with their vicarious trauma (Cerney, 1995).

Munroe et al. (1995) has enumerated several specific patterns of transferential and countertransferential traumatic engagement that may express themselves in the therapeutic process and that therapists must remain vigilant for, presented here along with my comments and suggestions:

Exploiter/exploited. In this pattern, the therapist is accused of being "just like all the others" who are abusing the patient or who have done so in the past. Variations of this pattern include the therapist "only being in it for the money," treating the patient as a "guinea pig," or "getting off on my suffering" or on the act of helping: "Who died and made you Mother Teresa?"

Allies/enemies. This pattern is often observed in combat veterans, but I've also encountered this pattern in police officers, in injured workers involved in legal or insurance claims against their employer, and in crime victims who may be wrestling with the criminal justice system (see chapter 16). Here, the therapist is conscripted into the role of either an adversary who is out to "get something on" the patient or, alternatively, as an idealized pal and confidant, "the only one who understands." The danger in both cases is that the therapist will fail to use appropriate therapeutic leverage and challenges, either to avoid confronting the patient in the enemy role or to avoid taking the shine off the idealized image in the ally role.

Aggressor/aggressee. This pattern is prominent in those patients who have grown up in a world of violence and intimidation (chapter 1). They have learned to use direct or implied threats to influence and manipulate people and may try this on the therapist. These patients may attempt to get the therapist to endorse violent revenge fantasies or to justify past acts of retaliatory aggression based on their victim status. Such patients may often have serious personality disorders in the antisocial-narcissistic-borderline spectrum that underlie their trauma syndrome (chapter 3), and these need to be addressed early and forthrightly.

Rescuer/rescuee. This is an unstable and potentially dangerous pattern, in which the crime victim shows up abruptly in breathless crisis, then drops out of sight until the next emergency. Therapists who play into this crisis cycle risk reinforcing the patient's view of the world as a hostile place where helping relationships occur only in emergencies and rescue relationships substitute for intimacy; this pattern is often seen in patients with dependent or bipolar personalities (chapter 3). The clinical challenge is for the therapist to provide a model of mature stability by being there when the patient needs her, while reinforcing the idea that dramatic displays are not necessary to elicit care and concern from others, and by emphasizing the necessity for the patient to build up inner resources by maintaining carefully modulated therapeutic contact that will head off crises before they escalate.

Lone Ranger. This is a variant of the rescuer pattern in which the therapist sets himself up as the sole sane voice, the only helper competent enough to protect the patient from the forces of evil pounding at the gate. While projecting a sense of professional competence and realistic hope is a necessary part of building the therapeutic alliance, an overly insulative us-against-the-world mentality may maladaptively reinforce the patient's traumatized view of the world as a hostile place where escape is possible only through an all-powerful rescuer who is stumbled upon by happenstance or beneficent fate, a variation of the Clarence-the-Angel fantasy described in chapter 7.

PSYCHOLOGICAL INTERVENTIONS WITH COUNSELORS AND THERAPISTS

As emphasized throughout this book, clinicians need to have available a wide range of counseling and therapeutic options to treat the wide variety of crime victim trauma syndromes and underlying personalities that they will encounter. Treatment often proceeds in stages or layers, with direct, symptom-moderating approaches often paving the way toward more exploratory, integrative modalities. It's the same with helping our own: We need a range of approaches to accommodate the diverse temperaments, cognitive styles, life experiences, and professional histories of our colleagues in distress.

Psychological Debriefing: Debriefing the Debriefers

Concepts like *vicarious traumatization* (McCann & Pearlman, 1990) and *compassion fatigue* (Figley, 1995) remind us of the cumulatively stressful effect on trauma therapists of working with successive cases of wounded and shattered patients, including crime victims. The very empathy we rely on to connect with our traumatized patients and establish a healing relationship also carries the risk of emotional contagion that may lead to therapeutic burnout or depression (Moon, 1999).

Chapter 12 introduced CISD in connection with treating survivors of workplace violence. Originally developed for the rapid psychological decompression of law enforcement and emergency services personnel, this model has shown its efficacy in a wide range of applications (Miller, 1999g). As psychotherapists become more involved in the critical incident stress field, it is inevitable that we will see more psychologically sophisticated analyses of the cognitive–behavioral and psychodynamic processes involved in debriefing methods, along with more complex and nuanced intervention approaches. Hopefully, this will not sacrifice the basic on-the-street adaptability and clinical user-friendliness of the stress debriefing model; indeed, it would be ironic if greater depth of understanding led to a more narrow range of practical applicability (Miller, 1999g).

Talbot et al. (1995) argue that psychotherapists, because of our training and experience, require specifically psychological understanding and integration to be able to function and intervene effectively. These authors' own program (Manton & Talbot, 1990; Talbot et al., 1995) has evolved largely through their work with bank employee victims of armed hold-ups and the mental health clinicians who debrief them. In this model of what they term *psychological debriefing*, the goal is to help mental health clinicians deal with the stresses of trauma work via ventilation, catharsis, and sharing of experiences, in order to achieve psychological mastery of the situation and prevent the development of more serious delayed stress syndromes. Particularly important for psychotherapists is the careful exploration of their identification with the victim's experience, which enables them to properly assimilate the burden of empathy. The therapists are helped to integrate the traumatic experience and make a transition back to everyday work and life.

Because of our training and experience, this model postulates, we psychotherapists need to know not only what happened, and when, how, and where it happened, but also *why* it happened. That is, the debriefing must incorporate not just emotional ventilation but also an integrative intellectual understanding of the traumatic event and the therapist's role in dealing with victims in the aftermath. Consequently, the debriefing process employed by Manton and Talbot (1990) and Talbot et al. (1995) includes making psychological sense of what occurred to the victims and the psychotherapists both personally and professionally.

In this model, the debriefing of the debriefers is attended by two or more psychologists who were not part of the original civilian debriefing; for clarity, I refer to them here as *secondary debriefers.* The therapist debriefing is held away from the crisis scene as soon as is possible for all involved therapists to attend.

In Talbot et al.'s (1995) psychological debriefing model, the debriefing procedure incorporates the crisis event, the responses to that event by the therapists, and the processes occurring in the debriefing itself. Its aim is to tie in and make sense of the crisis and the subsequent counseling so that a clear, total picture is formed. The secondary debriefer is consequently dealing with a number of different levels of the crisis: the event itself, the victims' responses to that event, the psychotherapists' responses to the event, the psychotherapists' responses to the victims, and each psychotherapist's personal and professional response to the event. In essence, the secondary debriefer assumes a clinical supervisor type of role to help each therapist reach an understanding of the interventions that were made, assess those that were useful, explore possible alternatives, and decide on future actions.

The secondary debriefer needs to normalize the experiences of fearfulness and sadness that follow the traumatic event. Part of his or her response may also involve what Talbot et al. (1995) call a *parallel process,* in which the psychotherapist tries to experience what the victims have experienced. Past unresolved issues may also come up, particularly if there have been violence or abuse experiences in the therapists' own histories. Fully dealing with countertransference issues is usually beyond the scope of a single debriefing, but this should be followed up by further treatment if necessary (Maier & Van Ryboeck, 1995; Miller, 1998c, 1998h).

In Talbot et al.'s (1995) system, to help make sense of the therapists' experiences in the original crisis and in the present debriefing, the secondary debriefer brings together his or her knowledge of the original crisis victims as individuals and as a group, and his or her understanding of the operative psychological processes. Because greater psychological knowledge is often associated with better intellectualized and sophisticated defenses, the secondary debriefer, consistent with the supervisor-type role, may need to be somewhat more directive or confrontive with the debriefed therapists than clinicians typically are with civilian victims or, for that matter, than debriefers might be with other crisis responders, such as police officers, firefighters, or paramedics. The ultimate goal is to tie in themes and personal issues, draw parallels, and put the incident into perspective.

Finally, as in a therapeutic session, the secondary debriefer needs to summarize, to contain, and to make sense of what occurred. Talbot et al. (1995) assert that it can be useful for the individual therapists to verbalize what they have gained and learned from working in the crisis and from the victim debriefings. To continue personally and professionally, psychotherapists need to have a sense of mastery of the experience, as well as the assurance of feeling valued, worthwhile, and positive about themselves and their work. Cognitive understanding and adaptive self-insight give psychotherapists mastery of the situation, objectivity, and a theoretical base from which to make further interventions. This is essential in order for them to continue to function as effective trauma therapists. Similar recommendations apply to therapists in all specialties (Miller, 1993a, 1998h).

Process Debriefing

Dyregrov (1997) describes a CISD-type model of intervention that he terms *process debriefing,* incorporating the same basic structure as the Mitchell and Everly (1996) model (chapter 12) but placing more emphasis on analyzing and addressing the group dynamics that actually take place in a debriefing. Characteristics of process debriefing include

- strong mobilization of group support,
- primary use of other group members to normalize reactions to stress,
- active use of the group as a resource,
- limiting the number of participants to 15 members per group in order to optimize the interaction, and
- emphasis on the role of the group leader and coleader in providing a model of communication by the way they interact with one another.

In this sense, process debriefing seems to represent a species of cognitive–behavioral group therapy more than being a strict CISD approach per se. Indeed, while pointing out that formal mental health credentials are no guarantee of therapeutic effectiveness, Dyregrov (1997) emphasizes the need for group leaders to have the necessary knowledge, training, and experience to positively influence the group experience. Accordingly, he cites several criteria for effective therapists, including genuineness in the helping relationship, provision of a safe and trusting atmosphere of nonpossessive warmth, and accurate, empathic, moment-by-moment understanding of the patient. Much of this will be familiar to practitioners of group therapy approaches, and of course, much of the same criteria for clinical effectiveness apply to therapists in all areas of practice (Miller, 1993a).

While a more intensive concern for group dynamics characterizes the content of Dyregrov's (1997) process debriefing, the structure of the session itself stays fairly close to the Mitchell model (Mitchell & Everly, 1996), with some modifications:

- The introduction and fact phases are consolidated into an inclusive *relationship phase,* in which the trust, authority, and structure of the group is established.
- The model stresses the importance of *predebriefing preparation* by the leader and coleader, in terms of learning about the nature of the critical incident and the composition of the group. This is in line with the principles of good history taking in other types of clinical assessment.
- There is an emphasis on the relationship between the leader and coleader during the debriefing in providing a *model of healthy interaction.* The participants learn how to process grief and pain in a mature, healthy way by watching others do so.
- The importance of *microcommunication* is highlighted, including such features as voice inflection, eye contact, and nonverbal signals.
- Sensitively *varying the intervention style* for different groups, for example, police officers, paramedics, nurses, or psychotherapists, is consistent with clinical flexibility and breadth of experience in applying nuanced interventions appropriately to various populations.
- The model points out the role of the *physical environment or setting* of the debriefing in influencing the group process. For example, respect for the attendees is shown by taking care to have the meeting in a quiet, private, comfortable locale, not in a noisy, smelly, cramped dump. Sometimes, however, reality may dictate the surroundings.

As highly trained clinical practitioners, we can well empathize with therapists who feel that their rich and varied clinical skills are often underutilized in the structured setting of an emergency service debriefing. However, we must remember that the CISD model was developed precisely for its utility as a first-line, first-aid approach to mental health crisis intervention and trauma care for law enforcement and emergency service personnel, not psychologically trained clinicians. The melding of more sophisticated psychodynamic group therapy approaches with the CISD model is certainly to be welcomed, and may in fact be an indispensable component for certain groups, such as traumatized psychotherapists (Miller, 1998c; Talbot et al., 1995).

But, as therapists, we need to take responsibility for knowing our patients and for tailoring our interventions accordingly. With certain groups, cognitively and psychodynamically rich and sophisticated clinical interventions may be piercingly effective in drawing out inhibited feelings and leading to shared expression and resolution of shock and trauma. For other groups, however, the therapist's knowledge and skills must remain more under the surface, the debriefing appearing to occur smoothly and naturally, while the unseen influence of the clinician's knowledge, talent, and training produces no brilliant therapeutic fireworks but is effective precisely because it makes the whole process look easy.

PSYCHOTHERAPY WITH CRIME VICTIM COUNSELORS AND TRAUMA THERAPISTS

Ironic but true: Many therapists don't like therapy—for themselves, that is. In order to reach this group of helpers, special adaptations to the therapeutic model and process are necessary.

General Decompression and Self-Help Measures

It sounds deceptively obvious that all therapists should establish and maintain a balance between their professional and personal lives, but for trauma therapists this is especially important (Cerney, 1995). Some authorities recommend that a sense of civic responsibility expressed in social activism can be an outlet for frustration and serve to productively bind anxiety and focus energies (Comas-Diaz & Padilla, 1990; Yassen, 1995)—as long as such activism does not become an obsessional, self-destructive crusade. Letting the public know your views, beliefs, and ideals can be a potent antidote to the secretive and silencing nature of the trauma. What may seem like small acts of activism can also combat powerlessness, the feeling that "with all I do, I don't make a dent," a commonly expressed sentiment among crime victim counselors. Just be careful that these types of advocacy activities not be seen as compromising your professional objectivity.

Self-help can also occur in the shape of formal or informal support groups or by incorporating stress-reduction activities and exercises into the therapist's daily life (Saakvitne & Pearlman, 1996).

Therapeutic Support for Traumatized Therapists

In cases where therapists have been directly traumatized, as when assaulted in mental health or criminal detention facilities, institutional leaders can take the following steps to ensure that traumatized workers are not stigmatized and ostracized by their colleagues (Catherall, 1995; also see chapter 12).

First, leaders must recognize that other employees may have an emotional reaction to the traumatized worker. This should be addressed by encouraging communication and by educating coworkers on the nature of traumatic stress and its expectable effects.

Second, leaders must create regular opportunities for the group to meet and talk about their exposure to traumatic stress. It is most effective if someone in a position of authority takes responsibility for normalizing the experience.

Finally, leaders must actively encourage the group to see the individual traumatized worker's reaction as a common group problem and deal with it on that basis.

In dealing with countertransferential reactions to aggressive and violent patients, Maier and Van Ryboek (1995) describe the following institutional policy and procedure. In this model, staff are asked to identify and share feelings with their peers and supervisors in forums provided by the clinical administration. Should these feelings interfere with the ability to provide effective and humane treatment to a patient, staff are expected to address the relevant issues. The formal personnel process and human resources channels may be utilized to shape the required change, including referral to the employee assistance program (EAP). If, over time, the staff member is unable to keep feelings of fear and anger from affecting her work performance, a change in work area or assignment may be in order.

Typically, nursing, mental health, and correctional staff victims of workplace violence, such as assaults by patients or inmates, experience intense emotional reactions (Lanza, 1995, 1996). They want to talk about their reactions but may feel it is unprofessional to do so. Victims often express that they do not expect to receive adequate support from hospital or correctional facility administrators, despite what may be a history of loyal service to the institution, and this may produce further anger and demoralization.

As we've discussed, blaming oneself is often a way to impute at least some kind of meaning and controllability to an otherwise incomprehensible catastrophic event. Self-blame can be functional, if it involves attributions to one's specific behavior in a specific situation, rather than to enduring personality characteristics, the often-cited difference between *behavioral self-blame* and *characterological self-blame*. But even behavioral self-blame is not helpful if victims feel that they used appropriate precautions and followed all the safety rules, and bad things happened anyway; this may induce a sense of helplessness and failure. Both administrators and clinicians can help threatened or assaulted staff sort out the realities of safe conduct from runaway catastrophic fears and fantasies.

Obviously, all of these supportive measures depend on a certain degree of trust and cooperation within an organization. This may not always be forthcoming, however, or it may not go far enough. In more complex cases, or those involving more disabling traumatization, crime victim trauma therapists and counselors may need more focused, individualized intervention.

PSYCHOTHERAPY WITH TRAUMATIZED THERAPISTS

Perhaps not surprisingly, the literature is sparse on therapeutic modalities for therapists themselves. Traumatized therapists who enter treatment require their own therapists to be accepting, nonjudgmental, and empathic, without becoming enmeshed or overawed. One of the most difficult issues traumatized therapists face is the assault on their perceptions of the world and its inhabitants (Cerney, 1995; Figley, 1995).

Cerney (1995) has treated a number of therapists suffering from secondary trauma, or vicarious traumatization, using a *suggestive imagery technique* (Grove & Panzer, 1991). Despite the name, the procedure involves no hypnotic induction per se. However, the author has noted that, when subjects are asked to form an image, they often spontaneously go into a suggestible trance state. When patients present a nightmare, flashback, or other type of intrusive thought or imagery, they are asked to "redream" the dream or go over the experience again. At the point at which the traumatic event is about to begin, the therapist suggests they freeze the scene so that they can program how the scenario is to proceed. They are then asked if they would like to enter the scene—be it a dream, memory, or flashback—from the distance of a mature, safe perspective. Or they may bring anyone they wish into the scene with them and thereby restructure it in a less threatening and more empowering way. Readers will note similarity of this approach to that of Matsakis (1994) and Solomon (1988, 1991) in chapter 7.

Specific techniques aside, when working with traumatized clinicians, I have found the biggest challenge to be that of maintaining flexibility of the therapist's role. At one moment, clinicians will want you to be a colleague with whom they can share war stories; the next moment, they may become helpless and dependent, expecting you to offer them some brilliant insight into restoring their motivation and revivifying their career. Complicating the process is the general sense of underlying stress and burnout we all feel in confronting the social and economic changes in mental health care.

In workshops and individual approaches, probably the most effective approach I've utilized is similar to that used with so-called burnout cases from other professions: Find a new way to use your talents and abilities (Miller, 1998h, 1999h, 2006m). As simplistic as this may sound, part of this approach comes from the field of rehabilitation (Miller, 1993e), which emphasizes the concept of *transferable skills*. If therapists can forge new niches for themselves, such as teaching, writing, consulting, or social activism, and if they can learn not to put all their technical eggs in one professional basket, a creative diversification of practice may be an antidote to demoralization and burnout. Alternatively, passionate devotion to a single worthy cause may be as effective, or more effective, in jump-starting the commitment process to renewed professional and personal growth. As we tell our patients, the proper solution depends on the nature of the problem and the nature of the person. This is true for ourselves as well.

> Therapist Smith was a 55-year-old married male psychologist who began work at a county court-supported counseling center to supplement his private practice income, which was beginning to dwindle under the onslaught of HMO regulation. Therapist Jones was a 29-year-old single female clinical social worker who had been a therapist and case manager at a shelter for abused women and children before beginning work as a clinician at the same center as Smith, at nearly the same time.

> Smith, after an almost 30-year career as an independent, outpatient clinical psychologist, resented the clinic job as an unwanted but necessary compromise to maintain his family's lifestyle. Jones, a 5-year veteran of domestic violence shelter work and suicide hotlines, saw the relatively normal crime victim and other forensic cases at the center as a professional respite from her prior steady clinical diet of acute crisis intervention work.

> One afternoon, the cocaine- and alcohol-dependent wife of a former patient, who had been treated at the center several weeks before, appeared abruptly at Smith and Jones's office to search for her erstwhile husband because, as she said, "I know he comes here, he told me." Failing to locate the missing spouse and believing she

was being duped, she picked up a pen from the receptionist's desk and demanded some paper, "so I can report you." Smith abruptly emerged from his office, surprising the woman, who proceeded to jab him in the arm with the pen, chasing him back into his office.

A few moments later, Jones came around a corner and confronted the scene of Smith held at bay by the pen-wielding, drugged-up woman, while the rest of the staff and patients stood around, waiting for security to arrive. Jones attempted to defuse the situation and talk down the disturbed intruder, but apparently moved too threateningly close and the woman suddenly grabbed Jones around the neck in a viselike chokehold. For several seconds, it looked like Jones was going to be strangled to death, but then two security guards and two police officers pulled the enraged woman off Jones and arrested the assailant. Jones spent the night in the hospital and went home the next day with a bruised trachea and sprained neck injury.

"I've had it with this," later exclaimed the minimally injured but clearly traumatized Smith during a mandated EAP counseling session. Rather than deal with the potential violence of the court counseling unit, he opted to go back to private practice, whatever the financial struggles might be, because "I don't get paid enough to get stabbed." Still, for months, he experienced nightmares, anxiety, and depression, had trouble concentrating during his clinical sessions, became irritable and detached with friends and family, and eventually retired from practice about a year after the incident. Through it all, he refused any kind of therapeutic help himself, because "What good would it be to talk about it, anyhow?"

COUNSELOR: If one of your patients told you that, what would you say?

SMITH: Probably what you're going to say: "You have to try to process it, not let it fester, get it out of your system," or something like that.

COUNSELOR: How about this: Bury it as long as that lets you get on with your life and your work. If it doesn't bother you, treat it like mental shrapnel, that is, it's in there but it's not worth all the painful digging around to get it out. But if it continues to really distract you and screw up your daily life, then at some point, once other parts of your life have stabilized, consider a "second opinion."

SMITH: You're right, I've got to first make up my mind what I want to do, then I'll consider the "baggage." I just didn't think I'd still be doing this at my age.

Jones took a few days off and returned to work at the end of the week, wearing a brightly colored padded cervical collar. She attended the first mandated EAP counseling session in her neck brace, but didn't like the counselor, so she sought her own therapist through her company insurance plan. She attended this therapy for about 4 weeks, then felt she had worked through the traumatic event and some associated issues sufficiently to continue her career and life. She noticed a tendency to become overinvolved in her work but was eager to move on in her career as a therapist and, eventually, supervisor.

THERAPIST: Overall, you seemed to have handled this event pretty well.

JONES: "Handle?" What do you mean, "handle"? Even now, every time I think about it, I almost pee in my pants. I can still feel those hands, like iron, around my neck. Nobody realizes how much being choked actually hurts. I remember almost blacking out—I could've been killed!

THERAPIST: But you're back at work.

JONES: Well, what am I supposed to do, just sit home and ruminate? Work gives me a chance to focus, to use my brain. But I still walk around edgy.

THERAPIST: That's PTSD 101, you know that. As far as classic symptoms and reactions, you're a case that reads the textbooks. And you'll probably follow the second half of the book that deals with recovery over the next few months. If work is your best therapy, then go for it. Just be careful not to let it get so intense that you burn yourself out.

JONES: No chance of that [laughs].

It is clear that Smith, already tired and demoralized from having to make a second-choice career move just to keep up financially, needed very little in the way of a traumatic event to propel him into full-scale burnout. Jones, on the other hand, although hardly happy about almost being fatally throttled in the first few weeks of a new job, was able to assimilate this traumatic event by virtue of her prior experience with hard-case clientele, of her ability to utilize adaptive defenses such as humor and sublimation, of her willingness to seek help as necessary, and of her goal-oriented ambition to advance in her career.

CONCLUSIONS

Trauma counselors and therapists who treat crime victims need to be mindful of our own needs as clinicians and as helping human beings who regularly deal with dark aspects of human nature and sometimes some of the toughest cases in the psychotherapy business. Continued education and training, interaction and cross-fertilization with peers, interdisciplinary collaboration, periodic diversion into pleasant activities, development of a sense of mission and purpose, and willingness to access help for ourselves when necessary can protect against premature burnout and contribute to our effectiveness as helpers and healers. And with crime victims, especially, part of this helping role may involve standing by them in their travels through the legal system and perhaps getting in the thick of the civil and criminal justice system ourselves.

CHAPTER 16

Your Day in Court

Crime Victims, Mental Health Clinicians, and the Legal System

Mental health clinicians who work with crime victims sooner or later find themselves involved with some aspects of the criminal justice system, from law enforcement response, to the arrest and prosecution of the offender, to the trial and sentencing, and perhaps into the years of parole hearings and eventual release of the perpetrator. In other cases, you will have to help your patient deal with no-arrest cases, acquittal of the suspect, or adjudication of a much-reduced sentence. In still other circumstances, you'll become involved in workers compensation, personal injury, or another civil case revolving around a criminal victimization. In all cases, counseling and therapeutic support may be vital for the crime victim to survive his or her ordeal psychologically intact.

CRIME VICTIM STRESSES IN THE CRIMINAL JUSTICE SYSTEM

There are several phases of the criminal justice process where crime victims' stresses may be heightened and in which the help of his or her counselor will be crucial. This applies to direct victims, as well as survivors of criminal homicide.

No-Arrest Cases

Statistics from the *Uniform Crime Reports* indicate that approximately one-third of homicides committed in the United States are never solved (FBI, 1994).

Officially, no-arrest murder cases are never closed because there is no statute of limitations for homicide, but, despite the recent media and entertainment industry interest in such cold cases, police know that with each passing day, week, month, and year, the opportunity for an arrest declines (Spungen, 1998). Exceptions may include high-profile cases such as serial killings, murders of police officers, and intrafamily homicides (Miller, 2000i, 2004c, 2006c, 2006m, 2007j; Miller & Schlesinger, 2000), but these will not characterize the cases of most victims and families.

No-arrest cases usually fall into one of two categories: (a) the police have insufficient clues regarding the identity of the suspect; or (b) there is an identifiable suspect but not enough evidence to make an arrest: A recently used term is *person of interest.* The latter situation seems to be more difficult for victims and family survivors to accept because they usually don't understand why the suspect cannot be taken into custody or more evidence gathered "if we already know who it is" (Spungen, 1998).

In homicide cases, no matter how many years have passed, most family survivors of a slain loved one never give up the belief that an arrest will be made. After a while, unrealistic high hopes may come to be invested in this some-day magical event, the future arrest representing, literally or symbolically, the redemptive, restorative process that will return their world to normal. Many victims and families, either through misinformation or self-delusion, come to believe that an arrest will automatically bring justice, being ill-prepared for the tortuous prosecutorial road ahead. As families become desperate, they may ceaselessly pester detectives for news of the case, thereby annoying and possibly alienating the very law enforcement personnel they depend on to solve the crime. Unless and until the criminal is apprehended, victims and survivors are deprived of a concrete, identifiable target for their anger. Absence of a perpetrator, or failure of the criminal justice system to prosecute, sets up an emotional vacuum, impeding the resolution of grief and anger, and potentially leading to helplessness and depression (Sprang & McNeil, 1995; Spungen, 1998).

However, families need not be either mute bystanders or obnoxious gadflies in the criminal investigation process. As long as they are in basic cooperation with the necessary procedures of law enforcement, taking an active role in the case can provide survivors with a productive channel for working out their anger and frustration, and it can afford a means of taking back some control. Families may hire private detectives to assist the police effort (be sure to check with them, first), or they may be able to provide investigators with certain specialized facts and information about the victim or crime circumstances that could aid police in their investigation. The goal for such families is to tread the thin line between making their case stand out among all the other unsolved crimes in their law enforcement jurisdiction, while at the same time avoiding being seen as intrusive pests who are meddling in the investigative process (Spungen, 1998).

In high profile multiple or serial murder or rape cases, victims or survivors may lose their individuality, with each family getting lost in the scale of the horror as the body count rises. It is this kind of high-profile serial offender case that has typically been referred to in the media, both past and present, by some tag line related to the perpetrator (Jack the Ripper, the Railway Killer, the College Dorm Rapist), which further seems to mockingly highlight the namelessness and facelessness of the victims and their families (Miller & Schlesinger, 2000; Spungen, 1998).

In high-profile cases, certain victims, because of their youth, attractiveness, social position, or intriguing lifestyle, may become the chosen victims of the media, replete with yearbook photos and home movie clips splattered over newspapers and TV screens. Other involved families may be relegated to second-class status by the media, and perhaps even by law enforcement, feeling shunted aside and neglected as the chosen victims become the poster children for the crime wave. For their part, the reluctant recipients of this special attention may feel abused and violated, as they or their loved one are involuntarily made the object of tabloid infotainment, while their own homes and workplaces are laid siege by battalions of reporters and curiosity seekers (Spungen, 1998).

Plea-Bargaining

The structure of the criminal justice process does not afford party status to family members of murder victims, and even surviving victims themselves may often feel like peripheral players in the prosecutor's main agenda of securing a conviction. Often, the police and prosecutor may disagree about the strength of the evidence needed to make an arrest, and their agendas concerning the case may differ. The first priority of police investigators is to close the case, while prosecutors want to be sure that sufficient evidence is collected to secure a conviction or, more commonly, to coerce a satisfactory plea agreement. The final arbiter in this process is usually the more conservative prosecutor. Most victims and families will never have their proverbial day in court because over 90% of cases are handled through plea agreement between defense attorneys and prosecutors, in which victims and families have little or no input (Sprang & McNeil, 1995; Spungen, 1998; Young, 1988).

The Trial

If the case does go to trial, some of the most difficult feelings to deal with involve the frustration and anger evoked by the impersonal attitude of the court and its participants. Typically, victims and families want justice; they want the criminal prosecuted and punished. Many victims and families report that the majority of their anger, anxiety, and depression relate directly to their dissatisfaction with the criminal justice system. Criminal trials often begin months or years after the crime, and, for many victims and families, the resolution of their grief and anger cannot be completed until they face that ordeal (Amick-McMullin et al., 1991; Ressler et al., 1988; Sprang & McNeil, 1995).

When the trial finally begins, victims or survivors may have to deal with another whole set of traumatic experiences that they are probably ill-prepared for. These include reliving the tragedy through the graphic testimony of witnesses and investigators, as well as the presentation of grisly crime scene and autopsy photos, bloody clothing and personal effects, restraint devices and weapons, and other grim exhibits and evidence. The trial may expose victims and families to information about the crime that they were not aware of or prepared for. Families may hear their injured or murdered loved one defiled and ridiculed as defense attorneys try to paint a picture of the victim as either lying or asking for it. In the courtroom, victims and families will probably come face-to-face with the accused perpetrator, whose reaction to the whole trial procedure may range from stony indifference to smirking bemusement. Victims or family members that become too emotional may be removed from the courtroom (Sprang & McNeil, 1995; Spungen, 1998).

Unless they are actually called as witnesses, the only real input to the judicial process that most families—and even many victims, themselves—will have occurs in the form of a *victim impact statement* that is filed with the judge, prosecutor, or Board of Pardons and Paroles, or may be read in court prior to sentencing. The victim impact statement allows the survivors to express the effect the crime has had on their physical, emotional, social, occupational, and economic well-being, and most victim advocates advise survivors to avail themselves of this mechanism if that is their wish (Hills & Thomson, 1999; Kilpatrick & Acierno, 2003; Kilpatrick et al., 1987; Sprang & McNeil, 1995; Spungen, 1998), although there is still controversy as to the practical effect of such statements on actual sentencing decisions, the psychological benefit obtained by the presenters, and even the constitutional legality of this measure (Chambers, Duff, & Leverick, 2007; Gordon & Brodsky, 2007; Nadler & Rose, 2003).

CRIME VICTIM PARTICIPATION IN THE CRIMINAL JUSTICE SYSTEM: POTENTIAL RISKS AND BENEFITS

Given the potential stresses and challenges noted above, the first choice many victims may have to make about whether or not to become involved in the criminal justice system involves the decision to report the crime in the first place.

Experiences With the Criminal Justice System

Although for many readers of this book it would seem inconceivable to let a serious crime against ourselves or a loved one go unreported, Herman (2003) points out that most crime victims, perhaps especially those most likely to be exposed to violence and least likely to have the legal, financial, or social resources to face a long journey through the courts, decline to involve themselves, apparently preferring to suffer the injustice of an unredressed offense rather than compromise their already shaky family relationships, community ties, privacy, safety, or mental health. Even following an initial police report, the dropout rate from the legal system remains high as the case proceeds through the criminal justice system. Many mental health clinicians who work with crime victims report that their patients' traumatic symptoms are worsened by adverse contacts with the legal process (Campbell & Raja, 1999; Freedy, Resnick, Kilpatrick, Dansky, & Tidwell, 1994).

Much of this reluctance may hinge on the nature and quality of the victim's contact with the criminal justice system. Victims' overall satisfaction appears to be directly related to their sense of inclusion and empowerment. Those who are given a chance to participate in the process and believe their participation to have an impact on their cases report more satisfaction with the system and show better mental health outcomes (Kilpatrick & Otto, 1987; Kilpatrick et al., 1987). Conversely, dissatisfaction appears to be highest among victims who are denied a chance to participate in the legal system, despite their expressed wish to do so.

For example, a study of 102 rape victims in a large midwestern city (Campbell, Wasco, Ahrens, Sefl, & Barnes, 2001) found that many had diligently reported their assaults, only to be frustrated when prosecutors declined to go forward with their cases. In this study, over half of the victims who sought help from the legal system rated their experiences as harmful, especially those whose cases were declined for prosecution. Conversely, victims whose cases were prosecuted in spite of their wishes exhibited similarly high levels of psychological distress. The results suggest that victim inclusion, choice, and empowerment may be the best predictors of mental health outcomes related to prosecution of the offender.

Thus, as much as this book advocates supporting victims through the criminal justice process, it is important to understand why many of your patients may choose not to become involved, because then you face the therapeutic challenge of standing by your patient and his or her decision.

Specific Risks and Benefits of Participation in the Legal System

Herman (2003) has described some of the potential risks and benefits of victim participation in the criminal justice system.

Physical risks include the threat of retaliation and/or harassment by the perpetrator or his allies:

- In cases of domestic violence or other intrafamily crimes, as well as in crimes involving people who live nearby and/or know each other, intimidation, threats, and harassment may be common. Although intimidation of a witness is technically a crime, authorities often have few means of enforcing this effectively.
- The accused perpetrator may use the legal system itself as an additional means to harass or humiliate the victim. For example, as a defendant in a civil or criminal case, the perpetrator can have his attorneys subpoena sensitive medical and other personal records or depose friends and relatives of the victim (Murphy, 1999).
- In domestic violence cases, the perpetrator may file for child custody or seek unlimited child visitation rights, which puts him in frequent contact with the victim and her home (Quirion, Lennett, Lund, & Tuck, 1997).

Psychological risks involve the inherent contradiction between the mental health needs of crime victims and the requirements of the criminal justice process:

- Victims need social acknowledgement and support; the court requires them to endure skepticism and a public challenge to their credibility.
- Victims need to establish a sense of stability and control over their lives; the court requires them to submit to a complex and poorly understood set of mandatory rules and procedures.
- Victims need the opportunity to tell their stories in their own way and at their own pace; the court requires them to respond to a rapid-

fire set of yes–no questions that focus selectively on the agenda of the cross-examining attorney and distort any coherent and meaningful narrative of the victim's overall crime experience.

- Victims may need temporary respite from exposure to trauma reminders and symptom triggers; the court procedure ensures that these will be thrown in their faces by being forced to recount the experience again and again and, in many cases, sit in the courtroom and face the perpetrator.

Potential benefits of participation in the criminal justice process largely relate to the increased sense of autonomy and control that such participation affords some victims (Clute, 1993). Potential benefits include the following:

- Greater sense of safety and protection for victims and enhanced sense of the power to protect others by deterring the offender from repeating his crimes.
- Access to a forum for public acknowledgment of their suffering, restitution for the harm done to them, and (in rare instances) an apology. There may be a restored faith in the institutions of society that are supposed to protect citizens and redress wrongs committed against them. Even if the perpetrator is acquitted, the fact that the victim took some action, "didn't let it go," can be an empowering experience. For example, the concept of *procedural justice* holds that litigants are likely to be satisfied with the justice system when they perceive that the process is respectful and fair, and when they have a voice in the proceedings. This appears to be true even when the desired outcome is not fully achieved (Lind & Tyler, 1988; Winick, 2000).

FORENSIC PSYCHOLOGICAL EVALUATION OF CRIME VICTIMS

If crime victims choose to participate in either the criminal or civil legal process, the psychological harm they have endured will likely be raised by their side and no doubt vigorously downplayed by the other side. Victims who claim psychological disability on the basis of PTSD or on the basis of another psychological syndrome may be court ordered to undergo a forensic psychiatric or psychological evaluation. In other cases, such as in civil lawsuits stemming from the crime (see below), the victim-plaintiff's attorney may arrange for the victim to undergo a psych eval for purposes of establishing the presence of a mental disorder caused by the victimization experience. Usually, the other side will request that the victim be evaluated by its doctor as well, accounting for the often seen battle of the experts that takes place in many civil and criminal cases.

If your patient is to undergo such an examination, there are some important things that you should know in order to fully support him or her through the process and provide the most accurate and sensible advice.

Nature and Purposes of a Forensic Psychological Evaluation

Most people are familiar with the fact that criminal suspects often undergo psychological examination and testing for purposes of establishing their competency to stand trial or to provide evidence for an insanity defense or mitigation. Less commonly, crime victims themselves may undergo forensic psychological evaluation (Carlson & Dutton, 2003) for several possible reasons:

- The prosecutor or plaintiff's attorney may order a psych eval to substantiate the presence of psychological trauma, other psychological disability, or neuropsychological impairment (Knight, 1997; Miller, 1993e) in order to highlight the severity of the crime.
- The defense may order a psych eval to establish the presence of preexisting psychological disorders in order to mitigate the effects of the present crime or to create a case for victim malingering or exaggeration of distress from the present crime (chapter 4).
- In a civil case filed against the perpetrator (see below), the plaintiff may seek to document psychological injury and disability to create a basis for demanding monetary damages. Conversely, the defense will usually order its own psych eval to document precisely the opposite: either that the plaintiff has suffered little or no psychological injury or that he or she is malingering and making it all up (chapter 4).

Forensic Versus Clinical Psychological Evaluations

If an adult patient voluntarily comes to you for help, the *fiduciary relationship* that exists is between you and your patient, and the purpose of any formal mental health evaluation is to diagnose and effectively treat that patient's disorder to help you help your patient with his or her problem. The content of the examination and any additional treatment records are confidential, and your patient is free to terminate the evaluation or treatment process at any time.

In the forensic setting, the fiduciary relationship exists between the psychologist and the court and/or the attorneys involved in the case. The purpose of the exam is to assess the aspects of the examinee's mental status that are relevant to the case at issue, not necessarily to help treat the patient's problem, although the examining psychologist may make treatment recommendations as part of his or her conclusions. The results of the exam typically go to the judge and the attorneys involved in the case, although your patient's attorney in a civil case or the prosecutor in a criminal case may share the report with a treating clinician if they want that clinician's perspective and opinion for purposes of strengthening their case. In some circumstances, either or both attorneys may arrange for the forensic psychological examination to be transcribed and/or videotaped.

If you are this patient's treating psychotherapist, or have been in the past, your clinical records may be subpoenaed. This is actually far less common in a criminal case, where courts generally go out of their way to preserve doctor–patient confidentiality, unless there are some extraordinary circumstances to the case. It is more common in civil cases, where a plaintiff sues a defendant for damages related to psychological injury; then, the defense will claim a right to ascertain whether such an injury in fact exists and, if so, whether it is related to the charge in question or was preexisting or coexisting. In rare instances, a past or present treating clinician may even be called to testify, although here, especially in criminal cases, the court will usually limit the scope of questioning to a very narrow issue that cannot be adequately answered in any other way but by direct questioning of the clinician.

Role of Victim Counselors in the Evaluation Process

Carlson and Dutton (2003) caution that assessing victims' symptoms and past trauma history could potentially be used against them. Many people have sought counseling or therapy for everyday relationship, family, or job problems, and this may be distorted by the other side by portraying the victim as a known mental patient. Conversely, the very ubiquity of psychotherapy in modern society may only serve to make judges and juries yawn when past treatment is presented in court. It is up to each attorney to decide how he or she wants to use this information in the best interests of his or her client.

Consequently, in order to allow victims to make informed choices about participation in a psychological assessment (where they have the option to choose) and to reduce anxiety about what will be taking place, the assessment process should be explained in detail. Practical advice should be provided to examinees about the evaluation process, as delineated below. Certainly, nothing should be told, implied, or coached regarding the content of the examinee's evaluation responses. At the end of the evaluation, the counselor should realistically point out some of the victim's strengths and successes in coping with both the original crime experience and the reliving of it necessitated by the criminal justice process in general and the psych eval in particular (Carlson & Dutton, 2003; Herman, 1992, 2003).

The Forensic Psychological Evaluation: Advice to Examinees

For individuals facing a forensic psych evaluation, whether they be a criminal defendant, plaintiff in a lawsuit, or worker undergoing a psychological fitness-for-duty examination (Miller, 2006j, 2006k, 2007d; Stone, 2000), I typically offer the following guidelines and recommendations.

To begin with, the exact procedures and measures utilized in the psychological exam will depend on the specific referral question. In the case of a crime victim examinee, this will usually involve his or her present mental state, compared to what it is claimed to have been prior to the victimization.

Virtually all forensic psychological exams begin with the doctor (these evaluations are almost always carried out by psychologists or psychiatrists) reviewing relevant records of the case to provide a background for the examination. A good portion of the exam will involve the examinee sitting face-to-face with the clinician, while the latter asks a set of questions relating to the circumstances of the present case; the examinee's medical, academic, and employment history; any current signs and symptoms he may be experiencing; and a set of mental status exam questions to assess his orientation, memory, reasoning, and emotional state.

Depending on the nature of the evaluation, the examinee may be administered a set of psychological tests, some requiring direct interaction with the examiner, others consisting of questionnaires and checklists. This can range from only a few quick standardized measures to an extensive battery of tests, depending on the forensic questions being addressed. The complete examination may therefore take a couple of hours, or extend over several days.

Although it's unlikely your patient is going to enjoy a forensic psychological evaluation, there are things he can do to help it go as smoothly and stress-free as possible and for the results to be an accurate representation of his true psychological status. Here are some recommendations you can give to your patients if they are about to undergo a forensic psychological evaluation.

> ***Don't assume the worst.*** Ideally, the psychologist, especially if a court-appointed expert, should be neither your patient's friend nor his enemy; this person's only job should be to objectively evaluate the examinee's mental status and relate it to the specific legal referral questions under consideration.

Know your rights and responsibilities. Not assuming the worst doesn't mean being uninformed or naïve. Either through his own research or in consultation with his legal representative, the examinee should know his rights and responsibilities with respect to the forensic psych exam. Again, the goal is not to be overly defensive and confrontational but for the examinee to be reasonably protected from unwarranted actions on the examiner's part or illegitimate use of the evaluation results.

Come prepared. The examinee should show up on time. He should bring any records or other materials that were requested. Other common-sense recommendations include bringing reading glasses and having a good lunch prior to an early afternoon exam. Accordingly, the examiner should make sure that he or she is ready at the appointed time and is prepared to conduct the evaluation.

Don't be afraid to ask questions. If the examinee has a question about something the examiner asks or a test that's being given, he should let the psychologist know. A reasonable examiner won't object to reasonable questions. Bear in mind, however, that the examiner may not be able to answer many of the questions—for example, "What does that test result mean?"—at the time of the evaluation. That's either because the examiner needs to score the test results against a normative table or because the actual results of the exam are owned by the legal agency making the referral. If the examiner can't answer a particular question, he or she should tell the examinee plainly. But the latter should not feel intimidated about asking reasonable questions.

Be honest and do your best. The entire validity of the forensic psychological evaluation hinges on the accuracy of the information obtained. Many interview protocols and psychological tests contain controls for inconsistency and response manipulation. In other words, if the examinee is lying or faking test results, the examiner will probably know about it. Then, even if the rest of the profile is relatively favorable, the psychologist will have no choice but to report that the examinee lied, and that's going to corrupt everything that victim says or does for the remainder of the trial. As a clinician looking out for the best interests of your patient, make sure he clearly understands this.

Expect to be treated courteously and behave accordingly. The examiner may have to ask some tough questions but should never gratuitously demean or humiliate the examinee or treat him like a criminal suspect. Indeed, there is nothing to be gained by making the examinee squirm because the more comfortable and less defensive the subject feels during the examination, the better his memory will be and the more accurate will be the information he provides. By the same token, examinees should behave with reasonable respect and decorum. If the examinee needs a bathroom, snack, or rest break, he should feel free to request one. The evaluation process should not be unnecessarily uncomfortable. Everybody knows that he probably doesn't want to be there, but both examiner and subject should keep in mind that they are each in that room to do a difficult but important job.

TESTIFYING IN COURT FOR MENTAL HEALTH CLINICIANS

One thing that mental health and law enforcement professionals have in common is that many of them cite testifying in court as one of the most stressful aspects of their work. Police officers have to testify regularly as part of their jobs, and some mental health professionals who specialize in forensic psychology do this for a living as well. As a nonforensic mental health clinician, however, you may think you never signed on for all this court business, but if you're reading this book, you are involved in, or have an interest in, working with crime victims, and that means that, at least sometimes, you will have to participate in a civil or criminal legal proceeding.

Your job as a clinician-witness is to ensure that the facts you present tell the complete story and that your delivery of these facts makes your testimony clear, credible, and convincing. This section provides some practical recommendations for testifying in court based on a survey of the literature, the experiences of my law enforcement and mental health colleagues, and my own experience as an expert witness in forensic psychology and neuropsychology (Goodman et al., 1992; Miller, 1996b, 1997d, 2006h, 2006i, 2007c; Miller & Dion, 2000; Miller & Magier, 1993; Mogil, 1989). The basic recommendations apply equally to forensic examiners, nonforensic clinicians, and the testifying victim-witness him- or herself.

Types of Witnesses and Testimony

A *fact witness* is someone who has personal knowledge of events pertaining to the case and can only testify as to things he or she has personally heard or observed ("Jenn told me that Gary assaulted her"; "I saw Gary and Jenn arguing and then I heard Jenn yelling"). They may not offer *opinions* ("Based on Jenn's behavior over the past couple of weeks, and Gary's history of being a hothead, I concluded that he probably assaulted Jenn"), which are the province of the *expert witness*, who is retained by the prosecution or defense, or appointed by the court, to make conclusions and statements about aspects of the case that he or she has personally not observed. Experts are there precisely to offer opinions that may assist the judge or jury in understanding specialized technical knowledge that would otherwise be beyond their expertise. This is typically the role of credentialed specialists in forensically related fields, such as a medical examiner, crime lab expert, firearms specialist, or forensic psychologist. Although experts are typically allowed more leeway in testimony than fact witnesses, the content of their testimony is still carefully vetted by the court for admissibility.

As a *treating clinician witness*, you may straddle the border between a fact and expert witness. You are not expected to be completely objective in your assessments and conclusions, as is the retained expert witness, because the court understands that the treatment relationship requires you in some ways to be an advocate for your patient, to be on her side. That is, even if you don't agree with everything she says or does, your primary interest in the case is your patient's improved mental health, not a dispassionate account of her diagnoses and disabilities. At the same time, your professional credentials and training allow you to make conclusions beyond the range of the knowledge and experience of the average juror, so you may be treated as an expert on that basis.

Preparing for Testimony

Actually, preparing for testimony begins from the moment you start treating your patient, whether you ever thought you'd end up in court or not:

> *Keep organized records.* Mental health clinicians, especially those whose work may potentially put them in contact with the legal system, should understand the importance of proper record keeping and strive to develop a well-organized, standardized, and readable style for note taking and report writing—not only because these may be one day read by probing, critical eyes, but because writing out your thoughts in words is an excellent way to clarify, organize, and remember the points you will want to get across, should any of your cases go to trial. Don't be afraid to supplement standard forms and checklists with your own words and illustrations if this will help you explain a potentially confusing scenario.
>
> *Review your case.* Review it as many times as necessary: There is no such thing as too much preparation. The more thoroughly you know your facts and opinions about the case, the easier it will be to answer questions thrown at you from left field, because you won't be relying on rote memorization of individual answers to different questions;

your knowledge and recollection will be an organic, holistic, automatic process that is hard to trip up by clever cross-examination. You will probably have one or more meetings with the prosecutor or plaintiff's attorney to go over your testimony and try to bullet proof it against the other side's questions. Ideally, the goal is not for the attorney to spoon-feed your words to you, but for both of you to clarify the substance of your testimony, to agree on a terminology that will most clearly and accurately express what you have to say, and to get a sense of what you will be asked by both sides.

Rehearse your testimony. Most of this will be mental rehearsal, going over the facts of the case and your testimony in your head. You might also rehearse out loud, while driving in your car or in front of a mirror at home. If trial testimony is unfamiliar to you, visit a court-room and observe other trials in progress. But even for the most sea-soned witness, there is still no substitute for adequate preparation, and many a veteran expert has let his or her overconfidence lead to loose ends, which are then used by a clever opposing counsel to hang them.

On the Stand

Certainly, most important aspects of courtroom demeanor cannot be pro-grammed; every witness brings his or her own unique style to the stand. Nevertheless, there are a few principles of effective testimony that all wit-nesses, whether first-timers or professional forensic experts, can productively apply (Kressel & Kressel, 2002; Mogil, 1989; Posey & Wrightsman, 2005; Spence, 2005; Vinson & Davis, 1993).

Attitude. Your general attitude should be one of confidence, not cocki-ness. To the average juror, a doctor or other professional clinician conveys an air of authority and respect; use this to your advantage. Maintain composure and dignity at all times. Remember, no matter how nasty the cross-examination, you are not the one on trial here. Nor is it you who is there to convict the criminal defendant; your job is to present the facts and evidence about your evaluation and/or treat-ment of the crime victim, and then let the legal process run its course. As with all aspects of clinical and forensic work, always remember this: *You are a professional.* Behave accordingly.

Demeanor. Body language is important. Like your mother said, sit up straight and don't slouch. If there is a microphone in front of you, sit close enough so that you don't have to lean over every time you speak.

Keep your presentation materials neatly organized in front of you, so you can find documents and exhibits when needed. While testifying, look at the attorney while he or she is questioning you, then switch your eye contact to the jury when answering the question; it's them you have to establish a connection with, and jurors tend to find witnesses more credible when witnesses "look straight at us." Be neither overly aloof nor overly intense. Open, friendly, and dignified are the attitudinal words to remember.

Speech tone. Speak as clearly, slowly, and concisely as possible to be understood. Keep sentences short and to the point. Keep your voice steady and use a normal conversational tone. Don't mumble, shout, or waffle, but avoid speaking in a robotic monotone. Your general attitude toward the jury should convey a sense of collegial respect: You are there to present the facts as you know them to a group of mature adults who, you are confident, will make the right decision.

Speech content. Listen carefully to each question before you respond. If you don't fully understand the question, ask the attorney to repeat it or rephrase it. Don't be baited into giving a quick answer; if you need a couple of seconds to compose your thoughts, take them. Speak as clearly and concisely as possible. Answer the question completely, but don't over elaborate or ramble. If you don't know the answer to the question, state plainly, "I don't know." Don't try to bluff your way out of a tricky question. The opposing attorney will try to seize on any inconsistency in your testimony to discredit you. Don't become defensive. Above all, be honest. If anyone in the courtroom detects even a whiff of deliberate bullshine, especially from a professional, it can stink up the rest of your testimony and possibly poison the entire case.

Attorney Tricks and Traps

Attorneys will often phrase a question in a way that constrains your answers in the direction they want you to go. If you feel you cannot honestly answer the question by a simple yes-no response, say so:

> "Sir, if I limit my answer to yes or no, I will not be able to give factual testimony. Do you still want me to answer that way?"

Sometimes, the attorney will voluntarily reword the question. If he presses for a yes-no answer, at that point, either your attorney will pop up to voice an objection or the judge will intervene. The latter may instruct the cross-examining attorney to allow you more latitude in responding, or to rephrase his question, or the judge may simply order you to answer the question as it has been asked, in which case that's what you do, as best you can, with a resigned look on your face.

Another attorney ploy is to phrase questions in such a way as to force you to respond in an ambiguous manner, often prefacing your answer with such wishy-washy phrases as "I believe," "I estimate," "I'm pretty sure that," "To the best of my knowledge/recollection," "As far as I know," and so on. If the facts warrant it, be as definite about your answers as possible; if they don't, honestly state that this particular piece of your testimony may not be a clear perception or recollection, but be firm about what you *are* sure about.

In general, try not to answer beyond the question. For example, if the attorney asks you to phrase your answers in precise measurements that are not relevant or that you cannot accurately recall, don't speculate, unless you're actually asked to do so.

ATTORNEY: Dr. Castille, you say in your notes that Ms. Tuller obtained a score of 40 on the Impact of Events Scale, indicating "moderate-to-severe posttraumatic stress disorder." Well, which is it, moderate or severe?

CLINICIAN: Forty-three is the cutoff score for severe PTSD, so Ms. Tuller was right on the borderline.

ATTORNEY: So then her posttraumatic stress wasn't severe?

CLINICIAN: The range for moderate PTSD is 26–43. Ms. Tuller's score was three points away from severe, but technically still in the moderate range, according to the scoring criteria.

ATTORNEY: So again you're telling us, doctor, that Ms. Tuller only suffers from moderate stress.

CLINICIAN: No, I'm saying that her score on this particular test came close to the severe range, but didn't quite reach it according to the norms of this one test. But, based on my overall examination of Ms. Tuller in the first few weeks after the assault, she was suffering from severe PTSD.

ATTORNEY: Yes, but as you just testified, according to the norms of this Impact of Events Scale, which you administer as part of your evaluation for PTSD, this patient's level of posttraumatic stress only falls in the moderate range, is that correct?

CLINICIAN: Yes, however . . .

ATTORNEY: Thank you, doctor, for clarifying that for us.

A related ploy is for the attorney to ask you to estimate something reasonable, like the amount of time that has passed (which most people can roughly gauge in terms of minutes or hours), and then switch to other topics, while maneuvering you to preserve the estimative mind-set. Now, everything you say has become an "estimate" or something recalled "to the best of my recollection." Later, in his or her summation, opposing counsel will state something like this:

> "And Dr. Castille really hasn't described anything solid has she? Everything is an estimate, a guess, an inference. Ladies and gentlemen of the jury, is a loose collection of "maybe's" and "I-guess-so's" sufficient evidence to convict a man and deprive him of his freedom because of psychological injuries that no one can see, no one can prove, and no one is sure of?"

Again, this doesn't mean you should inject false surety into naturally iffy data, but try to emphasize that the ambiguity lies with the subject matter, not with your own perceptions and interpretations.

ATTORNEY: Doctor, in your evaluation and treatment of Ms. Tuller, can you determine exactly how much of her present anxiety is related to the alleged assault and how much represents a continuation of the anxiety disorder for which she originally came to see you for treatment, as documented in your clinical notes?

CLINICIAN: Exactly?

ATTORNEY: Yes, did the alleged assault contribute to 10% of her current anxiety disorder? 20%?

CLINICIAN: I really can't put a percentage point on it.

ATTORNEY: So you can only guess how much of her anxiety was due to the alleged assault.

CLINICIAN: Well, certainly more than a guess. For example, when she first came to see me, her anxiety disorder mainly affected her socializing skills and being assertive with people, but she was able to attend classes, walk on campus, and study alone in her dorm room without undue fear. Now, after the assault, she is unable to do any of these things without being paralyzed with anxiety. So, one clear indicator of the effect of this assault has been its disrupting effect on significant life activities, such as attending college, which were not present prior to the assault.

Again, if you don't know the answer to a question, just say you don't know. Jurors will respect and appreciate honest ignorance or forgetting of a few details far more than a disingenuous attempt to make everything fit in with your testimony.

As noted earlier, nonforensic clinical treatment providers who are called to court may find that their testimony sometimes spans the domains of fact and expert witness. For example, you may be queried about what you and your patient discussed about the assault, like a fact witness, and then asked to state an opinion like an expert witness. Or you may state such an opinion, which the opposing attorney may challenge, and the judge must then decide whether or not to allow it to be admitted into the record.

ATTORNEY: Dr. Castille, can you tell us when you first became aware of Ms. Tuller's alleged assault?

CLINICIAN: She told me during a session.

ATTORNEY: Please explain.

CLINICIAN: I had been treating her for about 5 months and one day she came in and told me that a college classmate, Gary, who kept asking her out, was starting to follow her around the school, and that when she told him to leave her alone, he started shouting at her, and the next thing she knew, he had thrown her to the ground and was on top of her.

ATTORNEY: Just for clarity, doctor, you didn't review any police reports on this incident and certainly you weren't there to witness it, so what you're relating to us today is based solely on Ms. Tuller's account of the incident to you, is that correct?

CLINICIAN: Yes, that's what she told me in that session.

ATTORNEY: And doctor, in your work with patients with mental disorders, isn't it common for patients to misperceive and inaccurately remember events in their lives?

CLINICIAN: Well, for common, everyday events, that's often true, but usually for something as traumatic as an attempted sexual assault, people will basically remember what happened.

ATTORNEY: Isn't it the case, according to the professional literature on trauma syndromes, including the *DSM-IV-TR* that you cited earlier as an authoritative text, that highly traumatic events can often distort memory and recall?

CLINICIAN: I don't think that was the case with Ms. Tuller.

ATTORNEY: Doctor, are you an expert on posttraumatic stress disorder?

CLINICIAN: No, but I've been working with Ms. Tuller for 5 months, so I'm sort of an expert on Jenn Tuller.

In the end, if you have prepared well, communicated clearly, and testified honestly, you can take pride in having played your role in the legal system as a competent mental health professional.

VICTIM SUPPORT SERVICES AND THE CRIMINAL JUSTICE SYSTEM

Recall from chapters 6 and 7 that an essential part of comprehensive crime victim counseling and therapy is guiding your patient to appropriate support services in the community. Victim services, in one form or another, now exist in all 50 states, but budgetary considerations typically restrict the range of services offered. The victims most frequently targeted for assistance programs are sexual assault victims, domestic violence victims, and children. The National Organization for Victim Assistance (NOVA; www.trynova.org) has developed a generic model of victim services that contains three major components (Young, 1988):

1. Emergency response at the time of the crisis
2. Victim stabilization in the days following the trauma
3. Resource mobilization in the aftermath of the crime

As we've seen, all too often, attitudes and beliefs regarding the criminal justice system are sorely challenged following violent crime experiences. In response to this, a movement promoting the establishment of rights for crime victims has developed during the last two decades (Freedy et al., 1994). Victims and family members may find the legal maze intimidating, and interacting with criminal justice representatives may become a traumatic reminder of the painful and humiliating crime experience. If the perpetrator is known to the victim, as is common in cases of sexual assault or domestic violence, the victim may fear revenge if charges are pursued. Victims often fear the social stigma associated with media reporting, being questioned and disbelieved, and having temporarily lost control. Even when victims decide to press charges, ideal images of swift justice can quickly dissolve as legal proceedings drag on for months or years.

Studies have shown that the prevalence of PTSD is higher among victims who wade through the criminal justice system than among crime victims in general (Freedy et al., 1994). Crime victims most likely to develop PTSD are those who have suffered violent crimes, such as physical or sexual assault or homicide of a loved one, or who were in fear for their life or serious injury during the crime incident. However, support services for victims, including psychological counseling, are typically meager. A prevalent attitude among law enforcement seems to be that solving cases is paramount, with the needs of the victim often an afterthought (see chapters 5, 8).

However, direct clinical experience (Freedy et al., 1994) demonstrates that more humane treatment of victims and their families can foster optimum cooperation with the criminal justice system, which in turn may lead to an increase in the number of crimes reported and to quicker and more successful closure of cases and prosecution of offenders.

Freedy et al. (1994) examined the prevalence of PTSD and victim service utilization among crime victims and family members recently involved in the criminal justice system. About one-half of the participants met PTSD diagnostic criteria during their lifetime. Females were overrepresented among victims of more violent crimes, such as homicide and sexual assault. Victims of these more violent crimes—who sustained physical injuries, who perceived that they would be seriously injured, and who perceived their lives to be threatened—were more likely to suffer from PTSD than victims without these characteristics. While most subjects believed the criminal justice system should provide a range of victim services, including counseling and psychotherapy, most reported inadequate access to such services. The results imply that crime victims involved in the criminal justice system are at risk for developing PTSD, which is insufficiently addressed by mental health professionals due to inadequate access to health care services.

Kilpatrick and Acierno (2003) and Young (1988) have provided a model of victim assistance in criminal proceedings. As discussed earlier, the majority of victims never see their perpetrators and typically receive little information or consideration surrounding bail proceedings, pretrial hearings, plea bargains, trial proceedings, or sentencing. In most states, victims are even barred from observing the trial proceedings, except from the witness stand when they are called to testify. All this is further demoralizing to victims, many of whom believe that it is their case that is being prosecuted.

Prosecutor-based *victim/witness programs,* in part spurred by legislative *victims' bills of rights* in some jurisdictions, now inform victims of an arrest, seek their opinion at bail hearings, inform them of the prosecutor's decision as to what charges, if any, to file, and provide the victim with practical information about the procedures, language, and general philosophy of the criminal justice system. They also include the possibility of obtaining compensation for the expense of medical or mental health treatment, on the basis of an administrative complaint. However, such bills of rights are not self-executing, and victims may need help in accessing appropriate resources.

As we've discussed, therapists and counselors must be prepared to help crime victims face the frustrations and indignities of the criminal justice system (see www.ncvc.org). This includes pretrial appearances and court appearances, where the victim must face her assailant and withstand the sometimes withering cross-examination by defense attorneys. In homicide cases, the family must often sit there and hear the slain family member shamed and vilified. Young (1988) recommends that the victim/witness's counselor be especially available during the trial and perhaps even accompany her to court, but I recommend that you consult with the attorney first to avoid the appearance of conflict of interest in case you are called to testify.

With regard to sentencing, victims should be encouraged to file a *request for restitution* to be included in the proposed sentence, as well as a *victim impact statement* presented in person, in writing, or both, where such a statement is an option. After the sentencing, mental health services may become even more important. Many victims and their families essentially put their lives on hold while they pursue justice through prosecution and conviction. It is common for victims to return from a sentencing hearing, even if it went their way, feeling depressed, drained, and isolated. Also, murder convictions involving the death penalty or a lengthy prison term will almost certainly be appealed. A growing number of states now give victims an opportunity to express their opinions at offenders' parole hearings.

As discussed below, victims may wish to pursue legal recourse through the civil courts after the criminal case has concluded or even concurrently with it (Barton, 1990). This can include damage suits against offenders, as well as lawsuits against third parties who failed in meeting a duty to prevent the crime, for example, a negligence lawsuit in the case of an assault that took place on premises with insufficient lighting or lax security. Therapists should feel free to direct patients to appropriate legal resources, as long as these referrals don't constitute a conflict of interest of any kind. If such legal action is taken, victims may need continued support through that process in much the same way as they received it during the criminal trial (Kilpatrick & Acierno, 2003; Young, 1988).

CIVIL LITIGATION FOR CRIME VICTIMS

As a clinician who treats crime victims, most of your involvement in legal proceedings will be within the criminal justice system. But, increasingly, the civil court system is coming to be used as an alternative form of redress for criminal victimization; this has been made most famous by the O. J. Simpson case. Some studies (e.g., Des Rosiers, Feldthusen, & Hankivsky, 1998; Feldhausen et al., 2000) suggest that the primary goal of many crime victims who pursue civil litigation is to be heard and to obtain some sort of apology; most are sorely disappointed.

Clinicians who negotiate the legal system with crime victims thus need to have some understanding of the forensic issues involved in diagnosing and treating traumatically disabled patients in civil litigation, in order to properly advise and counsel their patients. At the same time, attorneys may appreciate some insight into the sometimes untidy real-life psychological worlds their clients commonly inhabit while pursuing their claims (Barton, 1990; Koch et al., 2006; Miller, 1993c, 1996b, 1997d, 1998f, 1998g, 1999a, 1999b, 1999j, 2000e, 2001e, 2005e, 2006l; Miller & Magier, 1993; Schouten, 1994; Simon, 1995; Slovenko, 1994; Sparr, 1990; Stone, 1993). This section will address these overlapping concerns and provide a basic understanding of the tort system of personal injury litigation.

Crime, Torts, and Psychological Injury

With the exception of divorce actions, it is estimated that half of all civil cases pending on American court dockets are personal injury cases (Modlin, 1983; Koch, 2006). The cost of personal crime victimization is estimated at $105 billion annually, including direct costs of medical treatment, lost earnings, and public victim assistance programs. Adding litigated compensation for pain, suffering, and loss of quality of life bumps the yearly figure up to $450 billion (Solomon & Davidson, 1997).

Burden of Proof

In most jurisdictions of the United States, for a guilty conviction in a criminal trial, a jury must be convinced *beyond a reasonable doubt,* which most courts interpret as greater than 90% certain. For civil cases, the burden of proof is determined *by a preponderance of the evidence,* which is usually interpreted as more likely than not, or just greater than 50% (Barton, 1990; Koch et al., 2006). This accounts for the phenomena of many criminal defendants being acquitted in criminal court but then being successfully sued in civil court.

Torts, Negligence, and Damages

The *law of torts* covers a variety of possible actions or inactions, such as trespass, invasion of privacy, plagiarism, negligence, false representation or deceit, slander, libel, and malicious prosecution (Modlin, 1983). Most personal injury suits are pursued under the *theory of negligence,* that is, unintentional breach of tort, which is the most common basis for third-party negligence suits (e.g., a poorly lit premises or lax security case). In cases of direct crime victimization, the legal theory usually entails *intentional infliction of emotional distress.* To pursue a lawsuit successfully, the plaintiff must assume the burden of proof and show that

1. a legal *duty* of care existed, which
2. the defendant *breached* willfully or fulfilled negligently, and which

3. was the *cause* of an event, which
4. produced significant *damages.*

The testimony of medical and psychological experts, especially with respect to causality and damages, expressed in a written report, deposition, or trial appearance, can often make or break a plaintiff's case (Barton, 1990; Feigenson, 2000; Miller, 1996b, 1997d, 2007c; Modlin, 1983; Simon, 1995; Taylor, 1997).

Causation and Responsibility

Causation need not be all-or-nothing. The law attempts to manage complex causation by the *chain of events* concept: If the index event set off a chain of events beyond the plaintiff's control, the tortfeasor may be held responsible for the adverse outcome. In some cases, this can get complicated; for example, what percentage of the disability from a criminal assault was caused by physical blows to the head and body; by the fear and pain attendant to the injury; by inept or insensitive handling of the incident by law enforcement officers, clinicians, and lawyers; or by preexisting or concomitant psychosocial problems?

The legal approach to causation may appear to differ markedly from the clinical approach to which most mental health clinicians are accustomed (Feigenson, 2000; Harsha, 1990). In viewing a patient's current symptoms and syndromes, medical and mental health clinicians typically search for both basic and complex causes which underlie the disorder, and they try to understand all aspects of the patient's condition. By contrast, judges, juries, and attorneys seek to determine whether one or more specific events precipitated or aggravated the plaintiff's current condition and to limit their concern to the precise proportion of the plaintiff's condition that allegedly has been precipitated, hastened, or exacerbated by the index event. That is, clinicians tend to think in terms of twists and turns; the legal system typically wants a straight line.

With regard to causation, the law is concerned with *proximate cause,* the legally definable cause for the claimed disability. A reasonable time relationship between cause and effect is usually sought, although, in cases of so-called delayed reaction, the psychological expert should be prepared to explain that a latency period is possible and symptoms of crime victim PTSD or another syndrome may not emerge fully until several weeks or months postinjury (Everstine & Everstine, 1993; Modlin, 1983).

With regard to a patient's predisposing conditions, the law of torts states that the tortfeasor is equally liable if the injury totally caused the disability, activated a latent condition, or worsened a preexisting condition. Any prior disorder that is exacerbated and thus produces significantly greater physical or emotional pain, discomfort, or torment than before the injury is still grounds for damages. This well-known *but-for* principle essentially states that the present level of disability would not have occurred "but for" the injury in question. A related concept is often articulated as the *thin skull* or *fragile eggshell* principle: The tortfeasor takes the victim as he finds him, prior weaknesses, vulnerabilities, and susceptibilities notwithstanding (Meek, 1990; Modlin, 1983, 1990; Sparr, 1990). Further, psychological traumatization in a criminal assault may render the patient more susceptible to the effects of future traumatic events (Bursztajn, Scherr, & Brodsky, 1994), which may have implications for the structure and amount of damage claims.

In other words, the defendant is not responsible for the plaintiff's anxiety or mood disorder if it predated the criminal act in its exact present form. However, even if a normal person would not have been incapacitated by the effects of the crime, the fact that the plaintiff's preexisting anxiety disorder made her more than usually susceptible to developing PTSD after the assault does not abrogate the defendant's responsibility for the ensuing traumatic disability—any more than illegally physically striking the head of someone with an abnormally thin skull relieves responsibility for ensuing brain damage because the blow wouldn't have fractured a normal skull. You picked your victim, the court tells the defendant, so you take him as you find him. But the defendant is not responsible if the brain damage existed in its entirety prior to the fateful blow. As expected, these can be complex issues to disentangle, clinically and legally.

When courts decide that a defendant is *not liable for damages* due to an intentional or negligent act, they most often cite the following factors:

- The injury is too remote from the source of the action (e.g., a firefighter claims to have just developed PTSD from the 9/11 terrorist attack 6 years ago).
- The injury is wholly out of proportion to the defendant's culpability (e.g., a teenager carjacks a woman's car without physical injury, and she becomes paralyzed and bedridden for the next year).
- It appears extraordinary that the action would have brought about the harm (e.g., the defendant drops a paper clip on the plaintiff's admittedly thin skull and severe brain damage ensues, or a woman has her purse snatched and develops a full-blown schizophrenic psychosis).
- Allowing recovery would place an unreasonable burden on the defendant (e.g., a man makes a snickering sexual remark at work and

the female victim is claiming total disability and demanding she receive employment compensation for the rest of her life).

- Allowing recovery would likely open the way for fraudulent claims (the Pandora's box argument; e.g., every time an employee said something stupid but harmless to another worker, a ruinous harassment lawsuit would ensue).
- Allowing recovery would create a field having "no sensible or just stopping point" (the slippery slope argument; e.g., why stop at words—what if someone looked at someone else the wrong way?).

Diagnosis of PTSD in the Litigation Setting

An actual psychiatric diagnosis is not essential to a legal cause of action if it can be shown that the plaintiff has suffered some kind of harm. However, plaintiffs' attorneys often wish to invoke PTSD in pursuing an award for mental stress because it supposedly gives the claim more medical legitimacy. In tort litigation, a diagnosis of PTSD can be related to a specific incident, allowing plaintiffs to argue that all of their psychological distress arose from the index traumatic event, such as a crime victimization. In contrast, a more mundane diagnosis such as anxiety disorder or depression dilutes the issue of causation because many factors other than, or in addition to, the index event can multiply determine these disorders.

Attorneys, then, apparently like the PTSD diagnosis because it sounds more objective and scientific than just mental stress. Indeed, in the face of impending tort reform's feared goal of limiting or even excluding damages for nonobjective and noneconomic losses such as pain, suffering, and emotional distress, PTSD may be seized upon as a bona fide neuropsychiatric diagnostic entity with a putative central nervous system basis (see chapter 2), thus scientifically skirting this threat by assuming the status of a legitimate medical disability, and thereby warranting compensation.

However, many authorities assert that, especially in the forensic context, PTSD should be diagnosed only if the clinical facts warrant such a conclusion; otherwise, both the diagnosis and the concept of PTSD risk becoming overutilized, diluted, and trivialized. In this view, the important role for the clinician is to communicate to insurance carriers, attorneys, judges, or juries that the plaintiff is experiencing psychological distress and impairment, and the precise diagnosis is less important than a thorough phenomenological description of the symptoms. Where diagnosis other than PTSD exists, this should be specified (Simon, 1995; Sparr, 1990).

Legal Stress Syndromes

Contact with the legal system may have deleterious effects of its own, such as loss of privacy, disempowerment, disruption of previously supportive relationships, and reliving of past traumas in an atmosphere of suspicion and hostility (Huffer, 1995; Winick, 2000). Bursztajn et al. (1994) use the term *critogenic,* or "judicially caused," to describe these legal stresses, by analogy to *iatrogenic,* or "medically caused" stresses. Indeed, the stresses of litigation can be so severe that Bursztajn et al. recommend that attorneys utilize informed consent with their plaintiff clients about the psychological risks of undertaking litigation; defendants presumably are afforded no such choice.

Similarly, Vesper and Cohen (1999) note that litigation can introduce its own set of secondary emotional injuries, a response they term *forensic traumatic stress disorder* (FTSD). The constant rehashing of the incident and the frequent discussions about the physical and psychological results of the ordeal tend to focus the victim and the family on the past, exacerbating flashbacks, nightmares, and dysfunction, entrenching the trauma as part of the patient's identity (Berntsen & Rubin, 2007), and undermining attempts to move toward recovery (see chapters 6 and 7). Counselors and therapists can play an important role in mitigating these critogenic or FTSD syndromes and should collaborate with their patient's attorney where this is clinically and forensically appropriate.

Clinicians, Lawyers, Patients, and Significant Others

Ideally, clinicians and attorneys should work together for the benefit of the crime victims under their care and guidance. This is not collusion, but rather collaboration in pursuing what is legally justifiable and clinically sound (Stolle, Wexler, Winick, & Dauer, 2000). According to Vesper and Cohen (1999), litigation need not be a destructive or negative experience. It can and should be an empowering process that provides the individual and the family with a voice in what probably seems to them an unjust situation. An attorney trained in litigating PTSD and a forensic psychologist specializing in the evaluation of PTSD comprise a formidable team that can help the victim and the victim's family overcome emotional consequences of the trauma by promoting self-esteem, dignity, and stability, while building a litigation case that can secure fair compensation.

Attorneys differ in their sensitivity to the impact of the litigation process on their client. Some lawyers believe that their role as professionals requires them to divorce themselves from their client's subjective reaction to the litigation process. Other lawyers believe that the client's emotional reaction to the litigation process must be taken into consideration in deciding whether and how to proceed with the litigation. Finally, some lawyers view themselves as mere instruments of the client (Vesper & Cohen, 1999; Winick, 2000).

Everstine (1986) points out that many people who would seem to have a close relationship to the victim (including some psychotherapists) are sometimes unsympathetic toward the idea of the victim suing for damages. For one thing, if the perpetrator has already been found guilty in a criminal proceeding, they may feel that he has paid his debt to society, and the notion of the victim profiting from tragedy may seem greedy. Conversely, well-meaning relatives and friends may mismanage the situation by acting too stridently as advocates, and attorneys and psychotherapists may do this as well. As emphasized throughout this book, what traumatized crime victims need most is to feel that the people they rely on are in control of themselves and capable of sanely and competently looking out for the victims' interests.

Everstine (1986) believes that therapists should support their patients' informed decisions to pursue criminal prosecution and civil charges against perpetrators. In many cases, there is a certain symbolic and healing value in a victim's reestablishing control by bringing a wrongdoer to justice. However, any decision to pursue civil litigation should not be made lightly. One needs to consider that many aspects of the victim's personal and professional life that are not admissible in criminal proceedings are discoverable in civil cases. In fact, there may be the clinician's obligation not only to advise the patient to consult with an attorney but, when appropriate, to educate the attorney about the subtleties of how the patient's psyche has become so deleteriously affected by the trauma and what might occur during the legal process.

As we've seen, one important role of the crime victim counselor or therapist is to help traumatized victims prepare emotionally for legal proceedings and examinations (Everstine, 1986). If a patient is especially vulnerable, the therapist may request that the victim's lawyer ask the court to protect the patient from an aggravating deposition. The court could order that (a) limitations be placed on the attorney's questions; (b) the therapist be present during the deposition; or (c) the deposition be taped. After a deposition, the patient should always request a copy of the deposition transcript to check it and correct any errors. In all cases, it is not the clinician's job to run the legal show but to make sure that the patient's role in it is as constructive as possible.

CONCLUSIONS

Helping your patient through the criminal justice or civil litigation system comes full circle in providing comprehensive good clinical and supportive care following crime victimization. I hope you'll assimilate and adapt some of this book's lessons to your own style of clinical practice and expand and deepen the concepts and strategies offered herein to extend their application to the varieties of victims of violence who will certainly need our aid in this uncertain, new, unfolding century.

Bibliography

Abel, E. M. (2001). Comparing the social service utilization, exposure to violence, and trauma symptomatology of domestic violence female "victims" and female "batterers." *Journal of Family Violence, 16,* 401–420.

Abueg, F. R., Drescher, K. D., & Kubany, E. S. (1994). Natural disasters. In F. M. Dattilio & A. Freeman (Eds.), *Cognitive-behavioral strategies in crisis intervention* (pp. 238–257). New York: Guilford.

Ackerly, G. D., Burnell, J., Holder, D. C., & Kurdek, L. A. (1988). Burnout among licensed psychologists. *Professional Psychology: Research & Practice, 19,* 624–631.

Adler, J. (1997, September 22). How kids mourn. *Newsweek,* 58–61.

Ahrens, W., Hart, R., & Maruyama, N. (1997). Pediatric death: Managing the aftermath in the emergency department. *Journal of Emergency Medicine, 15,* 601–603.

Alarcon, R. D. (1999). The cascade model: An alternative to comorbidity in the pathogenesis of posttraumatic stress disorder. *Psychiatry, 62,* 114–124.

Albrecht, S. (1996). *Crisis management for corporate self-defense.* New York: Amacom.

Albrecht, S. (1997). *Fear and violence on the job: Prevention solutions for the dangerous workplace.* Durham, NC: Carolina Academic Press.

Aldarondo, E., & Straus, M. A. (1994). Screening for physical violence in couple therapy: Methodological, practical, and ethical considerations. *Family Process, 33,* 425–439.

Aldwin, C. M. (1994). *Stress, coping, and development.* New York: Guilford.

Allen, D. M., & Farmer, R. G. (1996). Family relationships of adults with borderline personality disorder. *Comprehensive Psychiatry, 37,* 43–51.

Allen, N. E., Bybee, D. I., & Sullivan, C. M. (2004). Battered women's multitude of needs: Evidence supporting the need for comprehensive advocacy. *Violence Against Women, 10,* 1015–1035.

Allen, T. D. (2001). Family-supportive work environments: The role of organizational perceptions. *Journal of Vocational Behavior, 58,* 414–435.

Alvarez, J., & Hunt, M. (2005). Risk and resilience in canine search and rescue handlers after 9/11. *Journal of Traumatic Stress, 18,* 497–505.

American Psychiatric Association. (1994). *Diagnostic and statistical manual of mental disorders* (4th ed.). Washington, DC: American Psychiatric Association.

American Psychiatric Association. (2000). *Diagnostic and statistical manual of mental disorders* (4th ed., text revision). Washington, DC: American Psychiatric Association.

Amick-McMullan, A., Kilpatrick, D. G., & Resnick, H. S. (1991). Homicide as a risk factor for posttraumatic stress disorder among surviving family members. *Behavior Modification, 15,* 545–559.

Antonovsky, A. (1979). *Health, stress, and coping.* San Francisco: Jossey-Bass.

Antonovsky, A. (1987). *Unraveling the mystery of health: How people manage stress and stay well.* San Francisco: Jossey-Bass.

Antonovsky, A. (1990). Personality and health: Testing the sense of coherence model. In H. S. Friedman (Ed.), *Personality and disease* (pp. 155–177). New York: Wiley.

Appel, A. E., & Holden, G. W. (1998). The co-occurrence of spouse and physical child abuse: A review and appraisal. *Journal of Family Psychology, 12,* 578–599.

Arata, C. M. (2002). Child sexual abuse and sexual revictimization. *Clinical Psychology: Science and Practice, 9,* 135–164.

Arias, I., & Pape, K. T. (1999). Psychological abuse: Implications for adjustment and commitment to leave violent partners. *Violence and Victims, 14,* 55–67.

Armour, M. (2003). Meaning making in the aftermath of homicide. *Death Studies, 27,* 519–540.

Asken, M. J. (1993). *PsycheResponse: Psychological skills for optimal performance by emergency responders.* Englewood Cliffs, NJ: Regents/Prentice Hall.

Attig, T. (1996). *How we grieve: Relearning the world.* New York: Oxford University Press.

Bard, M., & Sangrey, D. (1986). *The crime victim's book.* New York: Brunner/Mazel.

Barnes, M. F. (1998). Understanding the secondary traumatic stress of parents. In C. R. Figley (Ed.), *Burnout in families: The systematic costs of caring* (pp.75–89). Boca Raton, FL: CRC Press.

Barton, W. A. (1990). *Recovering for psychological injuries.* Washington, DC: ATLA Press.

Bartone, P. T., Ursano, R. J., Wright, K. M., & Ingrahan, L. H. (1989). The impact of a military air disaster on the health of assistance workers. *Journal of Nervous and Mental Disease, 177,* 317–328.

Basoglu, M., Livanou, M., Crnobaric, C., Franciskovic, T., Suljic, E., Duric, D., et al. (2005). Psychiatric and cognitive effects of war in former Yugoslavia: Association of lack of redress for trauma and posttraumatic stress reactions. *Journal of the American Medical Association, 294,* 580–590.

Basoglu, M., Mineka, S., Paker, M., Aker, T., Livanou, M., & Gok, S. (1997). Psychological preparedness for trauma as a protective factor in survivors of torture. *Psychological Medicine, 27,* 1421–1433.

Baum, A. (1987). Toxins, technology, and natural disasters. In G. R. VandenBos & B. K. Bryant (Eds.), *Cataclysms, crises, and catastrophes* (pp. 5–53). Washington, DC: American Psychological Association.

Baum, A., & Fleming, I. (1993). Implications of psychological research on stress and technological accidents. *American Psychologist, 48,* 665–672.

Baum, A., Fleming, R., & Singer, J. E. (1983). Coping with victimization by technical disaster. *Journal of Social Issues, 39*, 117–138.

Beckmann, R. (1990). *Children who grieve: A manual for conducting support groups.* Holmes Beach, FL: Learning Publications.

Behncke, L. (2006). Mental skills training for sport: A brief review. *Athletic Insight: The Online Journal of Sport Psychology.* Retrieved from www.athleticinsight.com

Bender, W. N., & McLaughlin, P. J. (1997). Weapons violence in schools: Strategies for teachers confronting violence and hostage situations. *Intervention in School and Clinic, 32*, 211–216.

Bergen, R. K. (1996). *Wife rape: Understanding the response of survivors and service providers.* Thousand Oaks, CA: Sage.

Bernstein, D., & Borkovec, T. (1973). *Progressive relaxation training: A manual for the helping professions.* Champaign, IL: Research Press.

Berntsen, D., & Rubin, D. C. (2007). When a trauma becomes a key to identity: Enhanced integration of trauma memories predicts posttraumatic stress disorder symptoms. *Applied Cognitive Psychology, 21*, 417–431.

Bidinotto, R. J. (Ed.) (1996). *Criminal justice? The legal system vs. individual responsibility.* New York: Foundation for Economic Education.

Bifulco, A. T., Brown, G. W., & Harris, T. O. (1987). Childhood loss of parent, lack of adequate parental care and adult depression: A replication. *Journal of Affective Disorders, 12*, 115–128.

Bisson, J. I., Shepherd, J. P., & Dhutia, M. (1997). Psychosocial sequelae of facial trauma. *Journal of Trauma, 43*, 496–500.

Bjorkqvist, K. (1994). Sex differences in physical, verbal, and indirect aggression: A review of recent research. *Sex Roles, 30*, 177–188.

Blau, T. H. (1994). *Psychological services for law enforcement.* New York: Wiley.

Blount, E. C. (2003). *Occupational crime: Deterrence, investigation, and reporting in compliance with federal guidelines.* Boca Raton, FL: CRC Press.

Bluestein, J. (2001). *Creating emotionally safe schools: A guide for educators and parents.* Deerfield Beach, FL: Health Communications.

Blythe, B. T. (2002). *Blindsided: A manager's guide to catastrophic incidents in the workplace.* New York: Portfolio.

Bolz, F., Dudonis, K. J., & Schultz, D. P. (1996). *The counter-terrorism handbook: Tactics, procedures, and techniques.* Boca Raton: CRC Press.

Bonanno, G. A. (2005). Resilience in the face of potential trauma. *Current Directions in Psychological Science, 14*, 135–138.

Bongar, B. (2002). *The suicidal patient: Clinical and legal standards of care.* Washington, DC: American Psychological Association.

Bonwick, R. L., & Morris, P. L. P. (1996). Posttraumatic stress disorder in elderly war veterans. *International Journal of Geriatric Psychiatry, 11*, 1071–1076.

Boss, P. (1999). *Ambiguous loss: Learning to live with unresolved grief.* Cambridge, MA: Harvard University Press.

Boss, P. G. (2002). Ambiguous loss: Working with families of the missing. *Family Process, 41*, 14–17.

Boss, P., Beaulieu, L., Wieling, E., Turner, W., & La Cruz, S. (2003). Healing, loss, ambiguity, and trauma: A community-based intervention with families of union workers missing after the 9/11 attack in New York City. *Journal of Marital and Family Therapy, 29,* 455–467.

Bowman, M. L. (1997). *Individual differences in posttraumatic response: Problems with the stress-adversity connection.* Mahwah, NJ: Erlbaum.

Bowman, M. L. (1999). Individual differences in posttraumatic distress: Problems with the *DSM-IV* model. *Canadian Journal of Psychiatry, 44,* 21–33.

Brand, P. A., & Kidd, A. H. (1986). Frequency of physical aggression in heterosexual and female homosexual dyads. *Psychological Reports, 59,* 1307–1313.

Breitenbecher, K. H. (2001). Sexual revictimization among women: A review of the literature focusing on empirical investigations. *Aggression and Violent Behavior, 6,* 415–432.

Bremmer, J. D. (1999). Does stress damage the brain? *Biological Psychiatry, 45,* 797–805.

Bremmer, J. D. (2006). The relationship between cognitive and brain changes in posttraumatic stress disorder. *Annals of the New York Academy of Sciences, 1071,* 80–86.

Bremmer, J. D., Randall, P., Scott, T. M., Bronen, R. A., Seibyl, J. P., & Southwick, S. M. (1995). MRI-based measurement of hippocampal volume in patients with combat-related posttraumatic stress disorder. *American Journal of Psychiatry, 152,* 973–981.

Bremmer, J. D., Scott, T. M., Delaney, R. C., Southwick, S. M., Mason, J. W., Johnson, D. R., et al. (1993). Deficits in short-term memory in posttraumatic stress disorder. *American Journal of Psychiatry, 150,* 1015–1019.

Breslau, N., & Davis, G. C. (1992). Posttraumatic stress disorder in an urban population of young adults. *Archives of General Psychiatry, 149,* 671–675.

Breslau, N., Davis, G. C., Andreski, P., & Peterson, E. (1991). Traumatic events and posttraumatic stress disorder in an urban population of young adults. *Archives of General Psychiatry, 48,* 216–222.

Breslau, N., Kessler, R. C., Chilcoat, H. D., Schultz, L. R., Davis, G. C., & Andreski, P. (1998). Trauma and posttraumatic stress disorder in the community: The 1996 Detroit Area Survey of Trauma. *Archives of General Psychiatry, 55,* 626–632.

Brewin, C. R., Andrews, B., & Valentine, J. D. (2000). Meta-analysis of risk factors for posttraumatic stress disorder in trauma-exposed adults. *Journal of Consulting and Clinical Psychology, 68,* 748–766.

Brom, D., & Kleber, R. J. (1989). Prevention of posttraumatic stress disorders. *Journal of Traumatic Stress, 2,* 335–351.

Brom, D., Kleber, R. J., & Defares, P. B. (1989). Brief psychotherapy for posttraumatic stress disorder. *Journal of Consulting and Clinical Psychology, 57,* 607–612.

Brooks, G. (1998). *A new psychotherapy for traditional men.* San Francisco: Jossey-Bass.

Brown, C. G. (1993). *First get mad, then get justice.* New York: Birch Lane Press.

Browne, A. (1987). *When battered women kill.* New York: MacMillan.

Browne, A., & Williams, K. R. (1989). Exploring the effect of resource availability and the likelihood of female-perpetrated homicides. *Law and Society Review, 23,* 75–94.

Brownell, P. (1996). Domestic violence in the workplace: An emergent issue. *Crisis Intervention, 3,* 335–351.

Brush, L. (2003). Effects of work on hitting and hurting. *Violence Against Women, 9,* 1213–1230.

Bryant, R. A., Sackville, T., Dang, S. T., Moulds, M., & Guthrie, R. (1999). Treating acute stress disorder: An evaluation of cognitive-behavioral therapy and counseling techniques. *American Journal of Psychiatry, 156,* 1780–1786.

Budiansky, S., Gregory, S., Schmidt, K. F., & Bierk, R. (1996, March 4). Local TV: Mayhem central. *U.S. News and World Report,* 63–64.

Burke, A. S. (2007). Domestic violence as a crime of pattern and intent: An alternative reconceptualization. *George Washington Law Review, 75,* 552–612.

Bursztajn, H. J., Scherr, A. E., & Brodsky, A. (1994). The rebirth of forensic psychiatry in light of recent historical trends in criminal responsibility. *Psychiatric Clinics of North America, 17,* 611–635.

Bush, D. E., & O'Shea, P. G. (1996). Workplace violence: Comparative use of prevention practices and policies. In G. R. Vandenbos & E. Q. Bulatao (Eds.), *Violence on the job: Identifying risks and developing solutions* (pp. 283–297). Washington, DC: American Psychological Association.

Calhoun, K. S., & Atkeson, B. M. (1991). *Treatment of rape victims: Facilitating psychosocial adjustment.* New York: Pergamon.

Calhoun, L. G., & Tedeschi, R. G. (1999). *Facilitating posttraumatic growth.* Mahwah, NJ: Erlbaum.

Call, J. A. (2003). Negotiating crises: The evolution of hostage/barricade crisis negotiation. *Journal of Threat Assessment, 2,* 69–94.

Campbell, J. C. (1992). A review of nursing research on battering. In C. Sampselle (Ed.), *Violence against women: Nursing research, education, and practice issues* (pp. 69–89). London: Taylor & Francis.

Campbell, J. C. (1995). *Assessing dangerousness.* Newbury Park, CA: Sage.

Campbell, J. C. (2002). Health consequences of intimate partner violence. *Lancet, 359,* 1331–1336.

Campbell, R., & Raja, S. (1999). The secondary victimization of rape victims: Insights from mental health professionals who treat survivors of violence. *Violence and Victims, 14,* 261–275.

Campbell, R., Wasco, S. M., Ahrens, C. E., Sefl, T., & Barnes, H. E. (2001). Preventing the "second rape": Rape survivors' experiences with community service providers. *Journal of Interpersonal Violence, 16,* 1239–1259.

Caponigro, J. R. (2000). *The crisis counselor: A step-by-step guide to managing a business crisis.* Chicago: Contemporary Books.

Caraulia, A. P., & Steiger, L. K. (1997). *Nonviolent crisis intervention: Learning to defuse explosive behavior.* Brookfield, WI: CPI Publishing.

Carlson, E. B., & Dutton, M. A. (2003). Assessing experiences and responses of crime victims. *Journal of Traumatic Stress, 16,* 133–148.

Carson, L., & MacLeod, M. D. (1997). Explanations about crime and psychological distress in ethnic minority and white victims of crime: A qualitative explanation. *Journal of Community and Applied Social Psychology, 7,* 361–375.

Cascardi, M., O'Leary, K. D., & Schlee, K. A. (1999). Co-occurrence and correlates of posttraumatic stress disorder and major depression in physically abused women. *Journal of Family Violence, 14,* 227–249.

Casey, E. A., & Nurius, P. S. (2005). Trauma exposure and sexual revictimization risk comparisons across single, multiple incident, and multiple perpetrator victimizations. *Violence Against Women, 11,* 505–530.

Catherall, D. R. (1995). Preventing institutional secondary traumatic stress disorder. In C. R. Figley (Ed.), *Compassion fatigue: Coping with secondary traumatic stress disorder in those who treat the traumatized* (pp. 232–247). New York: Brunner/Mazel.

Cavanaugh, K., & Dobash, R. P. (2007). The murder of children by fathers in the context of child abuse. *Child Abuse and Neglect, 31,* 747–755.

Centonze, D., Siracusano, A., Calabresi, P., & Bernardi, G. (2005). Removing pathogenic memories: A neurobiology of psychotherapy. *Molecular Neurobiology, 32,* 123–132.

Cerney, M. S. (1995). Treating the "heroic treaters." An overview. In C. R. Figley (Ed.), *Compassion fatigue: Coping with secondary traumatic stress disorder in those who treat the traumatized* (pp. 131–149). New York: Brunner/Mazel.

Chambers, J., Duff, P., & Leverick, F. (2007). Victim impact statements: Can work, do work (for those who bother to make them). *Criminal Law Review,* 360–379.

Charney, D. S., Deutsch, A. Y., Krystal, J. H., Southwick, S. M., & Davis, M. (1993). Psychobiologic mechanisms of posttraumatic stress disorder. *Archives of General Psychiatry, 50,* 294–305.

Clark, D. W. (2007, August). Crisis response tools for law enforcement. *The Police Chief,* 94–101.

Clark, S. (1988, March). The violated victim: Prehospital psychological care for the crime victim. *Journal of Emergency Medical Services,* 48–51.

Classen, C. C., Koopman, C., Hales, R., & Spiegel, D. (1998). Acute stress reactions as a predictor of posttraumatic stress symptoms following office building shootings. *American Journal of Psychiatry, 155,* 620–624.

Classen, C. C., Palesh, O. G., & Aggarwal, R. (2005). Sexual revictimization: A review of the empirical literature. *Trauma, Violence, and Abuse, 6,* 103–129.

Clements, C., & Ogle, R. L. (2007). A comparison study of coping, family problem-solving, and emotional status in victims of domestic violence. *Journal of Psychological Trauma, 6,* 29–37.

Clute, S. (1993). Adult survivor litigation as an integral part of the therapeutic process. *Journal of Child Sexual Abuse, 2,* 121–127.

Cohen, R., Culp, C., & Genser, S. (1987). *Human problems in major disasters: A training curriculum for emergency medical personnel.* Washington, DC: U.S. Government Printing Office.

Coker, A. L., Davis, K. E., Arias, I., Desai, S., Sanderson, M., Brandt, H. M., et al. (2002). Physical and mental health effects of intimate partner violence for men and women. *American Journal of Preventative Medicine, 23,* 260–268.

Collins, S. (1989). Sudden death counseling protocol. *Dimensions of Critical Care Nursing, 8,* 375–382.

Coloroso, B. (2003). *The bully, the bullied, and the bystander: From preschool to high school—How parents and teachers can help break the cycle of violence.* New York: HarperResource.

Comas-Diaz, L., & Padilla, A. (1990). Countertransference in working with victims of political repression. *American Journal of Orthopsychiatry, 60,* 125–134.

Cooper, C. (1999). *Mediation and arbitration by patrol police officers.* New York: University Press of America.

Cooper, N. A., & Clum, G. A. (1989). Imaginal flooding as a supplementary treatment for PTSD in combat veterans: A controlled study. *Behavior Therapy, 20,* 381–391.

Costa, P. T., & McCrae, R. R. (1988). From catalog to classification: Murray's needs and the five-factor model. *Journal of Personality and Social Psychology, 55,* 258–265.

Cowie, H., & Olafsson, R. (2000). The role of peer support in helping victims of bullying in a school with high levels of aggression. *School Psychology International, 21,* 79–95.

Cozolino, L. (2002). *The neuroscience of psychotherapy: Building and rebuilding the human brain.* New York: Norton.

Crawley, J. (1992). *Constructive conflict management: Managing to make a difference.* London: Nicholas Brealey.

Crick, N. R., Wellman, N. E., Casas, J. F., O'Brien, K. M., Nelson, D. A., Grotpeter, J. K., et al. (1999). Childhood aggression and gender: A new look at an old problem. In D. Bernstein (Ed.), *Nebraska symposium on motivation, 45.* Lincoln: University of Nebraska Press.

Crofford, L. J. (2007). Violence, stress, and somatic syndromes. *Trauma, Violence, and Abuse, 8,* 299–313.

Dangler, L. A., O'Donnell, J., Gingrich, C., & Bope, E. T. (1996). What do family members expect from the family physician of a deceased loved one? *Family Medicine, 28,* 692–693.

Davis, C. G., Nolen-Hoeksema, S., & Larson, J. (1998). Making sense of loss and benefiting from the experience: Two construals of meaning. *Journal of Personality and Social Psychology, 59,* 561–574.

Davis, G. C., & Breslau, N. (1994). Post-traumatic stress disorder in victims of civilian and criminal violence. *Psychiatric Clinics of North America, 17,* 289–299.

Deitz, J. (1992). Self-psychological approach to posttraumatic stress disorder: Neurobiological aspects of transmuting internalization. *Journal of the American Academy of Psychoanalysis, 20,* 277–293.

Delosi, C., & Margolin, G. (2004). The role of family-of-origin violence in men's marital violence perpetration. *Clinical Psychology Review, 24,* 99–122.

Denenberg, R. V., & Braverman, M. (1999). *The violence-prone workplace: A new approach to dealing with hostile, threatening, and uncivil behavior.* Ithaca, NY: Cornell University Press.

Desai, S., Arias, I., Thompson, M. P., & Basile, K. C. (2002). Childhood victimization and subsequent adult revictimization assessed in a nationally representative sample of women and men. *Violence and Victims, 17,* 639–653.

Des Rosiers, N., Feldthusen, B., & Hankivsky, O. (1998). Legal compensation for sexual violence: Therapeutic consequences and consequences for the judicial system. *Psychology, Public Policy, and Law, 4,* 433–451.

Deutsch, C. J. (1984). Self-reported sources of stress among psychotherapists. *Professional Psychology: Research and Practice, 15,* 833–845.

Dezenhall, E., & Weber, J. (2007). *Damage control: Why everything you know about crisis management is wrong.* New York: Portfolio.

Dias, L., Chabner, B. A., Lynch, T. J., & Penson, R. T. (2003). Breaking bad news: A patient's perspective. *The Oncologist, 8,* 587–596.

Dienstbier, R. A. (1989). Arousal and physiological toughness: Implications for mental and physical health. *Psychological Review, 96,* 84–100.

Dienstbier, R. A. (1991). Behavioral correlates of sympathoadrenal reactivity: The toughness model. *Medical Science of Sports and Exercise, 23,* 846–852.

Difede, J., Apfeldorf, W. J., Cloitre, M., Spielman, L. A., & Perry, S. W. (1997). Acute psychiatric responses to the explosion at the World Trade Center: A case series. *Journal of Nervous and Mental Disease, 186,* 519–522.

DiGiuseppe, R. (1991). A rational-emotive model of assessment. In M. E. Bernard (Ed.), *Doing rational-emotive therapy effectively* (pp. 79–88). New York: Plenum.

Doka, K. (2002). *Disenfranchised grief.* Champaign, IL: Research Press.

Doss, W. (2006, March). Exercising emotional control. *Police,* 68–73.

Doss, W. (2007). *Condition to win: Dynamic techniques for performance oriented mental conditioning.* Flushing, NY: Looseleaf Law Press.

Dowden, J. S., & Keltner, N. L. (2007). Biological perspectives: Psychobiological substrates of posttraumatic stress. *Perspectives in Psychiatric Care, 43,* 147–150.

Dubin, W. R. (1995). Assaults with weapons. In B. S. Eichelman & A. C. Hartwig (Eds.), *Patient violence and the clinician* (pp. 139–154). Washington, DC: American Psychiatric Press.

Duhart, D. (2001). *Violence in the workplace, 1993–99.* Washington, DC: U.S. Department of Justice.

Dunning, C. (1999). Postintervention strategies to reduce police trauma: A paradigm shift. In J. M. Violanti & D. Paton (Eds.), *Police trauma: Psychological aftermath of civilian combat* (pp. 269–289). Springfield, IL: Charles C Thomas.

Durham, T. W., McCammon, S. L., & Allison, E. J. (1985). The psychological impact of disaster on rescue personnel. *Annals of Emergency Medicine, 14,* 664–668.

Dutton, D. G. (1995). Trauma symptoms and PTSD-like profiles in perpetrators of intimate abuse. *Journal of Traumatic Stress, 8,* 299–316.

Dyregrov, A. (1989). Caring for helpers in disaster situations: Psychological debriefing. *Disaster Management, 2,* 25–30.

Dyregrov, A. (1997). The process in psychological debriefing. *Journal of Traumatic Stress, 10,* 589–605.

Eberwein, K. E. (2006). A mental health clinician's guide to death notification. *International Journal of Emergency Mental Health, 8,* 117–126.

Eby, K., Campbell, J., Sullivan, C., & Davidson, W. (1995). Health effects of experiences of sexual violence for women with abusive partners. *Health Care for Women International, 16,* 563–576.

Echeburua, E., de Corral, P., Zubizarreta, I., & Sarasua, B. (1997). Psychological treatment of posttraumatic stress disorder in victims of sexual aggression. *Behavior Modification, 21,* 433–456.

Ehlers, A., & Clark, D. M. (2000). A cognitive model of posttraumatic stress disorder. *Behaviour Research and Therapy, 38,* 319–345.

Elliott, D. M., & Guy, J. D. (1993). Mental health professionals vs. non-mental health professionals: Childhood trauma and adult functioning. *Professional Psychology: Research and Practice, 24,* 83–90.

Elliott, D. M., Mok, D. S., & Briere, J. (2004). Adult sexual assault: Prevalence, symptomatology, and sex differences in the general population. *Journal of Traumatic Stress, 17,* 203–211.

Elzinga, B., & Bremmer, J. (2002). Are the neural substrates of memory the final pathway in posttraumatic stress disorder? *Journal of Affective Disorders, 70,* 1–17.

Ender, M. G., & Hermsen, J. M. (1996). Working with the bereaved: U.S. Army experiences with nontraditional families. *Death Studies, 20,* 557–575.

Etkin, A., Pittenger, C., Polan, H., & Kandel, E. (2005). Toward a neurobiology of psychotherapy: Basic science and clinical applications. *Journal of Neuropsychiatry and Clinical Neuroscience, 17,* 145–158.

Everly, G. S. (1994). Short-term psychotherapy of acute adult onset post-traumatic stress. *Stress Medicine, 10,* 191–196.

Everly, G. S. (1995). The neurocognitive theory of post-traumatic stress: A strategic metatherapeutic approach. In G. S. Everly & J. M. Lating (Eds.), *Psychotraumatology: Key papers and core concepts in post-traumatic stress* (pp. 159–169). New York: Plenum.

Everly, G. S., Flannery, R. B., & Mitchell, J. T. (1999). Critical incident stress management (CISM): A review of the literature. *Aggression and Violent Behavior, 5,* 23–40.

Everstine, D. S. (1986). Psychological trauma in personal injury cases. In L. Everstine & D. S. Everstine (Eds.), *Psychotherapy and the law* (pp. 27–45). New York: Grune & Stratton.

Everstine, D. S., & Everstine, L. (1993). *The trauma response: Treatment for emotional injury.* New York: Norton.

Eysenck, H. J. (1990). Genetic and environmental contributions to individual differences: The three major dimensions of personality. *Journal of Personality, 58,* 245–261.

Falsetti, S. A., & Resnick, H. S. (1995). Helping the victims of violent crime. In J. R. Freedy & S. E. Hobfoll (Eds.), *Traumatic stress: From theory to practice* (pp. 263–285). New York: Plenum.

Falsetti, S. A., Resnick, H. S., Dansky, B. S., Lydiard, R. B., & Kilpatrick, D. G. (1995). The relationship of stress to panic disorder: Cause or effect. In C. M. Mazure

(Ed.), *Does stress cause psychiatric illness?* (pp. 111–147). Washington, DC: American Psychiatric Press.

Farr, K. A. (2002). Battered women who were "being killed and survived it": Straight talk from survivors. *Violence and Victims, 17,* 267–281.

Federal Bureau of Investigation. (1994). *Crime in the United States, 1993: Uniform crime reports.* Washington, DC: U.S. Government Printing Office.

Feigenson, N. (2000). *Legal blame: How jurors think and talk about accidents.* Washington, DC: American Psychological Association.

Feldthausen, B., Hankivsky, O., & Greaves, L. (2000). Therapeutic consequences of civil actions for damages and compensation claims by victims of sexual abuse. *Canadian Journal of Women and the Law, 12,* 66–116.

Fergusson, D. M., & Horwood, L. J. (1987). Vulnerability to life events exposure. *Psychological Medicine, 17,* 739–749.

Figley, C. R. (1995). Compassion fatigue as secondary traumatic stress disorder: An overview. In C. R. Figley (Ed.), *Compassion fatigue: Coping with secondary traumatic stress disorder in those who treat the traumatized* (pp. 1–20). New York: Brunner/Mazel.

Finkelhor, D., & Yllo, K. (1985). *License to rape: Sexual abuse of wives.* New York: Free Press.

Flannery, R. B. (1995). *Violence in the workplace.* New York: Crossroad.

Flannery, R. B., Fulton, P., Tausch, J., & DeLoffi, A. (1991). A program to help staff cope with psychological sequelae of assaults by patients. *Hospital and Community Psychiatry, 42,* 935–942.

Flannery, R. B., Hanson, M. A., Penk, W. E., Goldfinger, S., Pastva, G. J., & Navon, M. A. (1998). Replicated declines in assault rates after implementation of the Assaulted Staff Action Program. *Psychiatric Services, 49,* 241–243.

Flannery, R. B., Penk, W. E., Hanson, M. A., & Flannery, G. J. (1996). The Assaulted Staff Action Program: Guidelines for fielding a team. In G. R. VandenBos & E. Q. Bulatao (Eds.), *Violence on the job: Identifying risks and developing solutions* (pp. 327–341). Washington, DC: American Psychological Association.

Flin, R. (1996). *Sitting in the hot seat: Leaders and teams for effective critical incident management.* New York: Wiley.

Foa, E. B., Hearst-Ikeda, D., & Perry, K. J. (1995). Evaluation of a brief cognitive-behavioral program for the prevention of chronic PTSD in recent assault victims. *Journal of Consulting and Clinical Psychology, 63,* 948–955.

Foa, E. B., & Kozak, M. J. (1986). Emotional processing of fear: Exposure to corrective information. *Psychological Bulletin, 99,* 20–35.

Foa, E. B., & Riggs, D. S. (1993). Posttraumatic stress disorder and rape. In J. Oldham, M. B. Riba, & A. Tasman (Eds.), *American Psychiatric Press review of psychiatry* (Vol. 12, pp. 273–303). Washington, DC: American Psychiatric Press.

Foa, E. B., Rothbaum, B. O., Riggs, D. S., & Murdock, T. B. (1991). Treatment of post-traumatic stress disorder in rape victims: A comparison between cognitive behavioral procedures and counseling. *Journal of Consulting and Clinical Psychology, 59,* 715–723.

Follette, V. M., Polusny, M. M., & Milbeck, K. (1994). Mental health and law enforcement professionals: Trauma history, psychological symptoms, and impact of providing services to child sexual abuse survivors. *Professional Psychology: Research and Practice, 25,* 275–282.

Follingstad, D. R., Wright, S., Lloyd, S., & Sebastian, J. A. (1991). Sex differences in motivations and effects in dating violence. *Family Relations, 40,* 51–57.

Ford, C. V. (1997–1978). A type of disability neurosis: The Humpty-Dumpty syndrome. *International Journal of Psychiatry in Medicine, 8,* 285–294.

Frank, E., & Stewart, B. D. (1984). Depressive symptoms in rape victims: A revisit. *Journal of Affective Disorders, 7,* 77–85.

Frederick, C. J. (1986). Post-traumatic stress responses to victims of violent crime: Information for law enforcement officials. In J. T. Reese & H. A. Goldstein (Eds.), *Psychological services for law enforcement* (pp. 341–350). Washington, DC: U.S. Government Printing Office.

Frederick, C. J. (1994). The psychology of terrorism and torture in war and peace: Diagnosis and treatment of victims. In R. P. Liberman & J. Yager (Eds.), *Stress in psychiatric disorders* (pp. 140–158). New York: Springer Publishing.

Freedy, J. R., Resnick, H. S., Kilpatrick, D. G., Dansky, B. S., & Tidwell, R. P. (1994). The psychological adjustment of recent crime victims in the criminal justice system. *Journal of Interpersonal Violence, 9,* 450–468.

Freidman, L. N., Tucker, S. B., Neville, P. R., & Imperial, M. (1996). The impact of domestic violence on the workplace. In G. R. Vandenbos & E. Q. Bulatao (Eds.), *Violence on the job: Identifying risks and developing solutions* (pp. 153–161). Washington, DC: American Psychological Association.

Freud, S. (1920). Beyond the pleasure principle. In J. Strachey (Ed. & Trans.), *The standard edition of the complete psychological works of Sigmund Freud* (Vol. 18, pp. 7–64). New York: Norton.

Frewen, P., & Lanius, R. (2006). Toward a psychobiology of posttraumatic self-dysregulation: Reexperiencing, hyperarousal, dissociation, and emotional numbing. *Annals of the New York Academy of Sciences, 1071,* 110–124.

Fry, W. F., & Salameh, W. A. (Eds.) (1987). *Handbook of humor and psychotherapy.* Sarasota, FL: Professional Resource Exchange.

Fukunishi, I. (1999). Relationship of cosmetic disfigurement to the severity of posttraumatic stress disorder in burn injury or digital amputation. *Psychotherapy and Psychosomatics, 68,* 82–86.

Fullerton, C. S., McCarroll, J. E., Ursano, R. J., & Wright, K. M. (1992). Psychological responses of rescue workers: Firefighters and trauma. *American Journal of Orthopsychiatry, 62,* 371–378.

Gallo, G. (2005, February). A family affair: Domestic violence in police families. *Police,* 36–40.

Garbarino, J. (1997). *Raising children in a socially toxic environment.* San Francisco: Jossey-Bass.

Gard, B. A., & Ruzek, J. I. (2006). Community mental health response to crisis. *Journal of Clinical Psychology: In Session, 62,* 1029–1041.

Garmezy, N. (1993). Children in poverty: Resilience despite risk. *Psychiatry, 56,* 127–136.

Garmezy, N., Masten, A. S., & Tellegen, A. (1984). The study of stress and competence in children: A building block for developmental psychopathology. *Child Development, 55,* 97–111.

Garner, G. W. (2005, January). Surviving domestic violence calls. *Police, 44–46.*

George, L. K., Winfield, I., & Blazer, D. G. (1992). Sociocultural factors in sexual assault: Comparison of two representative samples of women. *Journal of Social Issues, 48,* 105–125.

Getzel, G. S., & Masters, R. (1984). Serving families who survive homicide victims. *Social Casework, 65,* 138–144.

Gilligan, J. (1997). *Violence: Reflections on a national epidemic.* New York: Vintage.

Gilliland, B. E., & James, R. K. (1993). *Crisis intervention strategies* (2nd ed.). Pacific Grove, CA: Brooks/Cole.

Gleason, W. J. (1993). Mental disorders in battered women: An empirical study. *Violence and Victims, 8,* 53–68.

Golding, J. M. (1994). Sexual assault history and physical health in randomly selected Los Angeles women. *Health Psychology, 13,* 130–138.

Golding, J. M. (1999). Intimate partner violence as a risk factor for mental disorders: A meta-analysis. *Journal of Family Violence, 14,* 99–132.

Golding, J. M., Siegel, J. M., Sorenson, S. B., Burnam, M. A., & Stein, J. A. (1989). Social support sources following sexual assault. *Journal of Community Psychology, 17,* 92–107.

Goldstein, A. P. (1977). *Police crisis intervention.* Kalamazoo, MI: Behaviordelia.

Goodman, G. S., Taub, E., Jones, D., England, P., Port, L., & Ruby, L. (1992). Testifying in criminal court. *Monographs for the Society for Research in Child Development, 57*(5).

Gordon, T. M., & Brodsky, S. L. (2007). The influence of victim impact statements on sentencing in capital cases. *Journal of Forensic Psychology Practice, 7,* 45–52.

Gore-Felton, C., Gill, M., Koopman, C., & Spiegel, D. (1999). A review of acute stress reactions among victims of violence: Implications for early intervention. *Aggression and Violent Behavior, 4,* 293–306.

Green, B. L. (1991). Evaluating the effects of disasters. *Psychological Assessment, 3,* 538–546.

Green, M. A., & Berlin, M. A. (1987). Five psychosocial variables related to the existence of post-traumatic stress disorder symptoms. *Journal of Clinical Psychology, 43,* 643–649.

Grote, D. (1995). *Discipline without punishment: The proven strategy that turns problem employees into superior performers.* New York: Amacom.

Grove, D. J., & Panzer, B. I. (1991). *Resolving traumatic memories: Metaphors and symbols in psychotherapy.* New York: Irvington.

Hagh-Shenas, H., Goodarzi, M. A., Dehbozorgi, G., & Farashbandi, H. (2005). Psychological consequences of the Bam earthquake on professional and nonprofessional helpers. *Journal of Traumatic Stress, 18,* 477–483.

Hamberger, L. K., & Holtzworth-Munroe, A. (1994). Partner violence. In F. M. Dattilio & A. Freeman (Eds.), *Cognitive-behavioral strategies in crisis intervention* (pp. 302–324). New York: Guilford.

Hamblen, J. L., Gibson, L. E., Mueser, K. T., & Norris, F. H. (2006). Cognitive behavioral therapy for prolonged disaster distress. *Journal of Clinical Psychology: In Session, 62,* 1043–1052.

Hanneke, C. R., & Shields, N. A. (1985). Marital rape: Implications for the helping professions. *Social Casework, 66,* 451–458.

Hanscom, K. L. (2001). Treating survivors of war trauma and torture. *American Psychologist, 56,* 1032–1039.

Hardy, L., Jones, G., & Gould, D. (1996). *Understanding psychological preparation for sport: Theory and practice of elite performers.* New York: Wiley.

Harris, C. (1991). A family crisis-intervention model of treatment of post-traumatic stress reaction. *Journal of Traumatic Stress, 4,* 195–207.

Harsha, W. (1990). Understanding and treating low back pain. In R. S. Weiner (Ed.), *Innovations in pain management: A practical guide for clinicians* (pp. 9.1–9.17). Orlando: PMD Press.

Harvey, A. G., & Bryant, R. A. (1998). Predictors of acute stress following mild traumatic brain injury. *Brain Injury, 12,* 147–154.

Hassouneh-Phillips, D., & Curry, M. A. (2002). Abuse of women with disabilities: State of the science. *Rehabilitation Counseling Bulletin, 45,* 96–104.

Hatton, R. (2003). Homicide bereavement counseling: A survey of providers. *Death Studies, 27,* 427–448.

Hawker, D. S. J., & Boulton, M. J. (2000). Twenty years' research on peer victimization and psychosocial maladjustment: A meta-analytic review of cross-sectional studies. *Journal of Child Psychology and Psychiatry, 41,* 441–455.

Hays, K. F., & Brown, C. H. (2004). *You're on! Consulting for peak performance.* Washington, DC: American Psychological Association.

Helzer, J. E., Robins, L. N., & McEnvoi, L. (1987). Post-traumatic stress disorder in the general population. *New England Journal of Medicine, 317,* 1630–1634.

Hendler, N. (1982). The anatomy and psychopharmacology of chronic pain. *Journal of Clinical Psychiatry, 43,* 15–20.

Henry, V. E. (2004). *Death work: Police, trauma, and the psychology of survival.* New York: Oxford University Press.

Herman, J. L. (1992). *Trauma and recovery.* New York: Basic Books.

Herman, J. L. (2003). The mental health of crime victims: Impact of legal intervention. *Journal of Traumatic Stress, 16,* 159–166.

Herman, S. (2002, May). Law enforcement and victim services: Rebuilding lives together. *The Police Chief,* 34–37.

Hills, A. (2002). Responding to catastrophic terrorism. *Studies in Conflict & Terrorism, 25,* 245–261.

Hills, A., & Thomson, D. (1999). Should victim impact influence sentences? Understanding the community's justice reasoning. *Behavioral Sciences and the Law, 17,* 661–671.

Hirschel, D., & Buzawa, E. (2002). Understanding the context of dual arrest with directions for future research. *Violence Against Women, 8,* 1449–1473.

Hoagwood, K. E., Vogel, J. M., Levitt, J. M., D'Amico, P. J., Paisner, W. I., & Kaplan, S. J. (2007). Implementing an evidence-based trauma treatment in a state system after September 11: The CATS project. *Journal of the American Academy of Child and Adolescent Psychiatry, 46,* 1–7.

Hobfoll, S. E. (1989). Conservation of resources: A new attempt at conceptualizing stress. *American Psychologist, 44,* 513–524.

Hobfoll, S. E., Galai-Gat, T., Johnson, D. M., & Watson, P. J. (2007). Terrorism. In F. M. Dattilio & A. Freeman (Eds), *Cognitive-behavioral strategies in crisis intervention* (3rd ed., pp. 428–455). New York: Guilford Press.

Hobfoll, S. E., Hall, B. J., Canetti-Nisim, D., Galea, S., Johnson, R. J., & Palmieri, P. A. (2007). Refining our understanding of traumatic growth in the face of terrorism: Moving from meaning cognitions to doing what is meaningful. *Applied Psychology: An International Review, 56,* 345–366.

Hoffman, S., & Baron, S. A. (2001). Stalkers, stalking, and violence in the workplace. In J. A. Davis (Ed.), *Stalking crimes and victim protection: Prevention, intervention, threat assessment, and case management* (pp. 139–159). Boca Raton, FL: CRC Press.

Hoge, E. A., Austin, E. D., & Pollack, M. H. (2007). Resilience: Research evidence and conceptual considerations for posttraumatic stress disorder. *Depression and Anxiety, 24,* 139–152.

Holt, M. K., Finkelhor, D., & Kantor, G. K. (2007). Multiple victimization experiences of urban elementary school students: Associations with psychosocial functioning and academic performance. *Child Abuse & Neglect, 31,* 503–515.

Horowitz, M. J. (1986). *Stress response syndromes* (2nd ed.). New York: Jason Aronson.

Horowitz, M. J., Siegel, B., Holsen, A., Bonnano, G. A., Milbrath, C., & Stinson, C. H. (1997). Diagnostic criteria for complicated grief disorder. *American Journal of Psychiatry, 154,* 904–910.

Hough, M. (1985). The impact of victimization: Findings from the British Crime Survey. *Victimology, 10,* 498–511.

Hough, R. L., Vega, W., Valle, R., Kolody, B. R., del Castillo, R. G., & Tarke, H. (1990). Mental health consequences of the San Ysidro MacDonald's massacre: A community study. *Journal of Traumatic Stress, 3,* 71–92.

House, A. E. (1999). *DSM-IV diagnosis in the schools.* New York: Guilford Press.

Hoven, C. W., Duarte, C. S., & Mandell, D. J. (2003). Children's mental health after disasters: The impact of the World Trade Center attack. *Current Psychiatry Reports, 5,* 101–117.

Huffer, K. (1995). *Overcoming the devastation of legal abuse syndrome: Beyond rage.* Spirit Lake, ID: Fulkort Press.

Hughes, F. M., Stuart, G. L., Gordon, K. C., & Moore, T. M. (2007). Predicting the use of aggressive conflict tactics in a sample of women arrested for domestic violence. *Journal of Social and Personal Relationships, 24,* 155–176.

Huppert, J. D., & Baker-Morrisette, S. L. (2003). Beyond the manual: The insider's guide to panic control treatment. *Cognitive and Behavioral Practice, 10,* 2–13.

Hymer, S. (1984). The self in victimization: Conflict and developmental perspectives. *Victimology: An International Journal, 9,* 142–150.

Jacobson, E. (1938). *Progressive relaxation.* Chicago: University of Chicago Press.

James, B. (1989). *Treating traumatized children: New insights and creative interventions.* New York: Free Press.

Janik, J. (1991). What value are cognitive defenses in critical incident stress? In J. Reese, J. Horn, & C. Dunning (Eds.), *Critical incidents in policing* (pp.149–158). Washington, DC: U.S. Government Printing Office.

Janoff-Bulman, R. (1979). Characterological versus behavioral self-blame: Inquiries into depression and rape. *Journal of Personality and Social Psychology, 37,* 1798–1809.

Janoff-Bulman, R. (1992). *Shattered assumptions: Towards a new psychology of trauma.* New York: Free Press.

Javitt, D. (2004). Glutamate as a therapeutic target in psychiatric disorders. *Molecular Psychiatry, 9,* 984–997.

Jaycox, L. H., Marshall, G. N., & Schell, T. (2004). Use of mental health services by men injured through community violence. *Psychiatric Services, 55,* 415–420.

Jenkins, M. A., Langlais, P. J., Delis, D., & Cohen, R. A. (2000). Attention dysfunction associated with posttraumatic stress disorder among rape survivors. *The Clinical Neuropsychologist, 14,* 7–12.

Johnson, K. (1989). *Trauma in the lives of children: Crisis and stress management techniques for counselors and other professionals.* Alameda: Hunter House.

Johnson, K. (2000). Crisis response to schools. *International Journal of Emergency Mental Health, 2,* 173–180.

Johnson, M. P. (1995). Patriarchal terrorism and common couple violence: Two forms of violence against women. *Journal of Marriage and the Family, 57,* 283–294.

Johnson, P. R., & Indvik, J. (2000). Rebels, criticizers, backstabbers, and busybodies: Anger and aggression at work. *Public Personnel Management, 29,* 165–173.

Johnson, S. D., North, C. S., & Smith, E. M. (2002). Psychiatric disorders among victims of a courthouse shooting spree: A three-year follow-up study. *Community Mental Health Journal, 38,* 181–194.

Jones, C. A. (2002). Victim perspective of bank robbery: Trauma and recovery. *Traumatology, 8,* 191–204.

Jones, S. J., & Beck, E. (2007). Disenfranchised grief and nonfinite loss as experienced by the families of death row inmates. *Omega: Journal of Death and Dying, 54,* 281–299.

Joyce, T. (2006, March). Victimology awareness. *Law and Order,* 48–54.

Kabat-Zinn, J. (1994). *Wherever you go, there you are: Mindfulness meditation in everyday life.* New York: Hyperion.

Kabat-Zinn, J. (2003). Mindfulness-based interventions in context: Past, present, and future. *Clinical Psychology: Science and Practice, 10,* 144–156.

Kalb, R. (2002, August 19). How are we doing? *Newsweek,* 53.

Kaltiala-Heino, R., Rimpelae, M., & Rantanen, P. (2001). Bullying at school: An indicator for adolescents at risk for mental disorders. *Journal of Adolescence, 23,* 661–674.

Keane, T. M., Fairbank, J. A., Caddell, J. M., & Zimmerling, R. T. (1989). Implosive (flooding) therapy reduces symptoms of PTSD in Vietnam combat veterans: A controlled study. *Behavior Therapy, 20,* 245–260.

Keller, B. (2002, May 26). Nuclear nightmare. *New York Times Magazine,* 22–29, 51, 54–55, 57.

Kellerman, A. (1992). Gun ownership as a risk factor for homicide in the home. *New England Journal of Medicine, 329,* 1084–1091.

Kendler, K. S., & Eaves, L. J. (1986). Models for the joint effect of genotype and environment on liability to psychiatric illness. *American Journal of Psychiatry, 143,* 279–289.

Kendler, K. S., Neale, M., Kessler, R., Heath, A., & Eaves, L. (1993). A twin study of recent life events and difficulties. *Archives of General Psychiatry, 50,* 789–796.

Kennair, N., & Mellor, D. (2007). Parent abuse: A review. *Child Psychiatry and Human Development, 38,* 203–219.

Kennedy, D. B., & Homant, R. J. (1984). Battered women's evaluation of police response. *Victimology: An International Journal, 9,* 174–179.

Kennedy, D. B., & Homant, R. J. (1997). Problems with the use of criminal profiling in premises security litigation. *Trial Diplomacy Journal, 20,* 223–229.

Kenney, J. S. (2003). Gender roles and grief cycles: Observations on models of grief and coping in homicide cases. *International Review of Victimology, 10,* 19–47.

Kessler, R. C., Sonnega, A., Bromet, E., Hughes, M., Nelson, C. B., & Breslau, N. (1999). Epidemiological risk factors for trauma and PTSD. In R. Yehuda (Ed.), *Risk factors for posttraumatic stress disorder* (pp. 23–59). Washington, DC: American Psychiatric Press.

Kilpatrick, D. G., & Acierno, R. (2003). Mental health needs of crime victims: Epidemiology and outcomes. *Journal of Traumatic Stress, 16,* 119–132.

Kilpatrick, D. G., & Otto, R. K. (1987). Constitutionally guaranteed participation in criminal proceedings for victims: Potential effects on psychological functioning. *Wayne Law Review, 34,* 7–28.

Kilpatrick, D. G., & Resnick, H. S. (1993). Posttraumatic stress disorder associated with exposure to criminal victimization in clinical and community populations. In J. R. T. Davidson & E. B. Foa (Eds.), *Posttraumatic stress disorders: DSM-IV and beyond* (pp. 113–143). Washington, DC: American Psychiatric Press.

Kilpatrick, D. G., Saunders, B. E., Veronen, L. G., Best, C. L., & Von, J. M. (1987). Criminal victimization: Lifetime prevalence, reporting to police, and psychological impact. *Crime and Delinquency, 33,* 7–28.

Kilpatrick, D. G., Veronen, L. J., & Resnick, P. A. (1982). Psychological sequelae to rape: Assessment and treatment strategies. In D. M. Doleys, R. L. Meredith, & A. R. Ciminero (Eds.), *Behavioral medicine: Assessment and treatment strategies* (pp. 473–498). New York: Plenum.

Kimmel, M. (1996). *Manhood in America.* New York: Free Press.

King, L. A., King, D. W., Fairbank, J. A., Keane, T. M., & Adams, G. A. (1998). Resilience-recovery factors in post-traumatic stress disorder among female and male Vietnam veterans: Hardiness, postwar social support, and additional stressful life events. *Journal of Personality and Social Psychology, 74,* 420–434.

Kinney, J. A. (1995). *Violence at work: How to make your company safer for employees and customers.* Englewood Cliffs, NJ: Prentice-Hall.

Kinney, J. A. (1996). The dynamics of threat management. In G. R. Vandenbos & E. Q. Bulatao (Eds.), *Violence on the job: Identifying risks and developing solutions* (pp. 299–313). Washington, DC: American Psychological Association.

Kinston, W., & Rosser, R. (1974). Disaster: Effects on mental and physical state. *Journal of Psychosomatic Research, 18,* 437–456.

Kirwin, B. R. (1997). *The mad, the bad, and the innocent: The criminal mind on trial —Tales of a forensic psychologist.* Boston: Little Brown.

Kleepsies, P. M. (Ed.) (1998). *Emergencies in mental health practice: Evaluation and management.* New York: Guilford.

Klein, G. A. (1996). The effect of acute stressors on decision making. In J. Driskell & E. Salas (Eds.), *Stress and human performance* (pp. 49–88). Hillsdale, NJ: Erlbaum.

Knight, J. A. (1997). Neuropsychological assessment in posttraumatic stress disorder. In J. Wilson & T. M. Keane (Eds.), *Assessing psychological trauma and PTSD* (pp. 448–492). New York: Guilford Press.

Kobasa, S. C. (1979a). Personality and resistance to illness. *American Journal of Community Psychology, 7,* 413–423.

Kobasa, S. C. (1979b). Stressful life events, personality, and health: An inquiry into hardiness. *Journal of Personality and Social Psychology, 37,* 1–11.

Kobasa, S. C., Maddi, S. R., & Kahn, S. (1982). Hardiness and health: A prospective study. *Journal of Personality and Social Psychology, 42,* 168–177.

Koch, W. J., Douglas, K. S., Nichols, T. L., & O'Neill, M. L. (2006). *Psychological injuries: Forensic assessment, treatment, and the law.* New York: Oxford University Press.

Kolb, L. C. (1987). A neuropsychological hypothesis explaining posttraumatic stress disorders. *American Journal of Psychiatry, 144,* 989–995.

Koopman, C., Zarcone, J., Mann, M., Freinkel, A., & Spiegel, D. (1998). Acute stress reactions of psychiatry staff to a threatening patient. *Journal of Anxiety, Stress and Coping, 11,* 27–45.

Kratcoski, P. C., Edelbacher, M., & Das, D. K. (2001). Terrorist victimization: Prevention, control, and recovery. *International Review of Victimology, 8,* 257–268.

Kressel, N. J., & Kressel, D. F. (2002). *Stack and sway: The new science of jury consulting.* Cambridge: Westview.

Kruger, K. J., & Valltos, N. G. (2002, July). Dealing with domestic violence in law enforcement relationships. *FBI Law Enforcement Bulletin,* 1–7.

Kushner, M. G., Riggs, D. S., Foa, E. B., & Miller, S. M. (1993). Perceived controllability and the development of posttraumatic stress disorder (PTSD) in crime victims. *Behavior Research and Therapy, 31,* 105–110.

Kuzma, L. (2000). Trends: Terrorism in the United States. *Public Opinion Quarterly, 64,* 90–105.

Labig, C. E. (1995). *Preventing violence in the workplace.* New York: Amacom.

Lanceley, F. J. (1999). *On-scene guide for crisis negotiators.* Boca Raton, FL: CRC Press.

Lane, J. F. (1980). Improving athletic performance through visuo-motor behavior rehearsal. In R. M. Suinn (Ed.), *Psychology in sport: Methods and applications.* Minneapolis: Burgess.

Landau, J., & Saul, J. (2004). Family and community resilience in response to major disaster. In F. Walsh & M. Goldrick (Eds.), *Living beyond loss: Death in the family* (2nd ed., pp. 285–309). New York: Norton.

Lanza, M. L. (1995). Nursing staff as victims of patient assault. In C. R. Figley (Ed.), *Compassion fatigue: Coping with secondary traumatic stress disorder in those who treat the traumatized* (pp. 131–149). New York: Brunner/Mazel.

Lanza, M. L. (1996). Violence against nurses in hospitals. In G. R. VandenBos & E. Q. Bulatao (Eds.), *Violence on the job: Identifying risks and developing solutions* (pp. 189–198). Washington, DC: American Psychological Association.

Lazarus, A. A., & Mayne, T. J. (1990). Relaxation: Some limitations, side effects, and proposed solutions. *Psychotherapy, 27,* 261–266.

LeBlanc, M. M., & Barling, J. (2005). Understanding the many faces of workplace violence. In S. Fox & P. E. Spector (Eds.), *Counterproductive work behavior: Investigations of actors and targets* (pp. 41–63). Washington, DC: American Psychological Association.

LeDoux, J. E. (1996). *The emotional brain: The mysterious underpinnings of emotional life.* New York: Simon & Schuster.

Leone, J., Johnson, M., Cohan, C., & Lloyd, S. (2004). Consequences of male partner violence on low-income minority women. *Journal of Marriage and Family, 66,* 472–490.

Lesserman, J., & Drossman, D. A. (2007). Relationship of abuse history to functional gastrointestinal disorders and symptoms: Some possible mediating mechanisms. *Trauma, Violence, and Abuse, 8,* 331–343.

Letellier, P. (1994). Gay and bisexual male domestic violence victimization: Challenges to feminist theory and response to violence. *Violence and Victims, 9,* 95–106.

Levendosky, A. A., Bogat, G. A., Theran, S. A., Trotter, J. S., von Eye, A., & Davidson, W. S. (2004). The social networks of women experiencing domestic violence. *American Journal of Community Psychology, 34,* 95–109.

Levine, E., Degutis, L., Pruzinsky, T., Shin, J., & Persing, J. A. (2005). Quality of life and facial trauma: Psychological and body image effects. *Annals of Plastic Surgery, 54,* 502–510.

Lind, A., & Tyler, T. (1988). *The social psychology of procedural justice.* New York: Plenum.

Lindemann, E. (1944). Symptomatology and management of acute grief. *American Journal of Psychiatry, 101,* 141–148.

Lindy, J. D., Grace, M. C., & Green, B. L. (1981). Survivors: Outreach to a reluctant population. *American Journal of Orthopsychiatry, 51,* 468–478.

Linehan, M. (1993). *Cognitive behavioral treatment of borderline personality disorder.* New York: Guilford Press.

Lipman, F. D. (1962). Malingering in personal injury cases. *Temple Law Quarterly, 35,* 141–162.

Lipton, M. I., & Schaffer, W. R. (1986). Posttraumatic stress disorder in the older veteran. *Military Medicine, 151,* 522–524.

Litz, B. T. (2004). *Early intervention for trauma and traumatic loss.* New York: Guilford Press.

Litz, B. T., Gray, M. J., Bryant, R. A., & Adler, A. B. (2002). Early intervention for trauma: Current status and future directions. *Clinical Psychology: Science and Practice, 9,* 112–134.

Lloyd, S. (1997). The effects of domestic violence on women's employment. *Law and Policy, 19,* 139–167.

Loboprabhu, S., Molinari, V., Pate, J., & Lomax, J. (2007). The after-death call to family members: A clinical perspective. *Aging & Mental Health, 11,* 192–196.

Logan, T. K., Shannon, L., Cole, J., & Swanberg, J. (2007). Partner stalking and implications for women's employment. *Journal of Interpersonal Violence, 22,* 268–291.

Logan, T. K., Walker, R., Cole, J., & Leukefeld, C. (2002). Victimization and substance use among women: Contributing factors interventions, and implications. *Review of General Psychology, 6,* 325–397.

Logan, T. K., Walker, R., Jordan, C., & Campbell, J. (2004). An integrative review of separation in the context of victimization. *Trauma, Violence, and Abuse, 5,* 143–193.

Los Angeles Board of Police Commissioners. (1997). *Domestic violence in the Los Angeles Police Department: How well does the Los Angeles Police Department police its own? Report on the Domestic Violence Task Force.* Office of Inspector General, Los Angeles, CA.

Lott, L. D. (1999). Deadly secrets: Violence in the police family. In L. Territo & J. D. Sewell (Eds.), *Stress management in law enforcement* (pp. 149–155). Durham, NC: Carolina Academic Press.

Lubit, R. H. (2004). *Coping with toxic managers, subordinates . . . and other difficult people.* New York: Prentice Hall.

Lundy, S. E., & Leventhal, B. (Eds.) (1999). *Same-sex domestic violence: Strategies for change.* Thousand Oaks, CA: Sage.

Luthar, S. S. (1991). Vulnerability and resilience: A study of high-risk adolescents. *Child Development, 62,* 600–616.

Lynch, S., & Graham-Bermann, S. (2004). Exploring the relationship between positive work experiences and women's sense of self in the context of partner abuse. *Psychology of Women Quarterly, 28,* 159–167.

Lyons, M. J., Goldberg, J., Eisen, S. A., True, W., Tsuang, M. T., & Meyer, J. M. (1993). Do genes influence exposure to trauma? A twin study of combat. *American Journal of Medical Genetics, 48,* 22–27.

Mack, D. A., Shannon, C., Quick, J. D., & Quick, J. C. (1998). Stress and the preventive management of workplace violence. In R. W. Griffith, A. O'Leary-Kelly, & J. M. Collins (Eds.), *Dysfunctional behavior in organizations: Violent and deviant behavior* (pp. 119–141). Stanford: JAI Press.

MacLeod, M. D. (1999). Why did it happen to me? Social cognition processes in adjustment and recovery from criminal victimization and illness. *Current Psychology, 18*, 18–31.

Macy, R. J. (2007). A coping theory framework toward preventing sexual revictimization. *Aggression and Violent Behavior, 12*, 177–192.

Maddi, S. R., & Khoshaba, D. M. (1994). Hardiness and mental health. *Journal of Personality Assessment, 63*, 265–274.

Maier, G. J., & Van Ryboek, G. J. (1995). Managing countertransference reactions to aggressive patients. In B. S. Eichelman & A. C. Hartwig (Eds.), *Patient violence and the clinician* (pp. 73–104). Washington, DC: American Psychiatric Press.

Maker, A. H., Kemmelmeier, M., & Peterson, C. (2001). Child sexual abuse, peer sexual abuse, and sexual assault in adulthood: A multi-risk model of revictimization. *Journal of Traumatic Stress, 14*, 351–368.

Mandel, H. P. (1997). *Conduct disorder and underachievement: Risk factors, assessment, treatment, and prevention.* New York: Wiley.

Mantell, M., & Albrecht, S. (1994). *Ticking bombs: Defusing violence in the workplace.* New York: Irwin.

Manton, M., & Talbot, A. (1990). Crisis intervention after an armed hold-up: Guidelines for counselors. *Journal of Traumatic Stress, 3*, 507–522.

Marra, T. (2005). *Dialectical behavior therapy in private practice: A practical and comprehensive guide.* Oakland, CA: New Harbinger.

Marshall, L. L. (1996). Psychological abuse of women: Six distinct clusters. *Journal of Family Violence, 11*, 379–409.

Martin, E. K. (2007). A review of marital rape. *Aggression and Violent Behavior, 12*, 329–347.

Martin, M. E. (1997). Double your trouble: Dual arrest in family violence. *Journal of Family Violence, 12*, 139–157.

Martinko, M. J., Douglas, S. C., Harvey, P., & Joseph, C. (2005). Managing organizational aggression. In R. E. Kidwell & C. L. Martin (Eds.), *Managing organizational deviance* (pp. 237–259). Thousand Oaks, CA: Sage.

Masters, R., Friedman, L. N., & Getzel, G. (1988). Helping families of homicide victims: A multidimensional approach. *Journal of Traumatic Stress, 1*, 109–125.

Matsakis, A. (1994). *Post-traumatic stress disorder: A complete treatment guide.* Oakland, CA: New Harbinger.

Mbilinyi, L. F., Edleson, J. L., Hagemeister, A. K., & Beeman, S. K. (2007). What happens to children when their mothers are battered? Results from a four city anonymous telephone survey. *Journal of Family Violence, 22*, 309–317.

McCabe, M. P., & Di Battista, J. (2004). Role of health, relationships, work and coping on adjustment among people with multiple sclerosis: A longitudinal investigation. *Psychology, Health, and Medicine, 9*, 431–439.

McCann, I. L., & Pearlman, L. A. (1990). *Psychological trauma and the adult survivor: Theory, therapy, and transformation.* New York: Brunner/Mazel.

McCarroll, J. E., Ursano, R. J., & Fullerton, C. S. (1993). Traumatic responses to the recovery of war dead in Operation Desert Storm. *American Journal of Psychiatry, 150,* 1875–1877.

McCarroll, J. E., Ursano, R. J., & Fullerton, C. S. (1995). Symptoms of PTSD following recovery of war dead: 13–15 month follow-up. *American Journal of Psychiatry, 152,* 939–941.

McCrae, R. R., & Costa, P. T. (1990). *Personality in adulthood.* New York: Guilford.

McFarlane, A. C. (1988a). The phenomenology of posttraumatic stress disorders following a natural disaster. *Journal of Nervous and Mental Disease, 176,* 22–29.

McFarlane, A. C. (1988b). The longitudinal course of posttraumatic morbidity: The range of outcomes and their predictors. *Journal of Nervous and Mental Disease, 176,* 30–39.

McFarlane, A. C. (1997). The prevalence and longitudinal course of PTSD: Implications for the neurobiological models of PTSD. *Annals of the New York Academy of Sciences, 821,* 10–23.

McFarlane, A. C., Atchison, M., Rafalowicz, E., & Papay, P. (1994). Physical symptoms in posttraumatic stress disorder. *Journal of Psychosomatic Research, 38,* 715–726.

McFarlane, J., Campbell, J., & Watson, K. (2002). Intimate partner stalking and femicide: Urgent implications for women's safety. *Behavioral Sciences and the Law, 20,* 51–68.

McFarlane, J., Campbell, J., Wilt, S., Sachs, C., Ulrich, Y., & Xu, X. (1999). Stalking and intimate partner femicide. *Homicide Studies, 2,* 442–446.

McFarlane, J., Malecha, A., Watson, K., Gist, J., Batten, E., & Hall, I. (2005). Intimate partner sexual assault against women: Frequency, health consequences, and treatment outcomes. *Obstetrics & Gynecology, 105,* 99–108.

McGinn, L. K., & Spindel, C. B. (2007). Disaster trauma. In F. M. Dattilio & A. Freeman (Eds.), *Cognitive-behavioral strategies in crisis intervention* (3rd ed., pp. 399–427). New York: Guilford Press.

McMains, M. J. (2002). Active listening: The aspirin of negotiations. *Journal of Police Crisis Negotiations, 2,* 69–74.

McMains, M. J., & Mullins, W. C. (1996). *Crisis negotiations: Managing critical incidents and hostage situations in law enforcement and corrections.* Cincinnati, OH: Anderson.

McNally, R. J. (2007). Mechanisms of exposure therapy: How neuroscience can improve psychological treatments for anxiety disorders. *Clinical Psychology Review, 27,* 750–759.

Meek, C. L. (1990). Evaluation and assessment of post-traumatic and other stress-related disorders. In C. L. Meek (Ed.), *Post-traumatic stress disorder: Assessment, differential diagnosis, and forensic evaluation* (pp. 9–61). Sarasota, FL: Professional Resource Exchange.

Meichenbaum, D. H. (1985). *Stress inoculation training.* Elmsford, NY: Pergamon.

Meloy, J. R. (1997). The clinical risk management of stalking: "Someone is watching over me." *American Journal of Psychotherapy, 51,* 174–184.

Mercy, J. A., & Salzman, L. E. (1989). Fatal violence among spouses in the United States. *American Journal of Public Health, 79,* 595–599.

Merskey, H. (1992). Psychiatric aspects of the neurology of trauma. *Neurologic Clinics, 10,* 895–905.

Messman, T. L., & Long, P. J. (1996). Child sexual abuse and its relationship to revictimization in adult women: A review. *Clinical Psychology Review, 16,* 397–420.

Meyer, C. B., & Taylor, S. E. (1986). Adjustment to rape. *Journal of Personality and Social Psychology, 50,* 1226–1234.

Miller, A. K., Markman, K. D., & Handley, I. M. (2007). Self-blame among sexual assault victims prospectively predicts victimization: A perceived sociolegal context model of risk. *Basic and Applied Social Psychology, 29,* 129–136.

Miller, L. (1984). Neuropsychological concepts of somatoform disorders. *International Journal of Psychiatry in Medicine, 14,* 31–46.

Miller, L. (1985). Neuropsychological assessment of substance abusers: Review and recommendations. *Journal of Substance Abuse Treatment, 2,* 5–17.

Miller, L. (1987). Neuropsychology of the aggressive psychopath: An integrative review. *Aggressive Behavior, 13,* 119–140.

Miller, L. (1988). Neuropsychological perspectives on delinquency. *Behavioral Sciences and the Law, 6,* 409–428.

Miller, L. (1989a, November). What biofeedback does and doesn't do. *Psychology Today,* 22–23.

Miller, L. (1989b, December). To beat stress, don't relax: Get tough! *Psychology Today,* 62–63.

Miller, L. (1990). *Inner natures: Brain, self, and personality.* New York: St. Martin's Press.

Miller, L. (1991a). Psychotherapy of the brain-injured patient: Principles and practices. *Journal of Cognitive Rehabilitation, 9*(2), 24–30.

Miller, L. (1991b). *Freud's brain: Neuropsychodynamic foundations of psychoanalysis.* New York: Guilford.

Miller, L. (1993a). Who are the best psychotherapists? Qualities of the effective practitioner. *Psychotherapy in Private Practice, 12*(1), 1–18.

Miller, L. (1993b). Psychotherapeutic approaches to chronic pain. *Psychotherapy, 30,* 115–124.

Miller, L. (1993c). Toxic torts: Clinical, neuropsychological, and forensic aspects of chemical and electrical injuries. *Journal of Cognitive Rehabilitation, 11*(1), 6–20.

Miller, L. (1993d). The "trauma" of head trauma: Clinical, neuropsychological, and forensic aspects of posttraumatic stress syndromes in brain injury. *Journal of Cognitive Rehabilitation, 11*(4), 18–29.

Miller, L. (1993e). *Psychotherapy of the brain-injured patient: Reclaiming the shattered self.* New York: Norton.

Miller, L. (1994a). Biofeedback and behavioral medicine: Treating the symptom, the syndrome, or the person? *Psychotherapy, 31,* 161–169.

Miller, L. (1994b). Civilian posttraumatic stress disorder: Clinical syndromes and psychotherapeutic strategies. *Psychotherapy, 31*, 655–664.

Miller, L. (1994c). Traumatic brain injury and aggression. In M. Hillbrand & N. J. Pallone (Eds.), *The psychobiology of aggression: Engines, measurement, control* (pp. 91–103). New York: Haworth.

Miller, L. (1995a, May 18). *Reaching the breaking point: Are we becoming a more violent society?* [Television Broadcast]. West Palm Beach, FL: CBS Action News.

Miller, L. (1995b). Tough guys: Psychotherapeutic strategies with law enforcement and emergency services personnel. *Psychotherapy, 32*, 592–600.

Miller, L. (1995c). Toxic trauma and chemical sensitivity: Clinical syndromes and psychotherapeutic strategies. *Psychotherapy, 32*, 648–656.

Miller, L. (1995d, October 3). *Intervention strategies with victims of domestic violence.* Program presented at the Palm Beach County Victim Services Domestic Violence Seminar, West Palm Beach, FL.

Miller, L. (1996a, January 25). *Evaluation and treatment of posttraumatic stress disorder in victims of violent crime.* Program presented to Palm Beach County Victim Services, West Palm Beach, FL.

Miller, L. (1996b). Making the best use of your neuropsychology expert: What every neurolawyer should know. *Neurolaw Letter, 6*, 93–99.

Miller, L. (1997a). Workplace violence in the rehabilitation setting: How to prepare, respond, and survive. *Florida State Association of Rehabilitation Nurses Newsletter, 7*, 4–8.

Miller, L. (1997b, October 17). *Workplace violence and domestic violence: Prevention, response, and recovery.* Program presented at the Domestic Violence Awareness Month Seminar, Palm Beach County Victim Services, West Palm Beach, FL.

Miller, L. (1997c, November 20). *Workplace violence in the healthcare setting: Prevention, response, and recovery.* Inservice training program presented to the South Florida Pain and Rehabilitation Center, Lantana, FL.

Miller, L. (1997d). The neuropsychology expert witness: An attorney's guide to productive case collaboration. *Journal of Cognitive Rehabilitation, 15*(5), 12–17.

Miller, L. (1998a). Motor vehicle accidents: Clinical, neuropsychological, and forensic aspects. *Journal of Cognitive Rehabilitation, 16*(4), 10–23.

Miller, L. (1998b). Ego autonomy and the healthy personality: Psychodynamics, cognitive style, and clinical applications. *Psychoanalytic Review, 85*, 423–448.

Miller, L. (1998c). Our own medicine: Traumatized psychotherapists and the stresses of doing therapy. *Psychotherapy, 35*, 137–146.

Miller, L. (1998d). Brain injury and violent crime: Clinical, neuropsychological, and forensic considerations. *Journal of Cognitive Rehabilitation, 16*(6), 2–17.

Miller, L. (1998e). Psychotherapy of crime victims: Treating the aftermath of interpersonal violence. *Psychotherapy, 35*, 336–345.

Miller, L. (1998f). Not just malingering: Recognizing psychological syndromes in personal injury litigation. *Neurolaw Letter, 8*, 25–30.

Miller, L. (1998g). Malingering in brain injury and toxic tort cases. In E. Pierson (Ed.), *1998 Wiley expert witness update: New developments in personal injury litigation* (pp. 225–289). New York: Wiley.

Miller, L. (1998h). *Shocks to the system: Psychotherapy of traumatic disability syndromes.* New York: Norton.

Miller, L. (1999a). "Mental stress claims" and personal injury: Clinical, neuropsychological, and forensic issues. *Neurolaw Letter, 8,* 39–45.

Miller, L. (1999b, February 27). *Posttraumatic stress disorder after workplace violence: Making the case for psychological injury.* Program presented at the American Trial Lawyers Association Conference on Premises Liability, Inadequate Security, and Violent Crimes, Phoenix, AZ.

Miller, L. (1999c). Workplace violence: Prevention, response, and recovery. *Psychotherapy, 36,* 160–169.

Miller, L. (1999d). Treating posttraumatic stress disorder in children and families: Basic principles and clinical applications. *American Journal of Family Therapy, 27,* 21–34.

Miller, L. (1999e). Posttraumatic stress disorder in child victims of violent crime: Making the case for psychological injury. *Victim Advocate, 1*(1), 6–10.

Miller, L. (1999f). Posttraumatic stress disorder in elderly victims of violent crime: Making the case for psychological injury. *Victim Advocate, 1*(2), 7–10.

Miller, L. (1999g). Critical incident stress debriefing: Clinical applications and new directions. *International Journal of Emergency Mental Health, 1,* 253–265.

Miller, L. (1999h, October 18–19). *Beating burnout: Understanding and coping with vicarious traumatization and compassion fatigue for mental health clinicians and social service providers.* Seminar presented to AMCAL Family Services, Montreal, Canada.

Miller, L. (1999i, December 3). *Crime trauma: Victims and helpers.* Program presented at the South Florida Society for Trauma-Based Disorders Continuing Education Seminar, Hollywood, FL.

Miller, L. (1999j). Psychological syndromes in personal injury litigation. In E. Pierson (Ed.), *1999 Wiley expert witness update: New developments in personal injury litigation* (pp. 263–308). New York: Aspen.

Miller, L. (1999k). Tough guys: Psychotherapeutic strategies with law enforcement and emergency services personnel. In L. Territo & J. D. Sewell (Eds.), *Stress management in law enforcement* (pp. 317–332). Durham, NC: Carolina Academic Press.

Miller, L. (2000a). Law enforcement traumatic stress: Clinical syndromes and intervention strategies. *Trauma Response, 6*(1), 15–20.

Miller, L. (2000b, January 10). *Crime scene trauma: Effective modalities for victims and helpers.* Workshop presented to the Palm Beach County Victims Services, West Palm Beach, FL.

Miller, L. (2000c, February 3). *Crisis management of violent episodes in the health care setting.* Inservice training program presented to the Heartland Rehabilitation Center, Lantana, FL.

Miller, L. (2000d, May 17). *Workplace violence in the clinical healthcare setting: Prevention, response, and recovery.* Program presented to Intracorp, Coral Springs, FL.

Miller, L. (2000e, May 19). *Brain cases: Forensic neuropsychology in personal injury litigation*. Continuing Legal Education Seminar presented at Heartland Rehabilitation Centers, Lantana, FL.

Miller, L. (2000f, June 17). *Workplace violence in the clinical healthcare setting: Prevention, response, and recovery*. Program presented to the Gold Coast Network, West Palm Beach, FL.

Miller, L. (2000g, August 8). *Preventing and responding to school violence*. Roundtable panel discussion at the Barry Grunow Memorial Summit on Youth and School Violence, Center for Family Services, West Palm Beach, FL.

Miller, L. (2000h, December 1). *Crime victimization and workplace violence: A critical incident stress management approach*. Program presented to the Center for Family Services, West Palm Beach, FL.

Miller, L. (2000i). The predator's brain: Neuropsychodynamics of serial killers. In L. B. Schlesinger (Ed.), *Serial offenders: Current thought, recent findings, unusual syndromes* (pp. 135–166). Boca Raton, FL: CRC Press.

Miller, L. (2000j). Traumatized psychotherapists. In F. M. Dattilio & A. Freeman (Eds.), *Cognitive-behavioral strategies in crisis intervention* (2nd ed., pp. 429–445). New York: Guilford.

Miller, L. (2001a). Workplace violence and psychological trauma: Clinical disability, legal liability, and corporate policy. Part I. *Neurolaw Letter, 11,* 1–5.

Miller, L. (2001b). Workplace violence and psychological trauma: Clinical disability, legal liability, and corporate policy. Part II. *Neurolaw Letter, 11,* 7–13.

Miller, L. (2001c, April 18). *Workplace violence and domestic violence: Strategies for prevention, response, and recovery*. Training program presented to the Parkland Public Safety Department, Parkland, FL.

Miller, L. (2001d, September 15). *Psychology in the criminal justice system: Expanding roles for mental health services*. Program presented at the Florida Psychological Association Continuing Education Seminar, West Palm Beach, FL.

Miller, L. (2001e). Crime victim trauma and psychological injury: Clinical and forensic guidelines. In E. Pierson (Ed.), *2001 Wiley expert witness update: New developments in personal injury litigation* (pp. 171–205). New York: Aspen.

Miller, L. (2002a, March). How safe is your job? The threat of workplace violence. *USA Today Magazine, 52–54.*

Miller, L. (2002b). Posttraumatic stress disorder in school violence: Risk management lessons from the workplace. *Neurolaw Letter, 11,* 33, 36–40.

Miller, L. (2002c, September 20). *Terrorism: Psychological response syndromes and treatment strategies*. Seminar presented to the South Florida Society for Trauma-Based Disorders, Ft. Lauderdale, FL.

Miller, L. (2002d, December 19). *Crisis management in the healthcare setting: What front-line clinicians need to know*. Inservice program presented to the Heartland Rehabilitation Services, Boca Raton, FL.

Miller, L. (2002e). What is the true spectrum of functional disorders in rehabilitation? In N. D. Zasler & M. F. Martelli (Eds.), *Functional disorders* (pp. 1–20). Philadelphia: Hanley & Belfus.

Miller, L. (2003a). Personalities at work: Understanding and managing human nature on the job. *Public Personnel Management, 32,* 419–433.

Miller, L. (2003b, May). Police personalities: Understanding and managing the problem officer. *The Police Chief,* 53–60.

Miller, L. (2003c, May 8). *"School shock:" Preventing and responding to school violence.* Continuing education seminar, Boynton Beach, FL.

Miller, L. (2003d). Psychological interventions for terroristic trauma: Symptoms, syndromes, and treatment strategies. *Psychotherapy, 39,* 283–296.

Miller, L. (2003e). Family therapy of terroristic trauma: Psychological syndromes and treatment strategies. *American Journal of Family Therapy, 31,* 257–280.

Miller, L. (2003f). Law enforcement responses to violence against youth: Psychological dynamics and intervention strategies. In R. S. Moser & C. E. Franz (Ed.), *Shocking violence II: Violent disaster, war, and terrorism affecting our youth* (pp. 165–195). New York: Charles C. Thomas.

Miller, L. (2004a). Psychotherapeutic interventions for survivors of terrorism. *American Journal of Psychotherapy, 58,* 1–16.

Miller, L. (2004b, May 5). *Personalities at work: People-knowledge for effective business management.* Program presented at the 23rd Annual Broward Aging Network Conference, Coconut Creek, FL.

Miller, L. (2004c, June 9). *Serial killers: Who they are and what you can do to protect yourself.* [Television Broadcast]. West Palm Beach, FL: Interview on NBC Channel 5 News.

Miller, L. (2004d, August 19). *Building the bully-proof child: Recommendations for students, teachers, and parents.* Program presented to the Anti-Defamation League, West Palm Beach, FL.

Miller, L. (2004e, October 21). *Bully-proofing your child and school: Practical strategies for parents and educators.* Program presented at the Educator Appreciation Day Event of the Palm Beach County School System, Boynton Beach, FL.

Miller, L. (2004f). Good cop—bad cop: Problem officers, law enforcement culture, and strategies for success. *Journal of Police and Criminal Psychology, 19,* 30–48.

Miller, L. (2005a). Psychotherapy for terrorism survivors: New directions in evaluation and treatment. *Directions in Clinical and Counseling Psychology, 17,* 59–74.

Miller, L. (2005b). Psychotherapy for terrorism survivors: New directions in evaluation and treatment. *Directions in Psychiatric Nursing, 11,* 123–138.

Miller, L. (2005c). Hostage negotiation: Psychological principles and practices. *International Journal of Emergency Mental Health, 7,* 277–298.

Miller, L. (2005d, April). Critical incident stress: Myths and realities. *Law and Order, 31.*

Miller, L. (2005e). *Workplace violence and psychological trauma: Clinical disability, legal liability, and corporate policy.* Retrieved from www.doereport.com/article_workplaceviolence.php

Miller, L. (2006a). *Stress management: The good, the bad, and the healthy.* Retrieved from www.policeone.com/writers/columnists/LaurenceMiller/articles/508968/

Miller, L. (2006b, May 9). *Personalities on the job: How to survive and thrive with your colorful coworkers.* Program presented to the Area Conference on Aging, Broward County, FL.

Miller, L. (2006c, August 17). *Child killers: The JonBenet Ramsey case.* West Palm Beach, FL: Interview on NBC Channel 5 News.

Miller, L. (2006d). The terrorist mind: I. A psychological and political analysis. *International Journal of Offender Rehabilitation and Comparative Criminology, 50,* 121–138.

Miller, L. (2006e). The terrorist mind: II. Typologies, psychopathologies, and practical guidelines for investigation. *International Journal of Offender Rehabilitation and Comparative Criminology, 50,* 255–268.

Miller, L. (2006f). Critical incident stress debriefing for law enforcement: Practical models and special applications. *International Journal of Emergency Mental Health, 8,* 189–201.

Miller, L. (2006g, October). Psychological principles and practices for superior law enforcement leadership. *The Police Chief,* 160–168.

Miller, L. (2006h, October). On the spot: Testifying in court for law enforcement officers. *FBI Law Enforcement Bulletin,* 1–6.

Miller, L. (2006i). *May it please the court: Testifying tips for officers.* Retrieved from www.policeone.com/writers/columnists/LaurenceMiller/articles/1188765/

Miller, L. (2006j). *The forensic psychological examination: What every client should expect.* Retrieved from www.doereport.com/forensic_psych_exam.php

Miller, L. (2006k). *The psychological fitness-for-duty evaluation: What every police officer should know.* Retrieved from www.edpdlaw.com/FFDMiller.pdf

Miller, L. (2006l). *Posttraumatic stress disorder: Making the case for psychological injury.* Retrieved from www.doereport.com/posttraumatic_stress.php

Miller, L. (2006m). *Practical police psychology: Stress management and crisis intervention for law enforcement.* Springfield, IL: Charles C Thomas.

Miller, L. (2007a). Police families: Stresses, syndromes, and solutions. *American Journal of Family Therapy, 35,* 21–40.

Miller, L. (2007b). Negotiating with mentally disordered hostage takers: Guiding principles and practical strategies. *Journal of Police Crisis Negotiations, 7,* 63–83.

Miller, L. (2007c). *May it please the court: Testifying tips for expert witnesses.* Retrieved from www.doereport.com/article_testifying_tips.php

Miller, L. (2007d, August). The psychological fitness-for-duty evaluation. *FBI Law Enforcement Bulletin,* 10–16.

Miller, L. (2007e). *School violence: Effective response protocols for maximum safety and minimum liability.* Retrieved from www.doereport.com/article_school_violence.php

Miller, L. (2007f). *School violence: The psychology of youthful murder and what to do about it.* Retrieved from www.policeone.com/writers/columnists/LaurenceMiller/articles/1238618/

Miller, L. (2007g). *Domestic violence in police families: Causes, effects, and intervention strategies.* Retrieved from www.policeone.com/writers/columnists/Laurence Miller/articles/1350610/

Miller, L. (2007h). *Hostage negotiations: Psychological strategies for resolving crises safely.* Retrieved from www.policeone.com/writers/columnists/LaurenceMiller/articles/ 1247470/

Miller, L. (2007i). *The worst possible news: Death notification and body identification for law enforcement officers.* Retrieved from www.policeone.com/writers/columnists/ LaurenceMiller/articles/ 1267704/

Miller, L. (2007j, August 29). *Parent-child murder-suicide: What makes them do it?* West Palm Beach, FL: Interview on NBC Channel 5 News.

Miller, L. (2007k). Crisis intervention strategies for treating law enforcement and mental health professionals. In F. M. Dattilio & A. Freeman (Eds.), *Cognitive-behavioral strategies in crisis intervention* (3rd ed., pp. 93–121). New York: Guilford.

Miller, L. (2007l). Traumatic stress disorders. In F. M. Dattilio & A. Freeman (Eds.), *Cognitive-behavioral strategies in crisis intervention* (3rd ed., pp. 494–527). New York: Guilford.

Miller, L. (2007m). *METTLE: Mental toughness training for law enforcement.* Flushing, NY: Looseleaf Law Publications.

Miller, L. (2008). *From difficult to disturbed: Understanding and managing dysfunctional employees.* New York: Amacom.

Miller, L. (in press-a). Stress, traumatic stress, and posttraumatic stress syndromes. In L. Territo & J. D. Sewell (Eds.), *Stress management in law enforcement* (2nd ed.). Durham, NC: Carolina Academic Press.

Miller, L. (in press-b). The practice of crisis intervention. In J. Krzyzowski (Ed.), *Emergency psychiatry: Concepts and principles.* Warsaw: Medyk.

Miller, L. (in press-c). Role of the mental health consultant in police negotiation teams. In J. Krzyzowski (Ed.), *Emergency psychiatry: Concepts and principles.* Warsaw: Medyk.

Miller, L. (in press-d). *Criminal psychology: Nature, nurture, culture.* Boston: AB Longman/Pearson.

Miller, L., Agresti, M., & D'Eusanio, S. (1999, September 30). *Posttraumatic stress disorder in victims of violent crime.* WINQ Live Community Update, Lake Park, FL.

Miller, L., & Dion, J. R. (2000). Expert spotlight: Interview with Dr. Laurence Miller. *Victim Advocate, 1*(3), 10–11.

Miller, L., & Magier, M. (1993, June 1). *Brain cases: Forensic neuropsychology in personal injury litigation.* Neuropsychology Training Institute Continuing Legal Education Seminar, Boca Raton, FL.

Miller, L., Pirtle, C., & Bartlett, R. (1997, April 2). *Psychological responses to disasters: FEMA disaster management training course.* West Palm Beach, FL.

Miller, L., & Schlesinger, L. B. (2000). Survivors, families, and co-victims of serial offenders. In L. B. Schlesinger (Ed.), *Serial offenders: Current thought, recent findings, unusual syndromes* (pp. 309–334). Boca Raton, FL: CRC Press.

Millon, T., & Davis, R. (2000). *Personality disorders in modern life.* New York: Wiley.

Mitchell, J. T., & Everly, G. S. (1996). *Critical incident stress debriefing: Operations manual* (rev. ed.). Ellicott City, MD: Chevron.

Mitroff, I. I. (2001). *Managing crises before they happen: What every executive manager needs to know about crisis management.* New York: Amacom.

Modlin, H. C. (1983). Traumatic neurosis and other injuries. *Psychiatric Clinics of North America, 6,* 661–682.

Modlin, H. C. (1990). Post-traumatic stress disorder: Differential diagnosis. In C. L. Meek (Ed.), *Post-traumatic stress disorder: Assessment, differential diagnosis, and forensic evaluation* (pp. 63–89). Sarasota, FL: Professional Resource Exchange.

Mogil, M. (1989, May). Maximizing your courtroom testimony. *FBI Law Enforcement Bulletin,* 7–9.

Mollica, R. (2004). Surviving torture. *New England Journal of Medicine, 35,* 5–7.

Moon, E. (1999, February). How to handle the high cost of caring. *Professional Counselor,* 18–22.

Mueller, J. (2005). Six rather unusual propositions about terrorism. *Terrorism and Political Violence, 17,* 487–505.

Munroe, J. F., Shay, J., Fisher, L., Makay, C., Rapperport, K., & Zimering, R. (1995). Preventing compassion fatigue: A team treatment model. In C. R. Figley (Ed.), *Compassion fatigue: Coping with secondary traumatic stress disorder in those who treat the traumatized* (pp. 209–231). New York: Brunner/Mazel.

Muran, E., & DiGiuseppe, R. (2000). Rape trauma. In F. M. Dattilio & A. Freeman (Eds.), *Cognitive-behavioral strategies in crisis intervention* (2nd ed., pp. 150–165). New York: Guilford.

Murphy, S. A. (1999). PTSD among bereaved parents following the violent deaths of their 12-to-28-year-old children: A longitudinal prospective analysis. *Journal of Traumatic Stress, 12,* 273–291.

Murphy, S. A., Johnson, C., & Lohan, J. (2002). The aftermath of the violent death of a child: An integration of the assessments of parents' mental distress and PTSD during the first five years of bereavement. *Journal of Loss and Trauma, 7,* 203–222.

Mynard, H., Joseph, S., & Alexander, J. (2000). Peer-victimisation and posttraumatic stress in adolescents. *Personality and Individual Differences, 29,* 815–821.

Nadler, J., & Rose, M. R. (2003). Victim impact testimony and the psychology of punishment. *Cornell Law Review, 88,* 419–456.

Namie, G., & Namie, R. (2000). *The bully at work: What you can do to stop the hurt and reclaim your dignity on the job.* Naperville, IL: Sourcebooks.

Nansel, T. R., Overpeck, M. D., Haynie, D. L., Ruan, W. J., & Scheidt, P. C. (2003). Relationships between bullying and violence among U.S. youth. *Archives of Pediatrics and Adolescent Medicine, 157,* 348–353.

Nansel, T. R., Overpeck, M. D., Pilla, R. S., Ruan, W. J., Simons-Morton, B., & Scheidt, P. (2001). Bullying behaviors among U.S. youth. *Journal of the American Medical Association, 285,* 2094–2100.

Nardi, T. J., & Keefe-Cooperman, K. (2006). Communicating bad news: A model for emergency mental health helpers. *International Journal of Emergency Mental Health, 8,* 203–207.

Neidig, P. H., Russell, H. E., & Senig, A. F. (1992). Interpersonal aggression in law enforcement families: A preliminary investigation. *Police Studies, 15,* 30–38.

Neimeyer, R. A. (2000). Searching for the meaning of meaning: Grief therapy and the process of reconstruction. *Death Studies, 24,* 541–550.

Neimeyer, R. A. (2001). Reauthoring life narratives: Grief therapy as meaning reconstruction. *Israel Journal of Psychiatry and Related Sciences, 38,* 171–183.

Neimeyer, R. A., & Jordan, J. R. (2002). Disenfranchisement as empathic failure. In K. Doka (Ed.), *Disenfranchised grief: New directions, challenges, and strategies for practice* (pp. 95–117). San Francisco: Jossey-Bass.

Neimeyer, R. A., Prigerson, H. G., & Davies, B. (2002). Mourning and meaning. *American Behavioral Scientist, 46,* 235–251.

Neuman, J. H., & Baron, R. A. (1998). Workplace violence and workplace aggression: Evidence concerning specific forms, potential causes, and preferred targets. *Journal of Management, 24,* 391–419.

Neuman, J. H., & Baron, R. A. (2005). Aggression in the workplace: A social-psychological perspective. In S. Fox & P. E. Spector (Eds.), *Counterproductive work behavior: Investigations of actors and targets* (pp. 13–40). Washington, DC: American Psychological Association.

Nicastro, A., Cousins, A., & Spitzberg, B. (2000). The tactical face of stalking. *Journal of Criminal Justice, 28,* 69–82.

Nichols, B. L., & Czirr, D. K. (1986). Posttraumatic stress disorder: Hidden syndrome in elders. *Clinical Gerontologist, 5,* 417–433.

Nicoletti, J., & Spooner, K. (1996). Violence in the workplace: Response and intervention strategies. In G. R. Vandenbos & E. Q. Bulatao (Eds.), *Violence on the job: Identifying risks and developing solutions* (pp. 267–282). Washington, DC: American Psychological Association.

Nies, K. J., & Sweet, J. J. (1994). Neuropsycholological assessment and malingering: A critical review of past and present strategies. *Archives of Clinical Neuropsychology, 9,* 501–552.

Noesner, G. W. (1999, January). Negotiation concepts for commanders. *FBI Law Enforcement Bulletin,* 6–14.

Noesner, G. W., & Webster, M. (1997, August). Crisis intervention: Using active listening skills in negotiations. *FBI Law Enforcement Bulletin,* 13–19.

Norris, F. H. (1992). Epidemiology of trauma: Frequency and impact of different potentially traumatic events on different demographic groups. *Journal of Consulting and Clinical Psychology, 60,* 409–418.

Norris, F. H., Friedman, M. J., Watson, P. J., Byrne, C. M., Diaz, E., & Kaniasty, K. (2002a). 60,000 disaster victims speak: Part I. A review of the empirical literature, 1981–2001. *Psychiatry: Interpersonal and Biological Processes, 65,* 207–239.

Norris, F. H., Friedman, M. J., Watson, P. J., Byrne, C. M., Diaz, E., & Kaniasty, K. (2002b). 60,000 disaster victims speak: Part II. Summary and implications of the disaster mental health research. *Psychiatry: Interpersonal and Biological Processes, 65,* 240–260.

North, C. S., Nixon, S., Shariat, S., Mallonee, S., McMillan, J., Spitznagel, E. L., et al. (1999). Psychiatric disorders among survivors of the Oklahoma City bombing. *Journal of the American Medical Association, 282,* 755–762.

North, C. S., Smith, E. M., McCool, R. E., & Shea, J. M. (1989). Short-term psycho-pathology in eyewitnesses to mass murder. *Hospital and Community Psychiatry, 40,* 1293–1295.

North, C. S., Smith, E. M., & Spitznagel, E. L. (1994). Postttraumatic stress disorder in survivors of a mass shooting. *American Journal of Psychiatry, 151,* 82–88.

North, C. S., Smith, E. M., & Spitznagel, E. L. (1997). One-year follow-up of survivors of a mass shooting. *American Journal of Psychiatry, 154,* 1696–1702.

Norwood, A. E., Ursano, R. J., & Fullerton, C. S. (2000). Disaster psychiatry: Principles and practice. *Psychiatric Quarterly, 71,* 207–226.

Nurius, P. S., Norris, J., Young, D. S., Graham, T. L., & Gaylord, J. (2000). Interpret-ing and defensively responding to threat: Examining appraisals and coping with acquaintance sexual aggression. *Violence and Victims, 15,* 187–208.

Nutt, D., & Malizia, A. (2004). Structural and functional brain changes in posttrau-matic stress disorder. *Journal of Clinical Psychiatry, 65,* 11–17.

Olson, D. T. (1998, February). Improving deadly force decision making. *FBI Law Enforcement Bulletin,* 1–9.

Olweus, D. (1993). *Bullying at school: What we know and what we can do.* Cambridge: Blackwell.

Olweus, D. (1994). Annotation: Bullying at school: Basic facts and effects of a school based intervention program. *Journal of Child Psychology and Psychiatry, 35,* 1171–1190.

Orr, S. P., Claiborn, J. M., Altmann, B., Forgue, D. F., de Jong, J. B., & Pitman, R. K. (1990). Psychometric profile of posttraumatic stress disorder, anxious, and healthy Viet-nam veterans: Correlations with psychophysiologic responses. *Journal of Consult-ing and Clinical Psychology, 58,* 329–335.

Pam, E. (2001). Police homicide-suicide in relation to domestic violence. In D. C. Sheehan & J. I. Warren (Eds.), *Suicide and law enforcement.* Washington, DC: U.S. Government Printing Office.

Paris, J. (2000). Predispositions, personality traits, and posttraumatic stress disorder. *Harvard Review of Psychiatry, 8,* 175–183.

Park, C. L., & Folkman, S. (1997). Meaning in the context of stress and coping. *Review of General Psychology, 1,* 115–144.

Parker, R. S. (1990). *Traumatic brain injury and neuropsychological impairment: Senso-rimotor, cognitive, emotional, and adaptive problems in children and adults.* New York: Springer-Verlag.

Parker, R. S. (2001). *Concussive brain trauma: Neurobehavioral impairment and malad-aptation.* Boca Raton, FL: CRC Press.

Parkes, C. M. (1975). Determinants of outcome following bereavements. *Omega, 6,* 303–323.

Parkes, C. M., & Brown, R. (1972). Health after bereavement: A controlled study of young Boston widows and widowers. *Psychosomatic Medicine, 34,* 449–461.

Parrish, G. A., Holdren, K. S., Skiendzielewski, J. J., & Lumpkin, O. A. (1987). Emer-gency department experience with sudden death: A survey of survivors. *Annals of Emergency Medicine, 16,* 792–796.

Pavlov, I. P. (1927). *Conditioned reflexes: An investigation of the physiological activity of the cerebral cortex.* New York: Oxford University Press.

Peak, K. J. (2003). *Policing America: Methods, issues, challenges* (4th ed.). Upper Saddle River, NJ: Prentice-Hall.

Pearlman, L. A., & MacIan, P. S. (1995). Vicarious traumatization: An empirical study of the effects of trauma work on trauma therapists. *Professional Psychology: Research and Practice, 26,* 558–565.

Petty, R. A., & Kosch, L. M. (2001). Workplace violence and unwanted pursuit: From an employer's perspective. In J. A. Davis (Ed.), *Stalking crimes and victim protection: Prevention, intervention, threat assessment, and case management* (pp. 459–485). Boca Raton: CRC Press.

Phillips, D. A. (2007). Punking and bullying: Strategies in middle school, high school, and beyond. *Journal of Interpersonal Violence, 22,* 158–178.

Pierce, C. A., & Aguinis, H. (1997). The incubator: Bridging the gap between romantic relationships and sexual harassment in organizations. *Journal of Organizational Behavior, 18,* 197–200.

Pitcher, G. D., & Poland, S. (1992). *Crisis intervention in the schools.* New York: Guilford.

Pitman, R. K., Altman, B., Greenwald, E., Longpre, R. E., Macklin, M. L., Poire, R. E. & Steketee, G. S. (1991). Psychiatric complications during flooding therapy for posttraumatic stress disorder. *Journal of Clinical Psychiatry, 52,* 17–20.

Poltorak, D. Y., & Glazer, J. P. (2006). The development of children's understanding of death: Cognitive and psychodynamic considerations. *Child and Adolescent Psychiatric Clinics of North America, 15,* 567–573.

Popiel, D. A., & Susskind, E. C. (1985). The impact of rape: Social support as a moderator of stress. *American Journal of Community Psychology, 13,* 645–666.

Posey, A. J., & Wrightsman, L. S. (2005). *Trial consulting.* New York: Oxford University Press.

Potter-Efron, R. T. (1998). *Work rage: Preventing anger and resolving conflict on the job.* New York: Barnes & Noble.

Potts, M. K. (1994). Long-term effects of trauma: Posttraumatic stress among civilian internees of the Japanese during World War II. *Journal of Clinical Psychiatry, 50,* 681–698.

Prigerson, H. G., Bierhals, A. J., Stanislav, V. K., Raynolds, C. F., Shear, M. K., Day, N., et al. (1997). Traumatic grief as a risk factor for mental and physical morbidity. *American Journal of Psychiatry, 154,* 616–623.

Ptacek, J. T., & Eberhardt, T. L. (1996). Breaking bad news: A review of the literature. *Journal of the American Medical Association, 276,* 496–502.

Pynoos, R. S., Frederick, C., Nader, K., Arroyo, W., Steinberg, A., Eth, S., et al. (1987). Life threat and posttraumatic stress in school-age children. *Archives of General Psychiatry, 44,* 1057–1063.

Quinn, K. M. (1995). Guidelines for the psychiatric examination of posttraumatic stress disorder in children and adolescents. In R. I. Simon (Ed.), *Posttraumatic stress disorder in litigation: Guidelines for forensic assessment* (pp. 85–98). Washington, DC: American Psychiatric Press.

Quirion, P., Lennett, J., Lund, K., & Tuck, C. (1997). Protecting children exposed to domestic violence in contested custody and visitation litigation. *Boston Public Interest Law Journal, 6,* 501.

Raine, A. (1993). *The psychopathology of crime: Criminal behavior as a clinical disorder.* New York: Academic Press.

Randel, J., & Wells, K. (2003). Corporate approaches to reducing intimate partner violence through workplace initiatives. *Occupational and Environmental Medicine, 3,* 821–841.

Rando, T. A. (1993). *Treatment of complicated mourning.* Champaign, IL: Research Press.

Raphael, B. (1983). *The anatomy of bereavement.* New York: Basic Books.

Raphael, B. (1986). *When disaster strikes: How individuals and communities cope with catastrophe.* New York: Basic Books.

Regehr, C., & Bober, T. (2004). *In the line of fire: Trauma in the emergency services.* New York: Oxford University Press.

Regehr, C., & Gutheil, T. (2002). Apology, justice, and trauma recovery. *Journal of the American Academy of Psychiatry and the Law, 30,* 425–430.

Resick, P. A. (1993). The psychological impact of rape. *Journal of Interpersonal Violence, 8,* 223–255.

Resick, P. A., & Schnicke, M. K. (1992). Cognitive processing therapy for sexual assault victims. *Journal of Consulting and Clinical Psychology, 60,* 748–756.

Resnick, H. S., Acierno, R., & Kilpatrick, D. G. (1997). Health impact of interpersonal violence 2: Medical and mental health outcomes. *Behavioral Medicine, 23,* 65–78.

Resnick, H. S., Kilpatrick, D. G., Dansky, B. S., Saunders, B. E., & Best, C. L. (1993). Prevalence of civilian trauma and posttraumatic stress disorder in a representative national sample of women. *Journal of Consulting and Clinical Psychology, 61,* 984–991.

Resnick, H. S., Kilpatrick, D. G., Walsh, C., & Veronen, L. J. (1991). Marital rape. In R. T. Ammerman & M. Hersen (Eds.), *Case studies in family violence.* New York: Plenum.

Resnick, P. J. (1988). Malingering of post-traumatic disorder. In R. Rogers (Ed.), *Clinical assessment of malingering and deception.* New York: Guilford.

Ressler, R. K., Burgess, A. W., & Douglas, J. E. (1988). *Sexual homicide: Patterns and motives.* New York: Free Press.

Rigby, K. (2003). Consequences of bullying in school. *Canadian Journal of Psychiatry, 48,* 583–590.

Riger, S., Ahrens, C., & Bickenstaff, A. (2000). Measuring interference with employment and education reported by women of abusive partners: Preliminary data. *Violence and Victims, 15,* 161–172.

Riger, S., Raja, S., & Camacho, J. (2002). The radiating impact of intimate partner violence. *Journal of Interpersonal Violence, 17,* 184–205.

Ritter, R. (1994). Critical incident stress debriefing teams and schools. In R. G. Stevenson (Ed.), *What will we do? Preparing a school community to cope with crises* (pp.169–174). Amityville, NY: Baywood.

Robinette, H. M. (1987). *Burnout in blue: Managing the police marginal performer.* New York: Praeger.

Robinson, S., Rappaport-Bar-Server, M., & Rappaport, J. (1994). The present state of people who survived the Holocaust as children. *Acta Psychiatrica Scandinavica, 89,* 242–245.

Roccia, F., Dell'Acqua, A., Angelini, G., & Berrone, S. (2005). Maxillofacial trauma and psychiatric sequelae: Post-traumatic stress disorder. *Journal of Craniofacial Surgery, 16,* 355–360.

Rodgers, B. A. (2006). *Psychological aspects of police work: An officer's guide to street psychology.* Springfield, IL: Charles C Thomas.

Rodolfa, E. R., Kraft, W. A., & Reiley, R. R. (1988). Stressors of professionals and trainees at APA-approved counseling and VA medical center internship sites. *Professional Psychology: Research and Practice, 19,* 43–49.

Rogan, R. G., Donohoe, W. A., & Lyles, J. (1990). Gaining and exercising control in hostage taking negotiations using empathic perspective-taking. *International Journal of Group Tension, 20,* 77–90.

Rogan, R. G., & Hammer, M. R. (1995). Assessing message affect in crisis negotiations: An exploratory study. *Human Communication Research, 21,* 553–574.

Romano, J. A., & King, J. M. (2002). Chemical warfare and chemical terrorism: Psychological and performance outcomes. *Military Psychology, 14,* 85–92.

Ronen, T. (2002). Difficulties in assessing traumatic reactions in children. *Journal of Loss and Trauma, 7,* 87–106.

Rosenberg, T. (1997, December 28). To hell and back. *New York Times Magazine,* 32–36.

Ross, D. M. (1996). *Childhood bullying and teasing: What school personnel, other professionals, and parents can do.* Alexandria, VA: American Counseling Association.

Roth, S., & Cohen, L. J. (1986). Approach, avoidance, and coping with stress. *American Psychologist, 41,* 813–819.

Rothbaum, B. O., Foa, E. B., Riggs, D. S., Murdock, T., & Walsh, W. (1992). A prospective examination of posttraumatic stress disorder in rape victims. *Journal of Traumatic Stress, 5,* 455–475.

Rothman, E. F., Hathaway, J., Stidsen, A., & de Vries, H. F. (2007). How employment helps female victims of intimate partner violence: A qualitative study. *Journal of Occupational Health Psychology, 12,* 136–143.

Rubenstein, J. L., Heeren, T., Houseman, D., Rubin, C., & Stechler, G. (1989). Suicidal behavior in "normal" adolescents: Risk and protective factors. *American Journal of Orthopsychiatry, 59,* 59–71.

Rudofossi, D. (2007). *Working with traumatized police officer–patients: A clinician's guide to complex PTSD syndromes in public safety professionals.* Amityville, NY: Baywood.

Russell, H. E., & Beigel, A. (1990). *Understanding human behavior for effective police work* (3rd ed.). New York: Basic Books.

Rutter, M. (1985). Resilience in the face of adversity: Protective factors and resistance to psychiatric disorder. *British Journal of Psychiatry, 147,* 598–611.

Rutter, M. (1987). Psychosocial resilience and protective mechanisms. *American Journal of Orthopsychiatry, 57,* 316–331.

Rutter, M., Tizard, J., Yule, W., Graham, P., & Whitmore, K. (1976). Research report: Isle of Wight studies, 1964–1974. *Psychological Medicine, 6,* 313–332.

Rynearson, E. K. (1984). Bereavement after homicide: A descriptive study. *American Journal of Psychiatry, 141,* 1452–1454.

Rynearson, E. K. (1988). The homicide of a child. In F. M. Ochberg (Ed.), *Post-traumatic therapy and victims of violence* (pp. 213–224). New York: Brunner/Mazel.

Rynearson, E. K. (1994). Psychotherapy of bereavement after homicide. *Journal of Psychotherapy Practice and Research, 3,* 341–347.

Rynearson, E. K. (1996). Psychotherapy of bereavement after homicide: Be offensive. *In Session: Psychotherapy in Practice, 2,* 47–57.

Rynearson, E. K. (2001). *Retelling violent death.* Philadelphia: Brunner-Routledge.

Rynearson, E. K., & McCreery, J. M. (1993). Bereavement after homicide: A synergism of trauma and loss. *American Journal of Psychiatry, 150,* 258–261.

Saakvitne, K. W., & Pearlman, L. A. (1996). *Transforming the pain: A workbook on vicarious traumatization.* New York: Norton.

Sanders, A., Hoyle, C., Morgan, R., & Cape, E. (2001). Victim impact statements: Don't work, can't work. *Criminal Law Review,* 447–465.

Sanders, D. L. (1997, June). Responding to domestic violence. *The Police Chief,* 6.

Sapolsky, R. M. (1996). Why stress is bad for your brain. *Science, 273,* 749–750.

Sapolsky, R. M., Krey, L. C., & McEwen, B. S. (1984). Glucocorticoid-sensitive hippocampal neurons are involved in terminating the adrenocortical stress response. *Proceedings of the National Academy of Sciences, 81,* 6174–6177.

Sapolsky, R. M., Uno, H., Rebert, C. S., & Finch, C. E. (1990). Hippocampal damage associated with prolonged glucocorticoid exposure. *Journal of Neuroscience, 10,* 2897–2902.

Saunders, B. E., Kilpatrick, D. G., Resnick, H. S., & Tidwell, R. P. (1989). Brief screening for lifetime history of criminal victimization at mental health intake: A preliminary study. *Journal of Interpersonal Violence, 4,* 267–277.

Scarpa, A. (2001). Community violence exposure in a young adult sample: Lifetime prevalence and socioemotional effects. *Journal of Interpersonal Violence, 16,* 36–53.

Scarpa, A., Fikretoglu, D., Bowser, F., Hurley, J. D., Pappert, C. A., Romero, N., et al. (2002). Community violence exposure in university students: A replication and extension. *Journal of Interpersonal Violence, 17,* 253–272.

Scarpa, A., & Haden, S. C. (2006). Community violence victimization and aggressive behavior: The moderating effects of coping and social support. *Aggressive Behavior, 32,* 502–515.

Schafer, J., Caetano, R., & Clark, C. L. (1998). Rates of intimate partner violence in the United States. *American Journal of Public Health, 88,* 1702–1704.

Schaner, D. J. (1996). Have gun, will carry: Concealed handgun laws, workplace violence, and employer liability. *Employee Relations Law Journal, 22,* 83–100.

Schechter, D. S., & Davis, B. E. (2007). Parenting in times of crisis. *Psychiatric Annals, 36,* 216–222.

Schlosser, E. (1997, September). A grief like no other. *Atlantic Monthly, 37*–76.

Schmalleger, F. (2007). *Criminal justice today* (9th ed.). Upper Saddle River, NJ: Prentice Hall.

Schmid, A. P. (2000, April 12). *Magnitudes of terrorist victimization: Past, present and future.* Paper presented at the Ancillary Meeting on Terrorist Victimization Prevention, Control and Recovery, Tenth United Nations Congress on the Prevention of Crime and the Treatment of Offenders, Vienna, Austria.

Schneid, T. D. (1999). *Occupational health guide to violence in the workplace.* Boca Raton, FL: CRC Press.

Schouten, R. (1994). Distorting posttraumatic stress disorder for court. *Harvard Review of Psychiatry, 2,* 171–173.

Schouten, R. (1996). Sexual harassment and the role of psychiatry. *Harvard Review of Psychiatry, 3,* 296–298.

Schouten, R. (2006). Workplace violence: A overview for practicing clinicians. *Psychiatric Annals, 36,* 791–797.

Schretlen, D. J. (1988). The use of psychological tests to identify malingered symptoms of mental disorder. *Clinical Psychology Review, 8,* 451–476.

Schwartz, E. D., & Kowalski, J. M. (1991). Posttraumatic stress disorder after a school shooting: Effects of symptom threshold selection and diagnosis by DSM-III, DSM-III-R, or proposed DSM-IV. *American Journal of Psychiatry, 148,* 592–597.

Sewell, J. D. (1993). Traumatic stress in multiple murder investigations. *Journal of Traumatic Stress, 6,* 103–118.

Sewell, J. D. (1994). The stress of homicide investigations. *Death Studies, 18,* 565–582.

Shackleford, T. K., Buss, D. M., & Peters, J. (2000). Wife killing: Risk to women as a function of age. *Violence and Victims, 15,* 273–282.

Shafii, M., & Shafii, S. L. (Eds.) (2001). *School violence: Assessment, management, prevention.* Washington, DC: American Psychiatric Publishing.

Shalev, A. Y., Galai, T., & Eth, S. (1993). Levels of trauma: A multidimensional approach to the treatment of PTSD. *Psychiatry, 56,* 166–167.

Shapiro, R. M., Jankowski, M. A., & Dale, J. (2005). *Bullies, tyrants, and impossible people: How to beat them without joining them.* New York: Crown.

Sheehan, P. L. (1991). Critical incident trauma and intimacy. In J. T. Reese, J. M. Horn, & C. Dunning (Eds.), *Critical incidents in policing* (pp. 331–334). Washington, DC: Federal Bureau of Investigation.

Sheridan, D. J., & Nash, K. R. (2007). Acute injury patterns of intimate partner violence victims. *Trauma, Violence, and Abuse, 8,* 281–289.

Shorto, R. (2002, August 25). A life of crime. *New York Time Magazine,* 28–31.

Siegel, L. J. (2003). *Criminology* (8th ed.). Belmont, CA: Wadsworth/Thompson Learning.

Silbert, M. (1976). *Crisis identification and management: A training manual.* Oakland: California Planners.

Silva, M. N. (1991). The delivery of mental health services to law enforcement officers. In J. T. Reese, J. M. Horn, & C. Dunning (Eds.), *Critical incidents in policing* (Rev. ed., pp. 335–341). Washington, DC: U.S. Government Printing Office.

Silver, R., & Wortman, C. (1980). Coping with undesirable life events. In J. Garber & M. Seligman (Eds.), *Human helplessness* (pp. 279–340). New York: Academic Press.

Simmons, C. A., & Lehman, P. (2007). Exploring the link between pet abuse and controlling behavior in violent relationships. *Journal of Interpersonal Violence, 22,* 1211–1222.

Simon, R. I. (1995). Toward the development of guidelines in the forensic evaluation of posttraumatic stress disorder claims. In R. I. Simon (Ed.), *Posttraumatic stress disorder in litigation: Guidelines for forensic assessment* (pp. 31–84). Washington, DC: American Psychiatric Press.

Simon, R. I. (1996). *Bad men do what good men dream: A forensic psychiatrist illuminates the dark side of human behavior.* Washington, DC: American Psychiatric Press.

Slaikeu, K. A. (1996). *When push comes to shove: A practical guide to mediating disputes.* San Francisco: Jossey-Bass.

Slatkin, A. A. (1996, May). Enhancing negotiator training: Therapeutic communication. *FBI Law Enforcement Bulletin,* 1–6.

Slatkin, A. A. (2005). *Communication in crisis and hostage negotiations.* Springfield, IL: Charles C Thomas.

Slovenko, R. (1994). Legal aspects of posttraumatic stress disorder. *Psychiatric Clinics of North America, 17,* 439–446.

Smith, E. M., North, C. S., McCool, R. E., & Shea, J. M. (1990). Acute postdisaster psychiatric disorders: Identification of persons at risk. *American Journal of Psychiatry, 147,* 202–206.

Solomon, M. J., & Thompson, J. (1995). Anger and blame in three technological disasters. *Stress Medicine, 11,* 199–206.

Solomon, R. M. (1988). Mental conditioning: The utilization of fear. In J. T. Reese & J. M. Horn (Eds.), *Police psychology: Operational assistance* (pp. 391–407). Washington, DC: U.S. Government Printing Office.

Solomon, R. M. (1991). The dynamics of fear in critical incidents: Implications for training and treatment. In J. T. Reese, J. M. Horn, & C. Dunning (Eds.), *Critical incidents in policing* (pp. 347–358). Washington, DC: Federal Bureau of Investigation.

Solomon, S. D., & Davidson, J. R. T. (1997). Trauma: Prevalence, impairment, service use, and cost. *Journal of Clinical Psychiatry, 58,* 5–11.

Solomon, Z., Mikulincer, M., & Waysman, M. (1991). Delayed and immediate onset posttraumatic stress disorder: The role of life events and social resources. *Journal of Community Psychology, 19,* 231–236.

Southwestern Law Enforcement Institute. (1995). *Domestic assault among police: A survey of internal affairs policies.* Richardson, TX: Southwestern Law Enforcement Institute.

Sparr, L. F. (1990). Legal aspects of posttraumatic stress disorder: Uses and abuses. In M. E. Wolf & A. D. Mosnaim (Eds.), *Posttraumatic stress disorder: Etiology, phenomenology, and treatment* (pp. 239–264). Washington, DC: APA Press.

Spence, G. (2005). *Win your case: How to present, persuade, prevail—every place, every time.* New York: St. Martin's Press.

Sperry, L. (1995). *Handbook of the diagnosis and treatment of the DSM-IV personality disorders.* New York: Brunner/Mazel.

Sperry, L. (1999). *Cognitive behavior therapy of DSM-IV personality disorders: Highly effective interventions for the most common personality disorders.* New York: Brunner/Mazel.

Sprang, G., & McNeil, J. (1995). *The many faces of bereavement: The nature and treatment of natural, traumatic, and stigmatized grief.* New York: Brunner/Mazel.

Sprang, M. V., McNeil, J. S., & Wright, R. (1989). Psychological changes after the murder of a significant other. *Social Casework, 70,* 159–164.

Spungen, D. (1998). *Homicide: The hidden victims. A guide for professionals.* Thousand Oaks, CA: Sage.

Stark, E., & Flitcraft, A. (1996). *Women at risk: Domestic violence and women's health.* Thousand Oaks, CA: Sage.

Stebnicki, M. A. (2001). The psychosocial impact on survivors of extraordinary, stressful, and traumatic events: Principles and practices in critical incident response for rehabilitation counselors. *Directions in Rehabilitation Counseling, 12,* 57–72.

Stein, B. D., Jaycox, L. H., Kataoka, S. H., Wong, M., Tu, W., Elliott, M. N., et al. (2003). A mental health intervention for schoolchildren exposed to violence: A randomized controlled trial. *Journal of the American Medical Association, 290,* 603–611.

Stein, M. B., Walker, J. R., Hazen, A. L., & Forde, D. R. (1997). Full and partial posttraumatic stress disorder: Findings from a community survey. *American Journal of Psychiatry, 154,* 1114–1119.

Steinmetz, S. K. & Lucca, J. S. (1988). Husband battering. In V. B. Van Hasselt, R. L. Morrison, A. S. Bellack & M. Hersen (Eds.), *Handbook of family violence* (pp. 233–245). New York: Plenum.

Stewart, A. E. (1999). Complicated bereavement and posttraumatic stress disorder following fatal car crashes: Recommendations for death notification practice. *Death Studies, 23,* 289–321.

Stewart, J. S., Hardin, S. B., Weinrich, S. McGeorge, S., Lopez, J., & Pesut, D. (1992). Group protocol to mitigate disaster stress and enhance social support in adolescents exposed to Hurricane Hugo. *Issues in Mental Health Nursing, 13,* 105–109.

Stokes, J. W., & Bandaret, L. E. (1997). Psychological aspects of chemical defense and warfare. *Military Psychology, 9,* 395–415.

Stolle, D. P., Wexler, D. B., Winick, B. J., & Dauer, E. A. (2000). Integrating preventive law and therapeutic jurisprudence: A law and psychology based approach to lawyering. In D. P. Stolle, D. B. Wexler, & B. J. Winick (Eds.), *Practicing therapeutic jurisprudence: Law as a helping profession* (pp. 5–44). Durham, NC: Carolina Academic Press.

Stone, A. A. (1993). Post-traumatic stress disorder and the law: Critical review of the new frontier. *Bulletin of the American Academy of Psychiatry and Law, 21,* 23–36.

Stone, A. V. (2000). *Fitness for duty: Principles, methods, and legal issues.* Boca Raton, FL: CRC Press.

Strauss, I., & Savitsky, N. (1934). Head injury: Neurologic and psychiatric aspects. *Archives of Neurology and Psychiatry, 31,* 893–955.

Strentz, T. (1987). A hostage psychological survival guide. *FBI Law Enforcement Bulletin, 56,* 1–8.

Stroebe, M. (1992–1993). Coping with bereavement: A review of the grief work hypothesis. *Omega: Journal of Death and Dying, 26,* 19–42.

Strube, M., & Barbour, L. (1984). Factors related to the decision to leave an abusive relationship. *Journal of Marriage and the Family, 46,* 837–844.

Stuart, G. L., Moore, T. M., Ramsey, S. E., & Kahler, C. W. (2004). Hazardous drinking and relationship violence perpetration and victimization in women arrested for domestic violence. *Journal of Studies on Alcohol, 65,* 46–53.

Stuhlmiller, C., & Dunning, C. (2000). Challenging the mainstream: From pathogenic to salutogenic models of posttrauma intervention. In J. Violanti, D. Paton, & C. Dunning (Eds.), *Posttraumatic stress intervention: Challenges, issues, and perspectives* (pp. 10–42). Springfield, IL: Charles C Thomas.

Suinn, R. (1972). Removing emotional obstacles to learning and performance by visuo-motor behavior rehearsal. *Behavioral Therapy, 31,* 308–310.

Suinn, R. (1984). Visual motor behavior rehearsal: The basic technique. *Scandinavian Journal of Behavior Therapy, 13,* 131–142.

Suinn, R. (1985). Imagery rehearsal applications to performance enhancement. *The Behavior Therapist, 8,* 155–159.

Sullivan, C., Basta, J., Tan, C., & Davidson, W. (1992). After the crisis: A needs assessment of women leaving a domestic violence shelter. *Violence and Victims, 7,* 267–274.

Sullivan, C., Campbell, R., Angelique, H., Eby, K., & Davidson, W. (1994). An advocacy intervention program for women with abusive partners: Six month follow-up. *American Journal of Community Psychology, 11,* 101–122.

Sullivan, P. M., & Knutson, J. F. (2003). Maltreatment and disabilities: A population-based epidemiological study. *Journal of Early Intervention, 1,* 21–33.

Swanberg, J., & Logan, T. (2005). Domestic violence and employment: A qualitative study of rural and urban women. *Journal of Occupational Health Psychology, 10,* 3–17.

Swanberg, J., Logan, T. K., & Macke, C. (2005). Partner violence, employment, and the workplace: Consequences and future directions. *Trauma, Violence, and Abuse, 6,* 286–312.

Swanberg, J., Logan, T. K., & Macke, C. (2006). The consequences of partner violence on employment in the workplace. In K. Kelloway, J. Barling, & J. Hurrell (Eds.), *Handbook of workplace violence* (pp. 351–379). Thousand Oaks, CA: Sage.

Swanberg, J., Macke, C., & Logan, T. K. (2006). Intimate partner violence, women, and work: A descriptive look at work interference tactics, coping with violence on the job, and informal workplace support. *Violence and Victims, 21,* 561–578.

Swanberg, J., Macke, C., & Logan, T. K. (2007). Working women making it work: Intimate partner violence, employment, and workplace support. *Journal of Interpersonal Violence, 22,* 292–311.

Swisher, L. A., Nieman, L. Z., Nilsen, G. J., & Spivey, W. H. (1993). Death notification in the emergency department: A survey of residents and attending physicians. *Annals of Emergency Medicine, 22,* 102–106.

Talbot, A., Dutton, M., & Dunn, P. (1995). Debriefing the debriefers: An intervention strategy to assist psychologists after a crisis. In G. S. Everly & J. M. Lating (Eds.), *Psychotraumatology: Key papers and core concepts in posttraumatic stress* (pp. 281–298). New York: Plenum.

Taylor, J. S. (1997). *Neurolaw: Brain and spinal cord.* Washington, DC: ATLA Press.

Taylor, S. (2006). *Clinician's guide to PTSD: A cognitive-behavioral approach.* New York: Guilford.

Taylor, S., Wood, J. V., & Lechtman, R. R. (1983). It could be worse: Selective evaluation as a response to victimization. *Journal of Social Issues, 39,* 19–40.

Tedeschi, R. G., & Calhoun, L. G. (1995). *Trauma and transformation: Growing in the aftermath of suffering.* Thousand Oaks, CA: Sage.

Tedeschi, R. G., & Calhoun, L. G. (2004). Posttraumatic growth: Conceptual foundations and empirical evidence. *Psychological Inquiry, 15,* 1–18.

Tedeschi, R. G., & Kilmer, R. P. (2005). Assessing strengths, resilience, and growth to guide clinical interventions. *Professional Psychology: Research and Practice, 36,* 230–237.

Temple, S. (1997). Treating inner-city families of homicide victims: A contextually oriented approach. *Family Process, 36,* 133–149.

Thapar, A., & McGuffin, P. (1996). Genetic influences on life events in childhood. *Psychological Medicine, 26,* 813–830.

Thibault, G. E. (1992). Clinical problem solving: Failure to resolve a diagnostic inconsistency. *New England Journal of Medicine, 327,* 26–39.

Thompson, J. (1992). Stress theory and therapeutic practice. *Stress Medicine, 8,* 147–150.

Thompson, M. P., & Vardaman, P. J. (1997). The role of religion in coping with the loss of a family member to homicide. *Journal for the Scientific Study of Religion, 36,* 44–51.

Tjaden, P., & Thoennes, N. (2000). Prevalence and consequences of male-to-female and female-to-male intimate partner violence as measured by the National Violence Against Women Survey. *Violence Against Women, 6,* 142–161.

Tolman, R. M., & Raphael, J. (2000). A review of research on welfare and domestic violence. *Journal of Social Issues, 56,* 655–682.

Tolman, R. M., & Rosen, D. (2001). Domestic violence in the lives of women receiving welfare: Mental health, substance dependence, and economic well-being. *Violence Against Women, 7,* 141–158.

Trappler, B., & Friedman, S. (1996). Posttraumatic stress disorder in survivors of the Brooklyn Bridge shooting. *American Journal of Psychiatry, 153,* 705–707.

Travin, S., & Potter, B. (1984). Malingering and malingering-like behavior: Some clinical and conceptual issues. *Psychiatric Quarterly, 56,* 189–197.

Uhde, T. W., Boulenger, J. P., Roy-Byrne, P. P., Geraci, M. P., Vittone, B. J., & Post, R. M. (1985). Longitudinal course of panic disorder: Clinical and biological considerations. *Progress in Neuropharmacology and Biological Psychiatry, 9,* 39–51.

Ullman, S. E. (2007). Mental health services seeking in sexual assault victims. *Women & Therapy, 30,* 61–84.

Underwood, A., & Liu, M. (1996, August 12). "Why are you doing this?" *Newsweek,* 46–47.

Ursano, R. J., Fullerton, C. S., Bhartiya, V., & Kao, T. C. (1995). Longitudinal assessment of posttraumatic stress disorder and depression after exposure to traumatic death. *Journal of Nervous and Mental Disease, 183,* 36–42.

Ursano, R. J., Fullerton, C. S., & Norwood, A. E. (1995). Psychiatric dimensions of disaster: Patient care, community consultation, and preventive medicine. *Harvard Review of Psychiatry, 3,* 196–209.

Ursano, R. J., Kao, T. C., & Fullerton, C. S. (1992). Posttraumatic stress disorder and meaning: Structuring human chaos. *Journal of Nervous and Mental Disease, 180,* 756–759.

Ursano, R. J., & McCarroll, J. E. (1990). The nature of the traumatic stressor: Handling dead bodies. *Journal of Nervous and Mental Disease, 178,* 396–398.

van der Kolk, B. A. (1994). The body keeps the score: Memory and the evolving psychobiology of posttraumatic stress. *Harvard Review of Psychiatry, 1,* 253–265.

van der Kolk, B. A. (2003). Posttraumatic stress disorder and the nature of trauma. In M. Solomon & D. Siegel (Eds.), *Healing trauma* (pp. 168–195). New York: Norton.

Van Raalte, J. R., & Brewer, B. W. (2002). *Exploring sport and exercise psychology* (2nd ed.). Washington, DC: American Psychological Association.

Vega, G., & Comer, D. R. (2005). Bullying and harassment in the workplace. In R. E. Kidwell & C. L. Martin (Eds.), *Managing organizational deviance* (pp. 183–209). Thousand Oaks, CA: Sage.

Vernberg, E. M., & Vogel, J. M. (1993). Interventions with children after disasters. *Journal of Clinical Child Psychology, 22,* 485–498.

Vesper, J. H., & Cohen, L. J. (1999). Litigating posttraumatic stress disorder: Effects on the family. *Behavioral Sciences and the Law, 17,* 235–251.

Vinson, D. E., & Davis, D. S. (1993). *Jury persuasion: Psychological strategies and trial techniques.* Little Falls, NJ: Glasser Legalworks.

Violanti, J. M. (1999). Death on duty: Police survivor trauma. In J. M. Violanti & D. Paton (Eds.), *Police trauma: Psychological aftermath of civilian combat* (pp. 139–158). Springfield, IL: Charles C. Thomas.

Violanti, J. M. (2000). Scripting trauma: The impact of pathogenic intervention. In J. Violanti, D. Paton, & C. Dunning (Eds.), *Posttraumatic stress intervention: Challenges, issues, and perspectives* (pp. 153–165). Springfield, IL: Charles C Thomas.

Violanti, J. M. (2007). Homicide-suicide in police families: Aggression full circle. *International Journal of Emergency Mental Health, 9,* 97–104.

Vitanza, S., Vogel, L. C. M., & Marshall, L. L. (1995). Distress and symptoms of post-traumatic stress disorder in abused women. *Violence and Victims, 10,* 23–34.

Von Bloch, L. (1996). Breaking the bad news when sudden death occurs. *Social Work in Health Care, 24,* 91–97.

Walker, L. A. E. (1994). *Abused women and survivor therapy: A practical guide for the psychotherapist.* Washington, DC: American Psychological Association.

Walsh, F. (2002). Bouncing forward: Resilience in the aftermath of September 11. *Family Process, 41,* 34–36.

Walsh, F. (2007). Traumatic loss and major disasters: Strengthening family and community resilience. *Family Process, 46,* 207–227.

Weaver, T. L., & Clum, G. A. (1993). Early family environments and traumatic experiences associated with borderline personality disorder. *Journal of Consulting and Clinical Psychology, 61,* 1068–1075.

Weinberg, R. B. (1990). Serving large numbers of adolescent victim-survivors: Group interventions following trauma at school. *Professional Psychology: Research and Practice, 21,* 271–278.

Weiner, H. (1992). *Perturbing the organism: The biology of stressful experience.* Chicago: University of Chicago Press.

Weiss, S. J. (2007). Neurobiological alterations associated with traumatic stress. *Perspectives in Psychiatric Care, 43,* 114–122.

Wells, P. J. (1993). Preparing for sudden death: Social work in the emergency room. *Social Work, 38,* 339–342.

Werman, D. S. (1984). *The practice of supportive psychotherapy.* New York: Brunner/Mazel.

Werner, E. E. (1989). High-risk children in young adulthood: A longitudinal study from birth to 32 years. *American Journal of Orthopsychiatry, 59,* 72–81.

Werner, E. E., & Smith, R. S. (1982). *Vulnerable but invincible: A study of resilient children.* New York: McGraw-Hill.

Wester, S. R., & Lyubelsky, J. (2005). Supporting the thin blue line: Gender-sensitive therapy with male police officers. *Professional Psychology: Research and Practice, 36,* 51–58.

Westwell, C. A. (1998). Cognitive processing therapy in the treatment of marital rape. *Psychotherapy in Private Practice, 17,* 187–192.

Wettersten, K., Rudolf, S., Faul, K, Gallagher, K., Transgrud, H., & Adams, K. (2004). Freedom through self-sufficiency: A qualitative examination of the impact of domestic violence on the working lives of women in shelter. *Journal of Counseling Psychology, 5,* 447–462.

Wilson, M., Baglioni, A., & Downing, D. (1989). Analyzing factors influencing readmission to a battered women's shelter. *Journal of Family Violence, 4,* 275–284.

Wilson, M., & Daly, M. (1993). Spousal homicide risk and estrangement. *Violence and Victims, 8,* 3–16.

Winick, B. J. (2000). Therapeutic jurisprudence and the role of counsel in litigation. In D. P. Stolle, D. B. Wexler, & B. J. Winick (Eds.), *Practicing therapeutic jurisprudence: Law as a helping profession* (pp. 309–324). Durham, NC: Carolina Academic Press.

Wohlfarth, T., Winkel, F. W., & van den Brink, W. (2002). Identifying crime victims who are at high risk for post traumatic stress disorder: Developing a practical referral instrument. *Acta psychiatrica Scandinavica, 105,* 451–460.

Wolfe, J., & Charney, D. (1991). Use of neuropsychological assessment in posttraumatic stress disorder. *Psychological Assessment, 3,* 573–580.

Wong, E. C., Marshall, G. N., Shetty, V., Zhou, A., Belzberg, H., & Yamashita, D. D. R. (2007). Survivors of violence-related facial injury: Psychiatric needs and barriers to mental health care. *General Hospital Psychiatry, 29,* 117–122.

Worden, J. W. (1991). *Grief counseling and grief therapy.* New York: Springer Publishing.

Wright, J., Burgess, A., Laszlo, A., McCrary, G., & Douglas, J. (1996). A typology of interpersonal stalking. *Journal of Interpersonal Violence, 11,* 487–502.

Yalom, I. D. (1980). *Existential psychotherapy.* New York: Basic Books.

Yandrick, R. M. (1996). *Behavioral risk management: How to avoid preventable losses from mental health problems in the workplace.* San Francisco: Jossey-Bass.

Yassen, J. (1995). Preventing secondary traumatic stress disorder. In C. R. Figley (Ed.), *Compassion fatigue: Coping with secondary traumatic stress disorder in those who treat the traumatized* (pp. 178–208). New York: Brunner/Mazel.

Yehuda, R. (1998). Psychoneuroendocrinology of post-traumatic stress disorder. *Psychiatric Clinics of North America, 21,* 359–379.

Yehuda, R. (1999). Biological factors associated with susceptibility to posttraumatic stress disorder. *Canadian Journal of Psychiatry, 44,* 34–39.

Yehuda, R. (2002). Clinical relevance of biological findings in PTSD. *Psychiatric Quarterly, 73,* 123–133.

Young, M. A. (1988). Support services for victims. In F. M. Ochberg (Ed.), *Posttraumatic therapy and victims of violence* (pp. 330–351). New York: Brunner/Mazel.

Young, M. A. (1994). *Responding to communities in crisis: The training manual of the crisis response team.* Washington, DC: National Organization for Victim Assistance.

Zimrin, H. (1986). A profile of survival. *Child Abuse and Neglect, 10,* 339–349.

Index

Partner Stalking
How Women Respond, Cope, and Survive

TK Logan, PhD, **Jennifer Cole,** MSW
Lisa Shannon, MSW
Robert Walker, MSW, LCSW

It is estimated that a quarter of all women will be stalked in their lifetime. Stalkers put their victims in danger of losing their jobs, their support system, even their lives; and subject them to dangerously high levels of fear and stress. This book examines the multiple aspects of partner stalking from the victim's perspective. Female survivors share their personal stories of partner stalking, and the authors offer an extensive look at the latest stalking research, providing readers with the most relevant implications for practice and future research.

The book informs students, professionals, and researchers about:

• Women's perceptions and definitions of stalking

• The health and mental health problems that co-occur with partner stalking and violent relationships

• Levels of stress caused by and/or exacerbated by partner violence and stalking

• Impacts on financial and employment status, social activities, and relationships

• Victims' access to the justice system and the growing need for better and stronger policies and services to protect victims

Partial Contents:
• What Do We Know and What Do We Need to Know About Partner Stalking?
• Women's Perceptions of Partner Stalking
• Partner Stalking and Previous Victimization
• The Health and Mental Health Costs of Partner Stalking
• Partner Stalking and Co-Occurring Problems
• Partner Stalking and Coping Responses
• Partner Stalking and the Justice System Response

2006 · 368pp · hard · 978-0-8261-3756-2

Healing Crisis and Trauma with Mind, Body, and Spirit

Barbara Rubin Wainrib, EdD

We live in a changed world, a world where the enemy is no longer in uniform on the other side of a trench. There is no longer an identified "war zone" and the "enemy" may be the innocent looking person standing next to us. Clear boundaries and an assumption of safety no longer exist.

Healing Crisis and Trauma with Mind, Body, and Spirit

Barbara Rubin Wainrib

Learning new skills to address the injuries incurred by sudden trauma and unpredictable lives is essential. This book is written for those persons in the "helping professions." It is also written for those who have a sufficient understanding of psychology and a sufficient awareness of our current world, and want to gain some knowledge about being helpful.

This book offers the educator and the practitioner training methods, exercises, and intervention techniques applicable to the gamut of experiences that we currently encounter. It also will introduce readers to newer concepts and their applications such as role play, spirituality, the role of animals in healing, and the concept of forgiveness. Throughout the book, whether it is in those who represent the highly resilient or those who continue to struggle, a strengths perspective is emphasized. Finally, this book describes the "Phoenix Phenomenon", a concept Wainrib developed during the course of her teaching and practice, which articulates and illustrates an inherent ability to use resilience in the process of converting pain into growth.

Partial Contents:

Understanding Crisis Intervention and Trauma • Understanding Trauma and its Impact • Mass Trauma, Past and Present • Women and Trauma • Trauma from Within: Life Threatening Illness • Resilience and the Phoenix Phenomenon • Trauma and the Mind • Trauma and the Body • Spirituality and Trauma • New Sources of Healing • Forgiveness • Final Thoughts

2006 · 184pp · softcover · 978-0-8261-3245-1

11 West 42nd Street, New York, NY 10036-8002 • Fax: 212-941-7842
Order Toll-Free: 877-687-7476 • Order Online: www.springerpub.com

Victim Assistance

Exploring Individual Practice, Organizational Policy, and Societal Responses

Thomas L. Underwood, PhD
Christine Edmunds, Editors

Based on the acclaimed professional certificate program, Advanced Institute on Victim Studies: Critical Analysis of Victim Assistance, this book identifies core content areas essential for practitioners working with crime victims.

Recognizing the multidisciplined, multisystem field that encompasses victim assistance, the contributors present a solid foundation of the varying concepts and theories on victims and victims services. The balance of the text addresses the skills and strategies needed to enhance services to victims at the individual, organizational, and societal levels. Each chapter concludes with an analysis and application section, including representative scenarios and key questions for review.

Partial Contents:

*   Concepts of Victims Assistance
*   Ecological Perspective of Victimization
*   Exploring Attitudes Toward Violence and Victimization
*   The Psychological and Physiological Impact of Stress
*   Trauma and the Crime Victim
*   The Justice System and Victims
*   Victims of Sexual Abuse and Assault: Adults and Children
*   Victims of Criminal Death
*   Violence within Family Systems
*   Victims of Hate and Bias Crimes
*   Victim Advocacy and Public Policy
*   Issues for the Profession

2002 · 304pp · hardcover · 978-0-8261-4751-6

11 West 42nd Street, New York, NY 10036-8002 • Fax: 212-941-7842
Order Toll-Free: 877-687-7476 • Order Online: www.springerpub.com

SPRINGER / PUBLISHING COMPANY

Psychological Interventions in Times of Crisis

Laura Barbanel, EdD, ABPP
Robert Sternberg, PhD, Editors

Psychological
Interventions
in Times of
Crisis

Laura Barbanel
Robert J. Sternberg
Editors

"Psychological Interventions in Times of Crisis is an original contribution to the relatively new field of collective trauma. With the rigor of experienced academicians and clinicians Barbanel and Sternberg have managed to gather an outstanding group of international psychologists who attempt to conceptualize the responses that psychologists have made in the aftermath of disasters ranging from Chernobyl and West Africa to 9/11 USA. The scope of this volume transcends expectations. The chapters address theoretical as well as technical issues, offering a clear and substantial repertoire for psychologists invested in working outside of their offices. With respect and sensitivity to cultural diversity, the authors are most successful in devising frames capable of containing the complex need of non-pathological populations affected by disasters. Professionals and volunteers will benefit from Barbanel and Sternberg's thoughtful weaving of clinical practice and educational work. The in-depth exploration of psychological interventions offered by this book is bound to lessen the threat of secondary traumatization suffered by mental health professionals working in the area of trauma and disaster."

—**Isaac Tylim,** PsyD, ABPP
Secretary, International Psychoanalytic Association,
Committee on the United Nations
Co-Coordinator, New York University Post-Doctoral Program in Psychotherapy
and Psychoanalysis Trauma and Disaster Specialization Program

There is controversy as to whether psychological interventions in the aftermath of disaster are helpful or not. This book addresses these controversies and describes the responses that psychologists have made in different parts of the world to disaster.

2005 · 288pp · hardcover · 978-0-8261-3225-3

11 West 42nd Street, New York, NY 10036-8002 • Fax: 212-941-7842
Order Toll-Free: 877-687-7476 • Order Online: www.springerpub.com